D1107204

THE ECCENTRIC ARK

Frontispiece
Frank Buckland. Elgin, Scotland, June, 1870. He always carried a long bamboo pole marked off in feet when he inspected a salmon river.
From a photograph in the Library of the Royal College of Surgeons of England.

THE ECCENTRIC ARK

THE CURIOUS WORLD OF FRANK BUCKLAND

G. H. O. BURGESS

THE HORIZON PRESS, NEW YORK

Published in Great Britain
under the title of
"The Curious World of Frank Buckland"

First published in the
United States of America 1968 by

Horizon Press,
156 Fifth Avenue, New York,
N.Y. 10010

Library of Congress Catalog Card No.
67-31628

Printed in Great Britain

Contents

Illustrations

Acknowledgements

The author wishes to thank the following for permission to reproduce illustrations:

The Council of the Royal College of Surgeons of England for the Frontispiece and Plates II, III, IV, VI, XI, XIII and XV;

The County Archivist, The Devon Record Office and Exeter Diocesan Record Office for Plates I and XIV.

Preface

FRANK BUCKLAND was one of the most popular writers on natural history topics of the last century. His books were reprinted many times and he had a large and devoted circle of readers. He was, however, much more than a mere populariser and made significant contributions to the early development of both marine and freshwater fishery research and administration. Nevertheless, his name is now generally associated only with the Buckland Lectures, which were established under the terms of his will, and the major work of his life is forgotten.

He was an interesting person who lived through a fascinating period in British Science. He was born in 1826, when it was still just possible for one man to keep abreast of developments in all branches of science and when an untaught man like Hugh Miller could, by hard and unremitting labour, make himself an acknowledged authority in his own chosen field. When Buckland died in 1880, science had become a profession.

Frank Buckland was the eldest son of a gifted father who was Dean of Westminster and one of the founders of modern geology, and as a young man Frank met many of the famous people of the day. Buckland's success in life was partly due to the good fortune of his birth. In one sense he belonged to the first rather than the second half of the century for his attitude to science was essentially that of the gifted amateur. In other ways, however, he was in advance of his time and, particularly in the fisheries, foresaw the future needs much more clearly than most of his contemporaries. It was Buckland's weakness that he attempted to do too much; had he attempted less he might have achieved more and be better known today. On the other hand, his achievement was not inconsiderable for he was officially concerned with the fisheries only from his appointment as Inspector of Salmon Fisheries in 1867 until his death and he was too ill for the last year of his life, from the end of 1879, to do very much.

When Buckland died he bequeathed a sum of money for the establishment of the lectureship already mentioned. The income derived from this money is administered by the Trustees of the Buckland Foundation (1926). I was greatly honoured to be asked to give the lectures for 1964 and whilst preparing them I became interested in the life of the founder. There matters would perhaps have rested had it not been for the strong encouragement I received from the Trustees to continue my researches and prepare material for a biography. I should like here to acknowledge my gratitude to them for their interest and helpful criticism. They are C. E. Lucas, C.M.G., D.SC., F.R.S., F.R.S.E., F.I.BIOL., Director of the Marine Laboratory (Department of Agriculture and Fisheries for Scotland); H. A. Cole, D.SC., F.I.BIOL., Director of the Fisheries Laboratory, Lowestoft (Ministry of Agriculture, Fisheries and Food); and J. H. Ray, O.B.E., F.C.I.S., F.S.S., Secretary, The British Trawlers' Federation. The late F. T. K. Pentelow, O.B.E., M.A., F.I.BIOL., former Clerk to the Foundation, was particularly helpful in providing information and advice from his own wide experience of the salmon fisheries.

I should also like here to record my thanks to the very large number of people, too numerous to mention individually, who gave me assistance by providing information, by commenting on parts of the manuscript and in other ways. I know too well how much work can be involved in the apparently simple task of searching out information, and many of those I asked did far more than could have been expected of them, and correspondingly lightened my task considerably.

Particular thanks are due to the following:

W. R. Le Fanu, M.A., F.S.A., Librarian of the Royal College of Surgeons of England; R. N. Rose, formerly Editor of *The Field*; Major D. F. Robarts, M.B.E., Household Cavalry Museum; Miss E. Joyce, Clerk to Billingshurst Parish Council; H. P. Spratt, B.SC., A.S.M.E., Deputy Keeper, Science Museum, London; Mrs E. M. Rogers of Laleham; the late Brigadier F. E. Buckland, M.R.C.S., L.R.C.P., B.M., B.CH., D.M.; J. F. A. Mason, M.A., D.PHIL., F.S.A., Librarian, Christ Church, Oxford; T. C. Buckland of Bideford, Devon.

Special mention deserves to be made of the assistance I have received from the Chief Librarian and his staff of the Central Library of Kingston upon Hull, and from Mrs Alan Riches of the Humber Laboratory. Their help in tracing rare and little-sought works has proved invaluable.

Finally, I should like to place on record my deep gratitude to my wife, not only for converting my illegible handwriting into legible typescript, but also for her encouragement and interest throughout the work.

G. H. O. B.

Humber Laboratory,
Wassand Street,
Hull

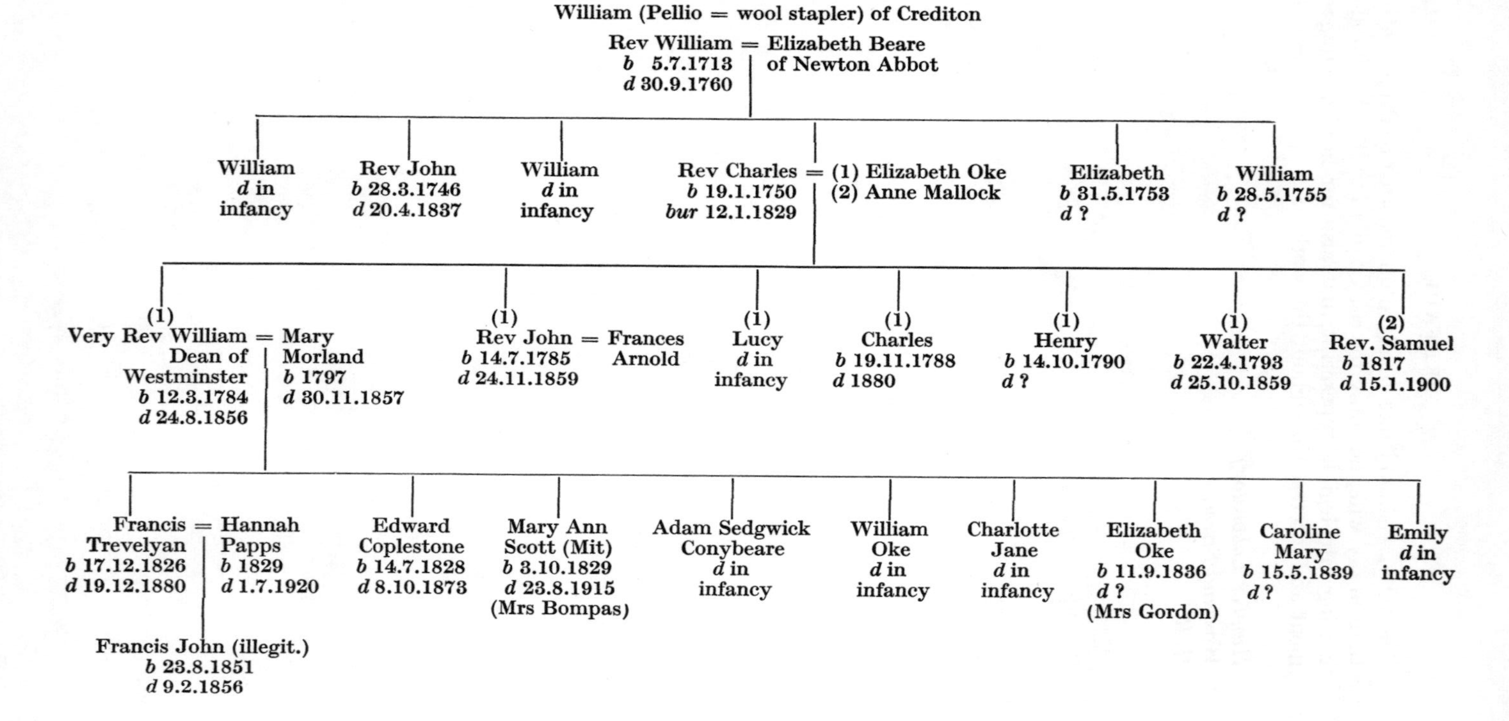
THE BUCKLAND STEM
William (Pellio = wool stapler) of Crediton
Rev William = Elizabeth Beare
b 5.7.1713
d 30.9.1760
of Newton Abbot
William
d in
infancy
Rev John
b 28.3.1746
d 20.4.1837
William
d in
infancy
Rev Charles = (1) Elizabeth Oke
(2) Anne Mallock
b 19.1.1750
bur 12.1.1829
Elizabeth
b 31.5.1753
d ?
William
b 28.5.1755
d ?
(1)
Very Rev William = Mary
Dean of
Westminster
b 12.3.1784
d 24.8.1856
Morland
b 1797
d 30.11.1857
(1)
Rev John = Frances
Arnold
b 14.7.1785
d 24.11.1859
(1)
Lucy
d in
infancy
(1)
Charles
b 19.11.1788
d 1880
(1)
Henry
b 14.10.1790
d ?
(1)
Walter
b 22.4.1793
d 25.10.1859
(2)
Rev. Samuel
b 1817
d 15.1.1900
Francis = Hannah
Trevelyan
b 17.12.1826
d 19.12.1880
Papps
b 1829
d 1.7.1920
Francis John (illegit.)
b 23.8.1851
d 9.2.1856
Edward
Coplestone
b 14.7.1828
d 8.10.1873
Mary Ann
Scott (Mit)
b 3.10.1829
d 23.8.1915
(Mrs Bompas)
Adam Sedgwick
Conybeare
d in
infancy
William
Oke
d in
infancy
Charlotte
Jane
d in
infancy
Elizabeth
Oke
b 11.9.1836
d ?
(Mrs Gordon)
Caroline
Mary
b 15.5.1839
d ?
Emily
d in
infancy

CHAPTER ONE

The Buckland Household

HOW MUCH DOES A MAN owe to his heredity and how much to his upbringing? The clay of nature is moulded on the wheel of nurture, and who shall say which is ultimately of greater importance? There is no doubt, however, that whatever he owed to his genetic inheritance, Frank Buckland owed an immense debt to his early training. 'My good Father and Mother trained me well in observation, note-taking and reflection; it has therefore become my habit to observe, record, and reflect upon everything I see in town or country, out of doors or indoors; and, as a Philosopher of old wrote of himself, so I am thankful to say I can write of myself, "Nunquam minus solus quam solus" ' (Never less alone than [when] alone).[1] In him was developed to a high degree the capacity to enjoy every situation, however apparently unpleasant, and in manhood he even seemed to carry his own environment with him wherever he went. Frank Buckland inherited all these qualities, and more besides, from his parents, particularly his remarkable father, William Buckland.

William Buckland was born at Axminster, Devon, on March 12, 1784. He was the eldest of seven children of the Reverend Charles Buckland, Rector of Templeton and Trusham, Devon, and of West Chelborough, Dorset. The Reverend Charles Buckland was a keen amateur naturalist, like so many other country parsons in that golden period, which began in the mid-eighteenth century and ended towards the close of the Victorian era, when educated men observed and recorded the living world around them. Father and son walked the country lanes together, and searched for fossils in the lias beds of the quarries near their house. William Buckland was a very observant child, and delighted in collecting birds' eggs and studying the behaviour of the fish in the River Axe.[2]

After spending a year at Blundell's School in Tiverton, he was sent, when he was 14 years old, to Winchester. His uncle, the Reverend John Buckland, Rector of Warborough near Oxford, a stern man without children of his own but who took a continuing interest in his nephew, wrote to his brother: 'As William appears to excel your other boys by many degrees in talent and industry and will add in many other respects he will probably make a better return for any extraordinary expense you may incur on his account. As there is the highest probability that there will be a vacancy for Devonshire at Corpus early in the year 1800, he ought to be ripened prematurely for such a purpose, which certainly cannot be done anywhere so well as at Winchester.'[3]

As a boy William Buckland was slow to learn but had an exceedingly retentive memory and an unusual facility for construing Latin. The curriculum of the school was, like that of other public schools of the period, almost exclusively classical.[4] Nevertheless, he retained his interest in nature, and in his rambles through the lush water meadows of the Itchen he studied the habits of the mole crickets; he, like his son forty years later, also trapped field-mice in the ancient earthworks that crown the summit of St Catherine's Hill, the playground known to generations of Wykehamists as 'Hills'. Years later he noted that he became familiar with the chalk formation from the fact that the path to 'Hills' led past chalk pits in which he found an abundance of sponges and other fossils.[2]

Public schools at this time were ill-disciplined and understaffed. The food was often poor and badly cooked and bullying of the younger boys by the older ones was commonplace. Masters often flogged their charges unmercifully and on occasions the pupils mutinied, as at Winchester in 1818. As Curtis has said: 'An age which began with the use of the pillory and stocks for minor offences and hanged the small pilferer, which later sanctioned transportation to Botany Bay and suffered the sight of the bodies of criminals hanging on gibbets, was not likely to be unduly disturbed by the flogging of schoolboys.'[5]

The extent of overcrowding was unbelievable. All the pupils assembled every working day in the building attributed to Wren and known as 'School', and Headmaster at one end and usher at the other, by the strength of their arms and power of their voices, somehow contrived to teach their various classes. The work demanded from the pupils was excessive; the normal day included over ten hours' study and Thomas Arnold, who went to Winchester six years after William Buckland left, '. . . once rose at 3 a.m. for six consecutive days in order to prepare himself for a recitation of some 3,000 lines of Homer'.[6] Nevertheless, in spite of the ferocious brutality of the conditions and the excessive demands upon the intellectual and physical abilities of the pupils, the public school system sometimes produced scholars of a high order.

In 1801, at the age of 17, after a rigorous examination lasting many days, William Buckland was elected to a scholarship at Corpus Christi College, Oxford. He obtained his B.A. degree in 1804 and now devoted time to studying geology. According to his son, he received his first lessons in this science from his lifelong friend William John Broderip (1789–1859), five years his junior but an enthusiastic collector and who, in later life when a successful lawyer, was frequently visited in his chambers in Gray's Inn by foreign professors anxious to see his treasures.[7] Buckland knew the Reverend Joseph Townsend, Rector of Pusey, Berkshire, friend and fellow-labourer of William Smith (1769–1839), the civil engineer whose original and acute observations led to the production of his geological map (1815) and earned him the title of the 'Father of English Geology'. William Buckland also attended the lectures on Anatomy of Sir Christopher Pegge, F.R.S., and those on Geology and Chemistry of Dr John Kidd. He obtained his M.A. in 1808 and his election to a Fellowship of Corpus Christi in 1809 gave him an assured income. In 1808 he began a series of tours on horseback, either alone or in company with one or two of his numerous geological friends; these tours took him through Britain and much of Western Europe and made his name famous within the next decade.

A year after Waterloo, in 1816, he toured Germany with two friends. 'At Weimar', he wrote, 'we saw Goethe, and at Freyberg visited Werner, who gave us a grand supper and talked learnedly of his books and music, and of anything but geology.' From 1812 to 1824 he rode once or twice a year from Oxford to visit his old blind father at Axminster, calling on geologist friends on the way.

His son wrote: 'Dr Buckland performed nearly all the geological excursions on horseback. He rode a favourite old black mare, which was frequently caparisoned all over with heavy bags of fossils and ponderous hammers. The old mare soon learnt her duty, and seemed to take interest in her master's pursuits; for she would remain quiet without anyone to hold her, while he was examining sections and strata, and then patiently submit to be loaded with interesting but weighty specimens. Ultimately she became so accustomed to her work that she invariably came to a full stop at a stone quarry, and nothing would persuade her to proceed until the rider had got off and examined (or, if a stranger to her, pretended to examine) the quarry.' Nevertheless, not all his geological excursions were performed on horseback, and William Buckland must surely be given credit as one of the pioneers of the mobile laboratory, for he had an extra strong travelling carriage built to carry his specimens '. . . and fitted up on the forepart with a furnace and implements for assays and analysis'.[8]

Dr John Kidd resigned in 1813 and Buckland was elected Reader in Mineralogy in his place. He was made a Fellow of the Royal Society in 1818 and in 1819 became the first Professor of Geology, a Chair newly created at the instigation of the Prince Regent, and with an annual stipend of £100, paid from the Treasury. Old Sir Joseph Banks, President of the Royal Society, a position he had occupied for forty years, fat and immobilized by gout, but still a man of great influence, commented that this was a position '. . . no one in England is so competent to fill'.

William Buckland resigned his Fellowship of Corpus Christi in March, 1824, since he was now contemplating marriage, and was appointed to a canonry of Christ Church, Oxford. He was now at the height of his powers; he was forty-one years old and following the publication in 1823 of his work, '*Reliquiae Diluvianiae*; or, Observations on the Organic Remains contained in Caves, Fissures, and Diluvial Gravel, and on other Geological Phenomena, attesting the Action of an Universal Deluge',[9] he was accepted as one of the foremost leaders of geological thought in western Europe. But his restless and bustling energy found many other outlets; in the face of strong opposition he, together with some of his influential friends, founded the

Oxford Gas Company, of which he was chairman for many years. He was an outstanding lecturer, with a gift of vivid yet economical description and '. . . extremely like Sydney Smith in his staple of character; no rival with him in wit, but like him in humour, common sense, and benevolently cheerful doctrine of Divinity . . .'.[10] A typical example of his humour was given by his son: 'There were some wonderful [fossil] footsteps once discovered near Dumfries, and my father had given a lecture upon them, I think at Edinburgh. During the discussion that followed the lecture, one of the visitors put the following question publicly: "I wish to ask the learned Doctor how it is that, according to his statement, the Cheirotherium seems always to have gone persistently in one and the same direction?" The Dean, who could give a witty answer when he liked, looked over his spectacles sternly at the questioner, and answered, "Sir – Cheirotherium was a Scotchman; he was ganging south, and na came back again," – a remark hailed with shouts of delight by a Scotch audience.'[1]

He was a born experimentalist and innovator; he was greatly interested in adult education, and played a leading part in the founding of the British Association. He was also a social reformer, and later in life, after his appointment as Dean of Westminster, initiated improvements in Westminster School and was a champion of the sanitary reforms advocated by Edwin Chadwick (1800–1890). Above all else, he had a craving to be useful in promoting the welfare of the world around him.[8] He was, as were most of his colleagues of the time, an adherent of the High Church party and a die-hard Tory.

On December 31, 1825, at Marcham Church, near Abingdon, William Buckland married Mary Morland, of Sheepstead House, near Abingdon, Berkshire. Mary Morland was a remarkable woman, and an ideal wife for Buckland. She had spent much of her childhood in Oxford in the home of Sir Christopher Pegge, M.D., F.R.S., and his wife who, to their sorrow, were childless. Mary's own mother had died soon after the birth of her daughter in 1797. Sir Christopher Pegge (1765–1822), Regius Professor of Physic at Oxford, was the son of Samuel Pegge the younger, antiquary poet and musician, who achieved fame as composer of several of the most popular songs for the Vauxhall Gardens. Sir Christopher Pegge was a chronic asthmatic and left Oxford for London in 1816 in the vain hope of alleviating his condition.[7]

Mary Morland undoubtedly owed much to this cultured home in Oxford, where she was allowed to develop an interest in geology. She made drawings of the fossils housed in Oxford; some of these drawings were used by Baron Cuvier (1769–1832) in his *Animaux Fossiles*. A sketch book belonging to Mary Morland which is now in the Devon Record Office shows her to have been a very competent and sensitive artist.[3] Mrs Gordon (born Elizabeth Oke Buckland), in the biography of her father,[8] recounts a story, '. . . which may have some foundation in fact . . .', of Dr Buckland's first encounter with his future wife. He was travelling in a coach somewhere in Dorsetshire and had just received from his bookseller Cuvier's latest book. A lady travelling in the same coach had the identical weighty volume which she had just received from the great Cuvier himself. 'They got into conversation, the drift of which was so peculiar that Dr Buckland at last exclaimed "You must be Miss Morland, to whom I am about to deliver a letter of introduction",' and '. . . she soon became Mrs Buckland.' In fact, he must have met her sooner, at least when he was writing his *Reliquiae Diluvianiae*, which was published in 1823 and contained some of her drawings, but perhaps even much earlier in the home of Sir Christopher Pegge.

Soon after the wedding, early in 1826, Dr and Mrs Buckland left for a wedding tour of Europe. This lasted most of the year, during which they visited places of geological interest. Everywhere Buckland was received with respect by his foreign colleagues. In the late autumn they returned to Oxford and their first child, Francis Trevelyan Buckland, was born on December 17, 1826, in the venerable house in Tom Quad that was to be his home for the first nineteen years of his life. When he was a man he recalled: 'I . . . am told that soon after I was hatched out my father and my godfather, the late Sir Francis Chantrey, weighed me in the kitchen scales against a leg of mutton, and that I was heavier than the joint provided for the family dinner that day.'[11]

The new baby was christened by his father in Christ Church on June 28 of the following year. Sir Francis Legatt Chantrey

(1781–1842), a close friend of Dr Buckland, was one of the sponsors and Sir John Trevelyan (1761–1828), of Nettlecombe, Somerset, was another. Chantrey, in spite of his lack of formal education, was one of the foremost sculptors of his period and at his death left his fortune to the Royal Academy. He showed something of north country brusqueness in his manner, but was at heart a kindly and considerate person, and a keen sportsman with rod and gun. The third godparent was Dr Thomas Arnold's sister Frances. She had married Dr Buckland's brother John in 1816, and had five children living; two more were born by the end of 1828.[12]

The baby was robust and lively, with the same retentive memory as his father and, no doubt stimulated by his parents, he early grew to love animals. His father clearly took pains to explain things to him, for Bompas[13] describes how, when Frank Buckland was about four years old '. . . a clergyman travelled from Devonshire to Oxford, to bring Dr Buckland some "very curious fossils". When he produced his treasures, Dr Buckland called his son, who was playing in the room, "Frankie, what are these?" "They are the vertebrae of an ichthyosaurus," lisped the child, who could not yet speak plain. The dumbfounded clergyman returned home crestfallen.'

The Buckland household was a happy and contented one. By the end of 1830 it contained three little boys and a girl; nine children were born altogether, although four died in infancy. The children were good natured, intelligent and affectionate, and their father was kind and enjoyed their company. He delighted to teach them to observe the world around them. When Black Will, the coachman of the 'Defiance' coach, bought two moribund crocodiles, each about four feet long, in Southampton in November, 1829, and carried them to Oxford as a speculation, Dr Buckland purchased them and allowed the children to play with the corpses. The scene was sketched by his friend Philip B. Duncan (1772–1863), Fellow of New College, Oxford, Keeper of the Ashmolean Museum and, perhaps slightly incongruously, founder of Savings Banks at Bath and Oxford (Plate I). Dr Buckland and another friend afterwards cooked a slice of crocodile to find out what it tasted like.[14]

There were few restrictions at home. Tables, chairs and even the floor were strewn in confusion with books, papers, geological specimens and objects of interest to the naturalist, and the brush and duster were rarely seen. Even some of the furniture itself testified to the interests of its owner, for one table was topped with specimens of lava found on Mount Etna while another was made entirely from coprolites (fossilized saurian faeces) and '. . . was often much admired by persons who had not the least idea of what they were looking at'.[15]

Although, however, it was peaceful at home, the times were troubled in the country at large. England was unsteadily recovering from the muscular cramp of war and was also suffering from the growing pains of industrialization. The Royal house was insecure and England dangerously near to revolution. George IV, gross, debauched and selfish, was unsteadily perched on the throne he had occupied since the death in 1820 of his insane old father, his unpopularity increasing. As Sir Llewellyn Woodward has pointed out: 'It may be said that he showed in his private life signs of his father's madness, and that, in his selfishness and low behaviour, he was no worse than four of his six brothers. It is difficult to find other arguments in his favour.'[16] Many Englishmen, broadminded though they may have been, held those in high places to be responsible for many of the ills of the country. Things were a little better after George IV died in June, 1830; his fat and tactless brother, William IV, in spite of his nickname 'Silly Billy', occasionally showed a sound and rugged common sense. The situation was still serious, however.

Attempts to maintain the price of corn after the Peace of 1815 by passing the Corn Laws had set landowner and manufacturer, already greatly out of sympathy with each other, even further at loggerheads. Workers in the factories and on the land were frequently inadequately paid. Where, as in the south of England, there was a labour surplus on the land, agricultural distress was widespread. Inadequate wages and the so-called 'Speenhamland Act', by which wages were made up from the poor rate, were rapidly turning the honest farm labourer into an idle pauper if not into a criminal.[17] Acts of violence were not infrequent, and rick-burning and wanton destruction of property manifestations of almost universal discontent.

Riots broke out during the autumn of 1830, when the starving field labourers of the counties south of the Thames marched about asking for a wage of half a crown a day. G. M. Trevelyan commented: 'The revenge taken by the Judges was terrible; three of the rioters were unjustly hanged and four hundred and twenty were torn from their families and transported to Australia, as convicts.'[17] In November, 1830, Dr Buckland wrote to the geologist Roderick Murchison, who later became Director General of the Geological Survey of the United Kingdom, that he was not anxious to leave Oxford at the present time '. . . for my wife's father and mother, six miles from here, are in hourly expectation of a mob from Abingdon to set fire to their premises, and there are threats of a mob coming into Oxford from the neighbourhood of Benson, and our streets, every night, are on the point of a row between town and gown.

'My brother-in-law has just come in with seven prisoners, and has lodged them in Oxford Castle for tonight. To-morrow he will take them to jail at Abingdon, where there was a rescue this morning of seven out of eight prisoners brought in from Hungerford, and a rescue will be attempted to-morrow when the men are taken over from Oxford Castle. Not one soldier is to be found in the land; and my brother-in-law* is fighting with a party of fox-hunters, turned into special constables, and galloping sixty or seventy miles a day during all the past week.'[7]

Dr Buckland, for all his bland good humour and tact, was also faced with personal opposition in the University of Oxford itself. There were some clerics who saw in geology a direct threat to their religious beliefs, and regarded Buckland with mistrust. It is true that in his *Reliquiae Diluvianiae* he had concluded that the bones found buried in the mud in caves in Britain and abroad were proof of the authenticity of Holy Writ because they belonged to animals that had roamed the countryside before the Flood, but many, such as the mammoth, were now extinct. In any event, however, it appeared that some revision of Bishop Ussher's original estimate of the age of the earth, based on the Bible, was now greatly overdue.

* Perhaps Thomas Thornhill Morland, of Sheepstead House, Master of Berkshire Fox Hounds.

Little wonder that Philip Shuttleworth, destined to become Bishop of Chichester, and fellow Wykehamist and friend of Buckland, wrote:

> Some doubts were once expressed about the Flood;
> Buckland arose, and all was clear as – mud.[8]

It is ironical, especially because of Frank Buckland's views in later life on evolution, that Dr Buckland was one of those who contributed to the corpus of knowledge that led to the publication of the *Origin of Species* in 1859. Baron von Bunsen, the German theologian and diplomatist, wrote to his wife in 1839: 'Buckland is persecuted by bigots for having asserted that among the fossils there may be a pre-Adamite species. "How" say they: "is that not direct, open infidelity? Did not death come into the world by Adam's sin?" I suppose then that the lions known to Adam were originally destined to roar throughout eternity.'[8]

Dr Buckland was also viewed with suspicion by some of his scientific colleagues, who felt that science was a serious matter and that Buckland treated it with too much levity. Charles Darwin perhaps summed up their feelings when he wrote: 'All the leading geologists were more or less known by me, at the time when geology was advancing with triumphant steps. I liked most of them, with the exception of Buckland, who though very good humoured and good-natured seemed to me a vulgar and almost coarse man. He was incited more by a craving for notoriety, which sometimes made him act like a buffoon, than by a love of science. He was not, however, selfish in his desire for notoriety; for Lyell, when a very young man, consulted him about communicating a poor paper to the Geol. Soc. which had been sent to him by a stranger, and Buckland answered—You had better do so, for it will be headed, "Communicated by Charles Lyell", and thus your name will be brought before the public.'[18]

Darwin in this instance seems to have misjudged his man. Buckland was, as already mentioned, an outstandingly good lecturer with a gift for popularizing his subject. His approach was original and sometimes dramatic, as on the occasion when he snapped at the face of a student with the skull of a hyaena. He used to begin his series of lectures by showing to the students the books that would be required and by explaining the meaning of the terms he would use. But he was very insistent on the need for field work, and often he would say at the end of his lecture: 'The next lecture will take place in the field above the quarries at Stonesfield', or, 'The class will meet at the Great Western Railway station at nine o'clock; when in the train, between Oxford and Bristol, I shall be able to point out and explain the several different formations we shall cross; and if you please, we will examine the rocks, and some of the most interesting geological features of *Clifton and its neighbourhood.*'[2]

There is no question, however, but that Buckland was eccentric. For some, the enjoyment of the distinguished company seated round his table for a meal could be marred by the bizarre foods that occasionally made their appearance. Hedgehog, of course, is not entirely unknown as a food in this country but puppy, crocodile and garden snail are perhaps more unusual. Richard Owen, the famous anatomist, and his wife, who were close friends of the family, were once given roast ostrich by the Bucklands. Mrs Owen noted in her diary that '. . . it was very much like a bit of coarse turkey'. Her husband had a very bad night after it.[19] Nevertheless, Ruskin wrote: 'I have always regretted a day of unlucky engagement on which I missed a delicate toast of mice; and remembered with delight being waited upon one hot summer morning by two graceful and polite little Caroline lizards, which kept off the flies.'[10] Frank Buckland and his father once visited a foreign cathedral '. . . where was exhibited a martyr's blood – dark spots on the pavement ever fresh and ineradicable'. Dr Buckland dropped to his knees and touched the spots with his tongue. 'I can tell you what it is; it is bat's urine.'[20]

Frank Buckland inherited both his father's happy facility as a lecturer, and also his inquisitive palate. One is reminded, for example, of his complaint to a fellow-student at Oxford about earwigs being 'so horribly bitter'.[21] The love of animals was an inescapable part of life in the Buckland household. The children were encouraged to have pets, and not only pets of the normal, mundane, variety, such as cavies or rabbits, but more exciting pets such as snakes and monkeys. Caroline Owen noted in her diary in November, 1838: 'A visit from Dr and Mrs Buckland and their two eldest boys, a friend, and a couple of live marmots . . . . The Doctor sat on the sofa with the two marmots and his bag on his lap. They were all going to Drury Lane. I don't know whether the marmots are going too!'[19]

Mrs Gordon, in her charming biography of her father,[8] has left a vivid picture of the training the children received. Their mother, kind but firm, saw to it that they were kept occupied in reading, gardening, looking after their pets, and doing useful jobs, for which they earned pocket money. Their father regarded laziness as a sin and he was strict only in this one particular, that he never allowed his children to be unemployed. He made sure that his children met the learned and distinguished visitors who constantly visited the house in Oxford, and they were taught to take an interest in the conversation at meals. Every evening, he would have some curious fact or anecdote to tell his children and in return he expected some observation or question from each of them.

Their mother would never allow gossip but would say: 'My dears, educated people always talk of things; it is only in the servants' hall that people talk gossip.' On Sundays, she took the younger children to a church where there was 'an excellent evangelical preacher' while Dr Buckland, in the summer wearing a flower in his buttonhole, took the older children to Christ Church. Frank Buckland recalled years later how pigeons were seen in Carfax only on Sundays because the farmers met at the cross-roads there on the previous evening to compare notes on the harvest.[22] After an early dinner the whole family would then walk in Christ Church meadow or, if this was flooded, Headington Hill. Dr Buckland, a keen gardener and botanist, and his family would then compare notes on the world of nature.

The scene painted by Mrs Gordon is indeed an attractive one, and also illustrative of an age that is gone and an attitude to life that it would be hard to find today. In fact the scene is almost too idyllic; it is perhaps merely the picture drawn by an elderly woman looking back upon her childhood. To quote again: 'Sometimes they were sent on an errand to take some "alicampane" – an old-fashioned herbal remedy made up with sugar in pink and white squares, bought from some old Meg

Merrilies in the market – to a barge-man with a bad cough, who, with the aid of his family was unloading the barge as it lay under the shadow of the fine old Norman keep from whose postern gate, as they were told, the Empress Maud escaped in a white sheet over the frozen river to Abingdon.

'The old-world corner of Oxford, with the high earth mound adjoining, and the Gaol, or Castle, as it was then called, was always full of mysterious interest to the little people. There were no railways then, and several gaily-painted barges were often to be seen moored along the Canal Wharf, supplying the city with coals, salt or pottery. However grimy their cargo might be, their owners contrived to keep fresh and bright the gay lines of colour on the sides of the little cabin at the end of the long black hull. Dr Buckland, or occasionally a good-natured bargee, would lift the children into the empty barge and allow them to peep into the snug little abode, reeking with the savoury smell which issued from a black iron pot on its small hob, while from the tiny low chimney-pipe curled the prettiest possible wreath of blue-grey smoke.'

Even if this does put too rosy a hue upon the scene, it indicates a very happy and contented childhood. Frank Buckland, besides inheriting his father's knack of lecturing well, and his interest in exotic food, also inherited the gift of keen and close observation. The greatest gift of all, however, was without doubt his humanity; this he acquired from both his parents in those early years in Oxford. It was to this happy, busy and cultured home that he returned during his holidays from school.

CHAPTER TWO

School

FRANK BUCKLAND received his earliest schooling from his mother, who spent her mornings superintending the instruction of her children '. . . . in sound and useful knowledge'.[2] Mrs Buckland was affectionate and deeply religious, and she took pains to inculcate these same qualities in her children. She gave her first-born a desk for his eighth birthday, in December, 1834; it was accompanied by a letter he treasured all his life:

> My dearest Frank, I hope you will like the Desk I have bought for you and that you will make good use of it both at home and at school. I daresay you will write many a Latin and perhaps a Greek exercise upon it – I hope too you will often remember the mother who gave it to you, and who loves you so dearly. Perhaps when you have a very hard lesson and feel inclined to be irritable and out of humour, you may look at your desk, and the thought may come into your heart 'would not my poor mother be vexed to see me so ill tempered,' and at this thought perhaps you may cast off the naughty fit, for the sake of the Parent who will never cease to pray that God will send his holy spirit upon you – God bless you my dear child – May you so give an account of the Talents committed to your charge, that like the faithful servant in the Parable, your heavenly master may say to you – 'Well done thou good and faithful servant. Enter thou into the joy of the Lord.' Your Grandmama has sent you another number of the Naturalist's Cabinet, and your Papa gives you the numbers that were wanted to make up the set, so you will have quite a Library of pretty books.
>
> Your affectionate mother,
> Mary Buckland.

Frank Buckland preserved another similar letter written to him by his mother on his fifth birthday (Plate II).

In 1835, when he was about eight and a half years of age, he was sent to the boarding-school run by the Reverend Alexander MacDonald, Vicar of Cotterstock, Northamptonshire. On August 8, 1835, he wrote his first letter from school to his mother, who was staying with the Chantreys in Pimlico. He was clearly very homesick.

> My dear mother will you right to me very often I do not like school so much as i thught I sude be sure and rite very often believ me youre affesenate sone frank buckland
> It is a very bad letter.
> be sure and right to me befor y. you saile.[23]

Shortly afterwards, his parents travelled to Europe on holiday, and visited France, Belgium and Germany. 'From Ostend to Ghent', his mother wrote to him in September, 'we travelled by the canal in very pretty Barges which were towed by four horses at the rate of 5 miles an hour; this was very dull travelling, for the banks of the canal were sometimes higher than the top of our boat.' She also referred to the great quantity of fruit on sale. 'Old women, very like the old women on Folly Bridge in Oxford, sit at stalls covered with apples, Pears, Peaches, Plums, Filberts etc. etc. which they sell very cheap.' Like many other tourists of the period, Dr and Mrs Buckland visited the battlefields of Waterloo; Mrs Buckland promised to tell her son all about it at Christmas time.[23]

After two years with Mr MacDonald, Frank Buckland was sent in 1837 to the school run by his uncle, the Reverend John Buckland, at Laleham, a typical Thames-side village, near Staines. John Buckland (1785–1859) went up to Trinity College, Oxford, in 1802, at the age of 16, and obtained his B.A. in 1806 and M.A. in 1809.[23] While still at Oxford, he became friendly with Thomas Arnold, who went up to Corpus Christi in 1811, and together with Trevenen Penrose, Arnold's future brother-in-law, they explored places of interest such as Blenheim, Stowe and Nuneham Courtenay. In July, 1816, Buckland married Thomas Arnold's sister, Frances.[6]

John Buckland in 1815 had set up a small school at Hampton on the Thames; in 1819 he and Thomas Arnold decided to go into partnership. Since, however, the accommodation in Hampton was too small, a search was made for more suitable premises. Two adjacent houses in Laleham, one belonging to a doctor, the other to an East Indian captain, were rented. Buckland taught the younger boys, and Arnold the older ones.[6]

Although the two establishments were run separately, it was the original intention to share profits and expenses. This arrangement did not apparently work very well, and in 1824 the business association was dissolved, although the two men remained good friends. In 1829, Thomas Arnold was appointed headmaster of Rugby, while John Buckland continued to run his school at Laleham and was later dubbed 'the Father of the English Preparatory School' by one headmaster of Winchester.*

John Buckland is said to have been a good teacher but a brutal pedagogue, and Frank Buckland's life at Laleham cannot have been an entirely happy one. In 1838 William Buckland drafted to his brother a letter which makes it quite clear that John Buckland was excessively harsh to his pupils. The scribbled insertions and vigorous deletions in this draft show the amount of thought put into its composition; it is probable that a letter was sent since otherwise there seems little point in preserving the copy.

> 'Dear John, I have been very unhappy since my boys' return from school and have postponed from day to day the very painful task which I feel is my Duty to perform of writing to remonstrate against your mode of punishing children with a round ruler, which is calculated to inflict on their hands and has inflicted on Frank an injury that he will carry to the Grave. I noticed this injury when I was at Laleham not long after the blow had been inflicted. A portion of the joint has been crushed and the injury is irremediable.
>
> On a former occasion he had a large wound and an extensive gash through the skin of a finger of his R. hand had been

* John Buckland retired in 1853 and died in 1859. His son Matthew (1822–1883) and grandson Francis Matthew (1854–1913) continued to run the school. It was moved to Bexhill-on-Sea in 1911, mainly because the views expressed by many doctors at that time that the Thames Valley was unhealthy were resulting in a fall in the number of pupils.[25]

cut by the end of the same ruler – and on Edward's first return [Edward Copleston Buckland, 1828–1873] a nail had recently been torn off from a finger by the same instrument.

I have put Frank's hand under the care of Mr Tuckwell who has a similar injury produced by a dislocation and fracture of a finger in a fall from his Horse, which will never be got rid of nor does he think that Frank's bone will ever recover the injury it has sustained. I feel it therefore my Duty to require from you as a condition of my boys' return again to Laleham, an assurance that they shall no more be punished by blows inflicted with a round ruler on the hand more specially on the *Right* Hand.

I have no objection to whipping or caning provided it be not on the Hand or Hands, be done with instruments that will not cut through the skin or break or crush the bones, but I protest against punishment accompanied with cutting, maiming and mutilating of that which next to the Head is the most important organ of the body, that is the hand.

The surface of the body affords abundant space for punishment by cane or birch which can leave only passing [?] scars but can inflict no permanent injury let boys be flogged or caned on the back and shoulders as much as may be needful but let them not be maimed with an inflexible round ruler it may lacerate a tendon and produce lock jaw, or break a bone, or injure for life a joint and at the heart must render callous and inflexible that skin at the extremities of the fingers in which Nature has placed the most delicate and important Nerves of Touch that occur in the Body.[23]

The draft continues in a similar vein for page after page. Frank Buckland was in fact branded for life by his uncle, and showed the injury on his hands to some of his friends only a year or two before his death.[26]

The school was not all work and punishment, however, and his grandmother Morland at Abingdon was sufficiently close for an occasional visit to be made to see her. Her husband, Mr Benjamin Morland, had died in 1833. Frank Buckland wrote to his mother in March, 1838:

We had a holiday on Teusday and I got so hoarse with hollowing that I quite lost my voice. I like old Priestly best he is the top of the school. I have been out evry day this week except Thursday and so have all the boys except one or two and we have had some very good games. Grandmama has been so kind as to give me such a lot of oranges for us evry time I go up. Next time you send a parcel send a piece of spunge apeace to wash our faces and a knife for me. Edward is got quite well.

Believe me your most affectionate son

F. T. Buckland.[23]

He remained at Laleham until he was twelve years old. His father, who took a close interest in the studies of his children, wrote in June, 1839:

Dear Frank,

I have been much pleased with the amended spelling in your last letter and now that you are going to Winchester presume you will feel it beneath your dignity to retain your former childish and careless habits of neglect as to this matter. I inclose a note to your Uncle desiring him if he think you equal to it to let you read a little of one of the easier plays of Euripides, because they read this author in the Class I think you will be placed in, if you have read ever so little of Euripides. I send a bottle of lemonade powder of which a tea spoon full put into a Tumbler of water will produce effervescence and remain with kind love to Edward

Your affectionate Father

W. Buckland.[23]

In July he was sent to Winchester, where he had been elected a Scholar on the nomination of his father's old school friend and colleague, Dr Philip Shuttleworth, Warden of New College, Oxford, and later to be appointed Bishop of Chichester.

William of Wykeham had intended to found a secular college for training boys for entry to New College, Oxford, which he also founded, and where they would fit themselves '. . . for the service of God in Church and State'. The original foundation of St Mary's College, Winchester, allowed for a Warden (custos), and ten Fellows, who were all priests, seventy Scholars, the Headmaster (informator), Undermaster (hostiarius), three Chaplains, three Clerks or singing men (capellani), and sixteen Choristers to sing in the college chapel. The Choristers and their schoolmaster were appointed by the Warden and, at least by the nineteenth century, had their own independent school and boarding establishment. They were '. . . poor boys of a lower rank in life than the Scholars.'[27]

Early in the history of the school, the Headmaster also taught a few of the *filii nobilium*, or sons of the nobility. This practice in time became greatly extended, as at many other schools of ancient foundation, and the Headmaster depended very largely, not only for his own income, but also for the funds necessary for running the whole school, upon the fees paid by the parents of these 'Commoners', or 'Gentlemen Commoners' as they were sometimes termed.

A curious result of this development was that whilst the Warden and Fellows were responsible for the administration of the Scholars, they had no responsibilities for, and little if any jurisdiction over, the Commoners, who were the concern solely of the Headmaster.[27] Commoners and Scholars were taught together, but fed, played and slept separately. There was, not unnaturally, some competition for election as a Scholar, which was done by nomination of a Fellow, since fees for Commoners in Buckland's time were about £120; Scholars had to pay only for 'extras' amounting to perhaps £30 or £40 a year. There was occasional friction between Commoners and Scholars.

The Headmaster of Winchester during Frank's time there was Dr George Moberly (1803–1885), who eventually became Bishop of Salisbury. Moberly, educated at Winchester and Balliol, was not an innovator. According to the Dictionary of National Biography, 'Although beloved by many of his pupils, it cannot be said that he gave any impulse to the fame or progress of the school . . .';[7] nevertheless, he appears to have reduced, to some small extent, the harsh conditions under which boys were '. . . roughed into manhood by intercourse with other boys', to repeat Farington's much-quoted phrase. He was a firm believer in the educational and disciplinary value of 'fagging', and prefects under his rule retained their considerable powers of 'tunding' junior boys with a ground-ash stick made from a sapling, popularly believed to be boiled with the mutton to get the grease into it and said by Frank Buckland to be as tough as whalebone.[28]

Dr Moberly did not, however, resort to anything like the same extent to the brutal flogging of boys in front of the whole school which had been customary before his time. He felt, he said, that this punishment was '. . . neither severe enough nor is it *nil*'. The instrument employed consisted of four strong apple twigs about three feet long, fixed to the end of a long wooden handle. This was applied vigorously to a bared region about the middle of the small of the back.[27]

The second master during Frank Buckland's day was Dr Charles Wordsworth (1806–1892). Wordsworth, nephew of the poet, was a brilliant classical scholar whose Greek Grammar was for a long time used almost everywhere in England. Together with the Warden, the Reverend Mr Barter, he was responsible for initiating a new period in the religious life of the school. He was tall, handsome and friendly, but could occasionally be severe. He eventually became Bishop of St Andrews, Dunkeld and Dunblane.[7]

Like all other Public Schools of the period, the curriculum was almost entirely classical. The day was spent in studying Greek and Latin grammar, composing verses, or vulguses as they were termed in schoolboy slang, and committing to memory long passages from the classics. Little time was devoted to arithmetic and modern languages, which were regarded as 'commercial' subjects, and geography and history were only studied as they applied to ancient Greece and Rome. No attention was paid to science.

The working day was long, and appears to have followed much the same pattern throughout the school. For example, in 1840, when he was thirteen years of age, Frank Buckland's time-table on a Monday – a full day's work – was as follows:

6.45	Chapel	1.15	Dinner
7.00	School	2.00	School
8.30	Breakfast	6.00	Supper
9.30	School	7.30	Play
12.00	Play	9.00	Chapel
1.00	Wash	9.15	Bed

Not every day was so full, however. On Tuesday only four hours were spent in school, the rest of the time was spent playing on 'Hills' which, as already mentioned, was St

PLATE I

Frank Buckland aged $2\frac{3}{4}$ years. One of the other children may be Edward Buckland, born in July, 1828. The crocodiles were purchased in Southampton by Black Will, the coachman of the 'Defiance' coach, and sold by him to Dr Buckland in Oxford. The sketch labelled 'The Last Hyaena' refers to Dr Buckland's work on cave deposits.

From a sketch by Philip Duncan in the Devon Record Office and Exeter Diocesan Record Office.

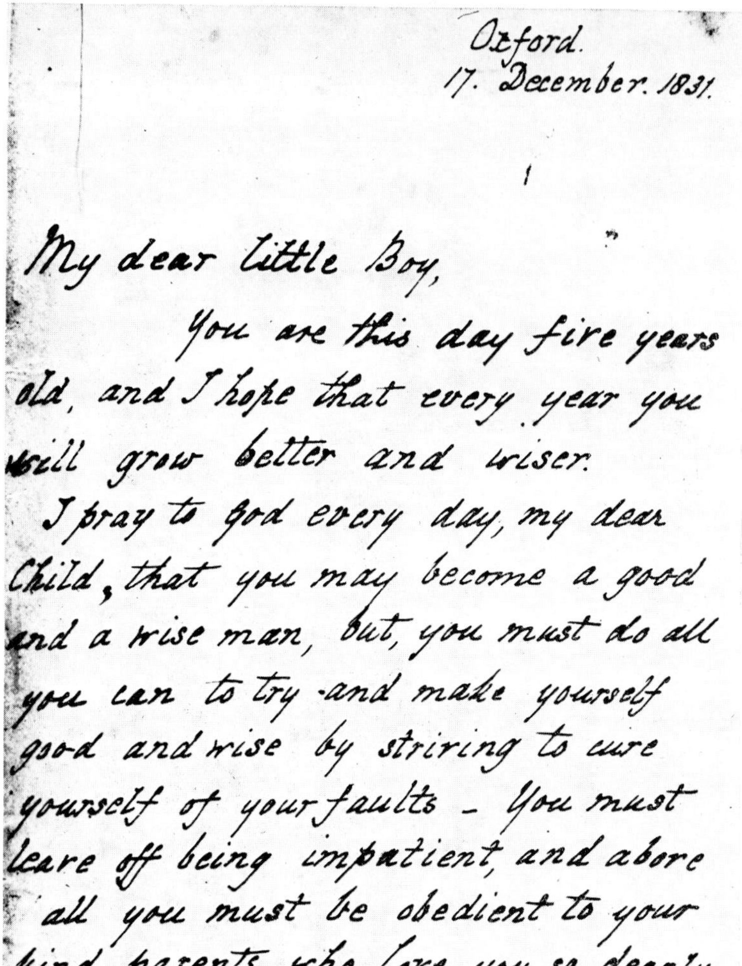

Oxford.
17. December. 1831.

My dear little Boy,

You are this day five years old, and I hope that every year you will grow better and wiser.

I pray to God every day, my dear Child, that you may become a good and a wise man, but, you must do all you can to try and make yourself good and wise by striving to cure yourself of your faults – You must leave off being impatient, and above all you must be obedient to your kind parents, who love you so dearly, and who never desire you to do any thing but what is for your good. God loves obedient, gentle children, but the disobedient he will surely punish. I hope my dearest Frank will be amongst the good and obedient children whom God will reward in this world and the next.

Your very affectionate mother, Mary Buckland.

PLATE II

Mary Buckland's letter to Frank on his fifth birthday. From the original in the Library of the Royal College of Surgeons of England.

Catherine's Hill behind the school. Wednesday followed the same pattern as Monday, except that beef was served at the midday meal. Thursday and Friday, however, were half-holidays and the afternoons were spent on 'Hills'. Saturday was a full day, but the only work done on Sunday was to learn an exercise or two for the following day. The time-table of the more senior boys allowed less time for play.[23]

Although the Public Schools had been severely criticized on numerous counts, including the almost entirely classical nature of the curricula, at least from early in the nineteenth century,[5] there could be little change until the Universities of Oxford and Cambridge altered their requirements. There could be no question of varying a boy's course of study according to his interests and abilities and one is reminded of Charles Darwin, nicknamed 'Gas' by his friends because of his interest in chemistry, who was publicly rebuked by his Headmaster at Shrewsbury, the great Dr Butler, for wasting his time on such useless subjects. Dr Moberly shared similar views; as a result of criticisms of the curriculum he introduced in the late 1850s an annual course of ten to twelve lectures on a scientific subject. When asked in 1862 by the Clarendon Commission whether he thought that these were of any value, he replied in the following manner:

> An amateur of science is the better for knowing the elements of it, and every man of liberal education is the better for not being ignorant of any thing, but compared with other things a scientific fact, either as conveyed by a lecturer, or as reproduced in examination, is a fact which produces nothing in a boy's mind. It is simply a barren fact, which after a few years becomes confused with other facts and is forgotten. It leads to nothing. It does not germinate, it is a perfectly unfruitful fact.[27]

Winchester, like most schools, suffered from under-staffing. Indeed the fagging system originally arose largely from this cause. At Winchester every prefect was made a 'tutor' of a group of junior boys and received a guinea every half-year from the parents of each boy he taught. Dr Wordsworth complained to the Warden of this practice and the duties of the 'boy tutors' were restricted in Frank Buckland's day to that of helping in the composition of the little boys.[4] They were still paid for their services, however, and each prefect had an annual income from this source of between £20 and £30.[27]

In later life, Buckland recalled his time at Winchester.[28] He described his first arrival as ' . . . a frightened and trembling lad'.

> In those days there was no railway to Winchester and I went from Oxford to Winchester in a four-horse coach, the driver of which wore most wonderful top-boots and a marvellous coat with gigantic buttons. I had great respect for this coachman, as he once brought my father a semi-dead crocodile, in the coach boot, from Southampton. My father turned the dead crocodile into the pond in the middle of the quadrangle at Christ Church, to revive him; but he refused to be revived, so I rode about upon him, Waterton fashion, and somehow I always associated the Southampton coachman with a crocodile. I recollect perfectly well that he once told me he had driven my mother to school at Southampton, and this made me think him very old. Soon after we had driven over Folly Bridge on our road to Winchester, crossing the Thames at Oxford, and were ascending the Bagley Wood Hill on the Abingdon Road, the rest of the passengers began to complain about a nasty unpleasant smell, which apparently proceeded from the luggage on the top of the coach. A bluebottle fly first appeared from out of Bagley Wood, than another, until a perfect swarm of flies soon followed the coach, hovering and buzzing over the luggage. The passengers were mostly Oxford boys, going to Winchester, and there was a strong idea among them that somehow or other *I* knew from whence this odour proceeded. I knew perfectly well the cause of the smell, but I said nothing. The 'governor', then Canon of Christ Church, had kept a haunch of venison for me to take as a present to the headmaster, Dr Moberly; he had kept it so long hanging up in the larder at Christ Church that it had become very 'exalted' indeed; nevertheless he packed it up, thinking to make it last anyhow as far as Winchester. His experiment failed, and the other boys punched my head on the top of the coach, and were very near throwing me and my venison overboard altogether.

Perhaps it was to this experience that he was referring in a cryptic sentence in one of his letters home in August, 1842: 'the venison stunck very much as we were going along in the coach'.[23]

He also described some of the experiences to be endured by new boys. Some, such as 'launching' across the floor of the dormitory, in the middle of the night, the bed with the sleeping new boy in it, leaving the frightened victim to rearrange his bed as best he could, were harmless enough. Others, at least by modern standards, were sadistically cruel.

The newest boy in each of the Scholars' dormitories was called 'Junior in chambers'. Buckland wrote that in his time the 'Junior in chambers' had a 'precious hard time of it'. 'He had to get up at "first peal", i.e. when the chapel bell rang – and this was awfully early in the morning – call all the boys in the room, light the fire, put out the prefects' washing apparatus, etc. The Winchester fires were large faggots burnt upon "dog-irons". It requires great art to make a faggot light quickly, and the burning sticks were awkward to handle. No tongs were allowed; so when a boy first took office he had a pair of "tin gloves" given him; i.e. one of the seniors took the red-hot end of a bit of stick, and blowing it to keep it alight made a mark down all the fingers and round the wrists; after he had received his 'tin gloves' woe be to the boy who managed the faggots clumsily, for he instantly was formally presented with another pair of "tin gloves".'[28]

Buckland was junior in the Second Chamber during the first half and '. . . had to keep the mess things of the family'. He also noted that he '. . . was ill towards the end of the half with boils on my arm. Went down to Lyme in the holydays.'[23] In the next half, however, he was the second junior in the Fifth Chamber, and his duties no doubt differed accordingly. The school year was still divided into two terms, or halves; Dr Thomas Arnold's practice at Rugby of dividing the year into three terms had not yet been adopted at Winchester.

Harsh, severe and brutal as the life at Winchester may appear, it was probably an improvement on what Frank Buckland's father had had to endure. It was probably also a great improvement on Laleham, where his uncle seems to have come near to breaking the boy's spirit. 'He is so perplext', wrote Dr Buckland to Dr Moberly, 'by the mixing up of other formulae [?] that a Confusion has come over him not easily to be got over.

'He can learn by heart and with understanding as rapidly as most boys but he has so low an estimation of his own powers and wants great encouragement. The least rebuke makes him Despair and pronounce himself a fool. He has evidently been cowed and is afraid of the ridicule of other boys and ashamed to risk a wrong answer.

'He gives up instantly in despair that which the least encouragement wd. enable him to accomplish.'[23]

His father, always interested in his son's progress, writing to him soon after he had arrived at Winchester, asked him what class he was in, whether he found the work easy or hard, what books he read, and many similar questions. As a footnote he added: 'You will not be sorry to have got rid of the Laleham Impositions.'[23]

'Fat Buckland' or 'Old Buckland' was a universal favourite. He was short and broad shouldered, with a shock of chestnut hair, which did not respond very readily to the comb, ruddy cheeks and eyes that sparkled with fun. 'Fast and furious was the fun in going home with him from Winchester on the coach-top; the quiet streets of Newbury and Abingdon, the summit of Ilsley Downs, the shades of Bagley Wood, echoing with his jokes, his great post-horn, his chaff of passers by, and the songs he elicited from purple-faced Old Stephens the coachman.'[29]

He was not an outstanding scholar, although he seems to have performed his tasks conscientiously, and Dr Wordsworth was able to write to Dr Buckland in January, 1842: 'Of your son, I have nothing to say, but what, I rejoice to think, *must give you pleasure*. He continues to make *good, steady*, – I might almost say – rapid progress, and to afford me *great* satisfaction by his diligence, and *behaviour in every respect*.' He wrote again in similar terms in July of the same year: he '. . . has been giving in uniformly in the same steady, industrious, attentive way as before – making very decided creditable progress – and giving me every reason to be pleased with his behaviour.'[23] The following year, Dr Moberly wrote to Dr Buckland: '. . . I am happy to be able to speak in high terms of your eldest son's uniform diligence and conduct during the last half year at Winchester. He is thoroughly steady and to be depended upon.'[23]

Frank Buckland had already developed a taste for natural history and much of his spare time was spent in catching and dissecting animals, or preparing and mounting their skins. The smaller bodies were frequently cooked and eaten; the larger ones were allowed to macerate in a pond until the flesh fell from the bones. He also kept pets in the school, including an owl, buzzard, magpie and raccoon. 'He brought back with him one half year a large white rat, which used to nestle in his bosom or sleeve, escaping, and contracting alliances with the old brown rats of founders kin behind the wainscoting, it peopled the school ere long with a race of piebalds.'[29]

He delighted to trap field mice on 'Hills', and used to cook them over a fire of twigs from the neighbouring farmer's fields, until complaints forced him to cook the mice in College. His ability as a poacher, however, made him much in demand by senior boys. He would 'wire' trout by slipping a fine wire over their heads. One of his friends in later life recalled some of these poaching excursions: 'Trout moreover could be "tickled" as well as wired: ascending the tiny open channels which flushed the main rivers, and lying with their heads against the stream, they were approached softly from behind, the fingers passed caressingly up their spotted sides until the gills were reached, when a sudden clutch secured and landed them. All this involved much trespassing and hedgebreaking, and vexed the righteous soul of Farmer Bridges – "Brodger" as we called him – who rented the meadows, and often appeared in person to remonstrate. Remonstrate, except at a distance, he could not: for he wore a pair of brick-red gaiters which advertised his approach from afar, and he was no match for our agility and speed. Once indeed he caught us, bringing with him labourers whom he disposed strategically behind trees and hedges, and who closed in upon us unexpectedly with one accord. We were between the devil and the deep sea – between Brodger and a deep part of the river known as "Goldfinch's." "We must swim for it, Tuckwell," said Frank, and in we went. Our sleeves were crammed with fish: comatose through exile from their native element, they revived on restoration to it. "By Jove," bubbled Frank as we swam, his mouth half full of water, "my trout have come alive." "So have mine, by Jove," I answered, and they kicked and floundered impedingly. However, we reached the further bank, emerged dripping like two water-gods, and securely paid our compliments across the river to Brodger and his grinning satellites.'[29]

His father took an interest in his hobbies as well as his work. 'I think the squirrel died of starvation,' wrote Frank to his father in July, 1842, 'for he only eat some buiscuit while he was here. I got up to see the Eclipse on Friday, but it was too cloudy to see any think which was great loss.'[23]

As he became older, it was decided that he should become a surgeon. He would often visit the local hospital in Winchester where he was on friendly terms with some of the staff and would exchange pieces of human anatomy for eels and trout. At this period, before the passing of the Medical Act of 1858, surgeons learnt their craft by a system very like apprenticeship, and there would have been little difficulty in his being shown all that went on in the hospital. He began to take a professional interest in his fellow pupils and would give sixpence to any junior who would allow himself to be bled. It is also recorded that a Commoner with a curiously shaped head once overheard Buckland muttering to himself: 'What wouldn't I give for that fellow's skull.'[13]

Dr Buckland was, however, anxious that his son should gain his degree at Oxford before beginning his surgical training. In any event, according to the statutes, he could not remain as Scholar at Winchester beyond the age of 18 years, when he was perhaps rather young to commence hospital work. As early as August, 1842, Dr Buckland wrote to his son:

> I have seen Dr Bridges who strongly advises your standing at Corpus. He was elected at 16 and a boy under 16 (Martin Woolcomb) the youngest of 12 candidates was elected with me in 1801. Among those not elected was your Warden's elder brother.
>
> In the Corpus election due allowance is made for Age and respect is had to Moral Character. Failure is no Disgrace and the Ceremony of an election will be useful acquisition of knowledge.

> There has never been an Hour for the last Century and a quarter in which some member of our family has not been on the foundation at Corpus, and I shd. regret much of your not availing yourself of the present occasion which may possibly place you in the steps of your Father's Great Uncle of Warborough.[23]

Dr Buckland began to coach his son by post for the Corpus Examination. 'I find Homer may be used in the Corpus Examination read therefore what I advise you', he wrote in a private letter, and set his son exercises to be sent to him by post, concluding with ' . . . all this for your private ear'.

In spite of these attempts, however, Frank failed to gain entry to Corpus. He also failed in 1844 to obtain a scholarship at Magdalen College, a fact he apparently regarded as lucky.[23] He matriculated at the end of May, 1844,[24] however, and his father wrote to him at Winchester early in July, 'I write this to desire you will resign immediately', adding as a postscript, 'write immediately to say when you will come home'.[23]

His schooldays were now at an end. He was a man and about to enter Christ Church. Dr Moberly wrote this valedictory letter to Dr Buckland:

> My dear Sir,
>
> On taking leave of your son Frank from Winchester, I am most anxious to express to you my high sense of his great good conduct and attention while he has been under my care. He has been unfailingly steady and careful in everything which he has had to do and carries away the character of a most amiable and right minded fellow. – I was very sorry to find that he had made so many mistakes in his examination at Christ Church – sorry, rather than surprized, I must say: for I know how strong his propensity to blunder is, even in matters which he knows. But I do trust that when he comes to be known, he will be found to have got more grammatical proficiency than he can yet have credit for. This same kind of inaccuracy however is what I have for a long while past most lamented in him.[23]

CHAPTER THREE

Oxford

THE DEATH OF HER SON Adam Sedgwick Conybeare Buckland at the age of six in September, 1844, was a great shock to Mrs Buckland, and her husband therefore took his family to Lyme by coach for a change of air. Here they collected geological specimens under his guidance and made the acquaintance of Miss Mary Anning, the remarkable woman who had devoted her life to collecting specimens of fossil saurians from the Dorsetshire lias.[8]

Frank Buckland returned from his holiday and entered Christ Church as a Commoner in October, 1844; he would not have been required to take a competitive entry examination, although he might have been asked to construe a few lines of Homer and Virgil, and to render a piece of English into Latin.[30] He had grown up in the shadow of Tom Tower, so that he knew well enough the life he was to lead for the next four years.

It was perhaps unfortunate that he had failed to gain a Scholarship to Corpus Christi; perhaps it was not only family sentiment that made Dr Buckland wish to see his son there. Corpus Christi, one of the smaller colleges, had maintained a remarkably high standard of scholastic achievement. Christ Church under Dean Gaisford, on the other hand, was in the middle of a period of temporary eclipse. Gaisford himself was a brilliant classical scholar, but he was not temperamentally suited to be head of a college like Christ Church at that period. Furthermore, he was not a believer in the value of the university examinations, did not encourage his men to do well in them, and in consequence the number of first class honours obtained by his undergraduates in the examination schools fell steeply during his rule.[30]

Another, and perhaps more important, cause of this

decline in standards of scholarship was the ancient system, which was abolished in 1854, of awarding Studentships by nomination of the Dean and Canons. The tutors of the college were chosen from the roll of Students, of whom there were one hundred and one. The Students were entitled to certain privileges and to a share in the income of the college; they had no voice in its government, however. Studentships were tenable for life, provided the recipient refrained from marriage and entered holy orders, although this latter condition was waived in certain special instances. This system clearly possessed inherent weaknesses and, if standards of teaching were to be maintained, demanded constant vigilance on the part of the college authorities.[31] Unfortunately, Students were all too frequently nominated '. . . on private grounds, irrespective of intellectual merit'.[30] The nominees were not, of course, necessarily destined to become tutors, but the numbers of really able men capable of becoming tutors were reduced by this system.

Frank Buckland himself, who was by no means an outstanding scholar, was formally admitted a Student on Christmas Eve, 1844, and received an income from this source until his marriage in 1863.[32] It was customary for the Student designate to write to the college authorities a formal letter in Latin asking to be admitted to the Studentship to which he had been nominated. A copy of Frank Buckland's letter, in somewhat deplorable medieval Latin, has survived.[23]

Gaisford was not good at handling men; in fairness to him, however, it should be added that some of the men were remarkably difficult to handle. The college was a large one and some of the undergraduates were not disposed to work. One of Frank Buckland's contemporaries remarked: 'There was a precious mischievous lot at Christ Church in my day, and we used to take a pride in annoying the old Dean in every conceivable way.'[33] Buckland certainly did not belong to this set.

Order was maintained by the levying of fines, by the imposition of the writing of lines or, in more serious matters, by confining the undergraduate within the college precincts, or forbidding his presence in college for a period. The ultimate punishment was to expel him altogether. For the wealthy, the fines mattered little, and the lines could be purchased from an individual named Boddington, who dwelt in Oriel Lane; the rates were 1s 6d for 100 Latin lines and 2s 0d for 100 Greek ones.[33]

Like most other undergraduates of the period Frank Buckland largely studied the classics, in which he seems to have displayed an average proficiency.[34] According to a colleague of later years, however, '. . . he contrived to acquire a large share of classical knowledge. He had whole passages of Virgil at his fingers' ends. He used to say, when he could not understand an act of parliament, that he always turned it into Latin.'[26]

His interests ranged widely; he attended his father's lectures in geology, Dr Daubeny's in chemistry, and others in electricity, mechanics and acoustics. A sketch of his rooms made by his friend Philip Shuttleworth clearly shows his absorbing passion for natural history (Plate III). His rooms were on the ground floor in the corner of what had come to be known as Fell's Buildings. These were erected in 1672–1679 during Dr John Fell's period as Dean, and were demolished in 1863 to make way for the present pseudo-Venetian Gothic Meadow Buildings.[35] They were described by Thompson, the author of the standard history of the college, as 'a somewhat mean block of buildings',[30] and the tractarian Frederick Oakeley, who perhaps deserves to be remembered at least for his translation of 'Adeste Fideles', in commenting on his experience as a raw young undergraduate, said: 'I used to find relief in a good cry when I came to my unutterably dismal rooms in Fell's Buildings.'[36] By the 1840s the structure was dilapidated and damp and infested with mice.

If the buildings were depressing, however, Frank Buckland did his utmost to enliven the inmates. He would entertain his friends to breakfast in his rooms, wearing a blue pea-jacket and a German student's red cap with a gold tassel. At irregular intervals during the day and night he would perform erratic exercises on a tremendous wooden horn or halloo an imaginary fox.[20] He appears to have played the French horn with some proficiency, for Caroline Owen, wife of the great anatomist, noted in her diary her attendance at a dinner party and added, 'Frank Buckland afterwards favoured us with a solo on the French horn. . . .'[19]

He kept a small menagerie in and about his rooms. A contemporary speaks of marmots, snakes, guinea pigs, a dove, monkey and chameleon which shared his rooms, and an eagle, jackal, pariah dog and baby bear which lived at one time or another in the vicinity.[20] Bompas tells how some of the pets tended to stray; one morning Frank was called in haste to remove a marmot from the Chapter House, where the Chapter was about to meet. The eagle escaped one Sunday morning and entered the chapel during the eight o'clock service, advancing with wings outstretched until it was recaptured. Dean Gaisford looked unspeakable things.[13] No doubt, however, Buckland was given more latitude than was allowed to many of his fellow undergraduates. There was, for example, a rule against the keeping of dogs which was strictly enforced.

His father's long official connexion with Christ Church ended in 1845 when he was appointed by the Prime Minister, Sir Robert Peel, to the Deanery at Westminster. Dr Buckland, however, retained the Chair of Mineralogy and Geology, to which he had been appointed in 1818; he had earlier refused Peel's offer of the Canonry of Lincoln because there he would have been required to resign his Chair.[3] He was a close friend of Peel, and a frequent visitor to his house. Peel, who had the distinction of being the first man to obtain a double 'first' at Oxford, delighted in the company of clever people, especially scientists and engineers, and he would frequently entertain a party of five or six of them at Drayton Manor; Buckland himself was almost invariably present. 'Three weeks ago we had an Agricultural Party at Sir Robert Peel's at Drayton Manor', Buckland wrote to Liebig in January, 1845. 'Lord Talbot, Professor Owen, Dr Lyon Playfair, Smith of Clifton, Mr Pusey, myself, Mr Geo. Stephenson the Engineer, Mr Wheatstone. Your presence would have made the assembly perfect.'[37]

Peel appears to have relied largely upon Dr Buckland as his scientific adviser, and they were frequently in conference during the potato famine over the causes of the potato blight. Those who knew Dr Buckland well, therefore, cannot have been unduly surprised when he was appointed to succeed Dean Samuel Wilberforce at Westminster, the latter having been promoted to the See of Oxford. Mrs Buckland wrote to

Sir Philip Egerton, a long-standing family friend and one of her husband's erstwhile pupils, confirming that the family was moving to London, and added that it would be very convenient; one son, Edward Buckland, was at the Treasury and the other, Frank, would soon also be resident in London, pursuing his call to surgery. The Dean was installed on December 12, 1845, and the family moved in January, 1846. Frank, of course, remained at Christ Church, but he still saw much of his family, since his father had also taken the living of Islip, five miles north of Oxford, which was bequeathed by Edward the Confessor to the Abbot of Westminster.[8]

It was clearly now accepted that Frank was to become a surgeon. Dr Buckland was already planning the early stages of his son's career in consultation with some of his eminent acquaintances and, indeed, Frank perhaps took up surgery mainly to please his father, as is implied by Spencer Walpole,[26] for he continued to be interested in the animal kingdom as a whole.

It was apparently his father's friend William Daniel Conybeare (1787–1857), a Christ Church man, who suggested a visit to Liebig's laboratory at the University of Giessen. Conybeare, a friend with whom Dr Buckland in his bachelor days had shared many a geological excursion, had only recently been installed as Dean of Llandaff when he heard of his friend's appointment to the Deanery at Westminster. He wrote a charming letter of congratulation to his old colleague and added: '. . . my young friend Frank with his own talents and your reputation is quite sure of running a very brilliant career in the profession he has chosen with all the ardour and interest that marks genius. Do send him to Liebig in the long vacation – that I am sure will be every way most useful in his career. Even I, though hard on 60 (I shall be 58 in June) may hope to live to see him Sir Francis Buckland, Chirurgeon in Ordinary to Her Majesty – he is a great friend of mine and I *like* him as much for his modesty and civil attention to his seniors as I respect him for the talents and keen powers of attention which he has inherited and learnt from you.'[23]

Conybeare's suggestion was acted upon, and Frank Buckland spent two long vacations in Giessen. Dr and Mrs Buckland arranged to look after the Liebigs' son Georg during a prolonged stay in England in return for Frank's visit to Giessen. Dr Buckland wrote to Liebig in January, 1845, suggesting that Frank should postpone his visit until 1846, since he knew no chemistry and no German. 'He will attend Dr Daubeny's Chemistry lectures in February and March and Dr Lyon Playfair has kindly offered to take him into his lodgings and let him work in his laboratory in Manchester and to help him in his German during the next Oxford summer vacation, 1845.'[37] This excellent plan was not, however, adopted, and Frank went to Giessen in June, 1845, and again in 1846.

Liebig, who began his career as an apothecary's apprentice, had by this time become one of the best known chemists in the world, and was busily engaged in etching his name indelibly upon the tablets of history. His main contribution was perhaps in his improvement in methods of analysis, but this in turn led to much deeper insight into some of the chemical processes occurring in plants and animals. In 1842, for example, he clearly stated for the first time that the chief organic constituents of plant and animal tissues could be divided into proteins, fats and carbohydrates.[38] Liebig was a great admirer of Britain; he first visited the country in 1837, when he was treated with considerable deference at the British Association meeting at Liverpool. He certainly met Dr Buckland during his stay in Oxford in 1842, for his host, Dr Daubeny, effected the introduction,[39] but Buckland may have met him earlier. They later became very friendly.

Even without this friendship there would probably have been little difficulty in arranging for Frank to study in the laboratory. Numerous foreign workers, the majority English, were studying there,[40] and many of the famous British chemists of the mid-nineteenth century spent some time with Liebig, learning his new techniques. Liebig's institute had been greatly enlarged in 1839; it consisted of two working rooms with places for twenty-two students altogether, one for advanced pupils, the other, with inadequate lighting and ventilation, for beginners (Plate IV). There was also a lecture room which, although it seated about sixty, was generally filled with an audience of twice this number when Liebig lectured. In summer time it became so intolerably hot that those sitting on the back row lowered themselves gently out of the windows and sought to cool themselves inside and out in an adjacent wine-cellar.

In the laboratory itself the air was also frequently unbearably hot. Any operation involving the use of heat, for example evaporation or distillation, required a coal fire, for Bunsen burners were not yet in use. Fans or bellows were employed when it was desired to make the coals burn more fiercely, and inevitably a large quantity of powdery coal ash was blown into the air. The students protected their hair with a bizarre assortment of head gear, ranging from conventional felt hats to paper bags. They were mostly dressed in blue protective smocks, beneath which they perspired freely. The sulphurous atmosphere also induced a disagreeable itching.[39]

Bompas quotes from many letters, which unfortunately do not seem to have survived, written home by Frank Buckland during this period in Giessen. Frank knew little if any German when first he arrived and his first few weeks were spent in acquiring a smattering of the language. After two months in the laboratory he commented: 'I understand much more than I did at first, and generally manage to get two or three facts out of the lectures, though of course these intricate combinations, explained in a language which I must construe in my mind before I can understand, are rather difficult.'

He also gave some interesting information on the training received by students at that time:

> When a young man begins here, he generally goes through the course of analysing a set of one hundred bottles, which takes him sometimes a year. These bottles are various compounds, which he must find out – viz. in the first ten he has only to find one metal, etc; in the second, two metals or substances, etc; till at last the highest bottles contain six or seven substances, all of which he must find out. Liebig thought I had better not begin these, as I had to learn German, and to stay only a short time here. However, I think I know more chemistry than when I came. About 3 o'clock Liebig comes into the laboratory, and he seems to be able to tell everybody, whatever they may be doing, what to expect, and how to proceed.[13]

It is plain from his letters home, however, that his interests mainly lay outside the laboratory. He observed the local inhabitants, and their manner of living; he rambled in the surrounding woods and studied the animal life; he visited the neighbouring manganese mines with Liebig and shared in the pleasures of eating and drinking with his fellow students; and he wrote home letters which began to bear that stamp of original description and lively narrative for which he was later to become famous. There is little evidence in anything that he wrote at the time or subsequently that he acquired anything more than a smattering of chemical knowledge.

An interesting letter written by Frank to his father's half-brother Samuel, who later became Vicar of Torrington, Devon, indicates how much the young man enjoyed his visit to Germany. The letter is dated August 1, 1845, and is unfortunately too long to quote in full.

> I have been here now nearly two months and have enjoyed myself very much all the time. Professor Liebig has been very kind to me, he has hired for me very nice lodgings outside the town which are light and airy, and from which I have a good view. I go every day to dine at his house at one o'clock and to supper at nine. The family consists of Mrs, a son about 18 and two daughters . . . I do German all the morning till eleven, when I go to the lecture on Chemistry which lasts till ½ past 12 and then dinner till two, after dinner I generally work in the laboratory till 5 or 6. Two days a week I have a drawing lesson with the Professor who teaches the students here, and also two days an anatomy lecture on bones. I did not at first understand a single word of the lectures but do now a little. Both German and Chemistry (in a strange language) are rather hard at first . . . The students live about in the town wherever they can get lodgings, they seem altogether a very orderly sett. Their chief amusements are drinking bad beer, smoking and fighting duels with swords. . . . Most of the students have a cut somewhere in their faces from duelling. . . . They have no amusements such as cricket, rowing etc. but meet every evening to drink and smoke. . . . There are very few horses seen about here, but cows are used everywhere. These cows (universally red) draw by a yoke fastened to their horns, the poor beasts seem very much fatigued sometimes, they make them drag immense loads, in carts, quite different from those

> in England. They are all shod with iron. The country women here are all dressed buy-a-broom fashion with a curious cap and an immense bustle, and altogether look rather curious. They twist their hair upon the top of the head from all sides, and so make a cushion to carry their baskets upon. I have seen them carrying large pails of water etc. this way, with the greatest dexterity. The men all wear blue smock frocks and the old fellows cocked hats, knee britches, stockings and buckle shoes. They seem to leave all the work to the women and so do nothing else but sit in their carts and drive their cows about. . . . Most of the country women on Sundays and holidays wear high heeled shoes and the wives wear an additional peticoat for every hundred guldens (a gulden is 1*s* 8*d*) their husbands have got so that on some an immense hill of short peticoats is seen. The rhy [rye] about here is now nearly all cut, from this black bread is made, which I now like very much. White rolls can also be obtained, but nothing like a loaf of white bread is seen, the black bread is a little sour. The drink here is light wine and very little beer is to be got. It is also very bad.[41]

He once gave an amusing account of his attempt in 1845 to carry home some of the green tree frogs (*Hyla arborea*) which he found in the woods around Giessen, and which are capable of producing a croak worthy of a much larger animal. After much effort he captured a dozen specimens. He said: 'I started at night on my homeward journey by the diligence, and I put the bottle containing the frogs into the pocket inside the diligence. My fellow passengers were sleepy old smoke-dried Germans. Very little conversation took place, and, after the first mile, every one settled himself to sleep, and soon all were snoring. I suddenly awoke with a start, and found all the sleepers had been roused at the same moment. On their sleepy faces were depicted fear and anger. What had woke us all up so suddenly? The morning was just breaking, and my frogs, though in the dark pocket of the coach, had found it out, and, with one accord, all twelve of them had begun their morning song. As if at a given signal, they one and all of them began to croak as hard as ever they could. The noise their united concert made, seemed, in the closed compartment of the coach, quite deafening: well might the Germans look angry; they wanted to throw the frogs, bottle and all, out of the

PLATE III

A sketch entitled 'The Wizard's Cave' by Philip Ughtred Shuttleworth, son of the Warden of New College, Oxford. The sketch is intended to represent Buckland's room in Fell's Buildings.
From the original in the Library of the Royal College of Surgeons of England.

PLATE IV

Liebig's Laboratory at Giessen. About 1845. From a contemporary print in the Library of the Royal College of Surgeons of England.

window, but I gave the bottle a good shaking, and made the frogs keep quiet.' He remained awake for the rest of the journey, shaking the bottle every time his amphibian choir began their chorus anew.[14] His attempt in 1846 to import into Britain some of the characteristic red slugs of the Giessen area was equally disastrous, for he awoke in the coach to see two of his specimens weaving devious paths over the expansive bald pate of the sleeping German opposite. He left the coach at the next stop, rather than try to explain what had happened.

On his way to Giessen in June, 1846, he stopped in Brussels for a brief period, having sailed from Ramsgate to Ostend. He wrote to his father: 'I got to Brussels about 9 that evening [Saturday, June 26] . . . and got a general view of the place. This morning we went out again and saw the Town Hall and the market, which was filled with people selling pigeons. I there bought for a franc a live red-headed woodpecker. I hope to stuff him soon. . . . At two o'clock the band played in the park and to my great delight the King came out to walk there with the Queen and I saw them both well.'[23]

He returned to Christ Church in October. 'I found my rooms nearly in the same state as I left them,' he wrote to his mother, 'every thing horribly damp and on my entry the first thing I saw on the floor was a horrid old donkey's skin which I condemned last term, as consisting more of moths' reliquiae than anything else. This horrid thing my scout had put again into my room, and the consequence is that the whole place is well stocked with moths, which have done me an immense deal of damage having quite devoured my beautiful Tiger's skin, and made a colony in almost every bit of animality in the place, particularly the birds.' Perhaps this was the skin of the donkey dissected long before by Frank in so leisurely a manner that when the time came to dispose of the corpse '. . . . the remains of the departed had to be taken away in buckets.'[23]

In June, 1847, the British Association met in Oxford, and the serious business of the meetings was interspersed by various social functions, some of which were enlivened by the presence of Frank's baby bear, Tiglath-Pileser, dressed in cap and gown. Tiglath-Pileser, or Tig for short, had obtained its name only shortly before; it had escaped and, like some other pets, had made for the Chapel. A Student was reading the first lesson, and was describing how King Ahaz was on his way to Damascus to meet Tiglath-Pileser, king of the Assyrians. The name of this monarch froze upon his lips, however, as he looked up to see the bear trotting towards him. Dean Gaisford sent for Frank: 'You or that animal, Mr Buckland, must quit the College.'[20]

Sir Charles Lyell described an immense garden party held in the Botanic Gardens. The bear, still dressed in cap and gown, was introduced to various celebrities, including the Prince of Canino (Charles Bonaparte, nephew of Napoleon I) and the French biologist Milne Edwards. Florence Nightingale was also present with her parents and her devoted admirer, Richard Monckton Milnes, afterwards Lord Houghton. It was apparently her suggestion that the bear should be hypnotized: 'Mr Milnes followed the suggestion and in ½ minute the little bear began to yawn, in less than 3 min. was stretched fast asleep on the gravel.'[42]

Tig was taken shortly afterwards to Islip, but, after escaping on a number of occasions and putting the village into uproar by robbing the local store of sugar and sweet stuffs, was presented in November, 1847, to the Zoological Society of London, of which Dr Buckland was a founder member. D. W. Mitchell, recently appointed as the first paid secretary of the Society, wrote to Frank: 'I am not at all surprised at your having difficulties about him at Christ Church. My recollections of the Dean do not recall any philozoic tenderness. If he ever read Aristotle on Animals it must have been for anything but the subject matter; for he persecuted hunters, dogs and two monkeys without mercy – one of the monkeys exhibited himself in a state of inebriety at the cellar window next to the Deanery one Sunday afternoon and was led out of College the next morning for the last time with an air of dejection in his countenance which is not always seen in humans under similar circumstances.'[23]

Frank tried for his B.A. degree in October, 1847, but failed and was obliged to remain at Christ Church until he tried again the following year. His failure was no doubt a disappointment to him. Dr John Kidd wrote, 'I have not known you, now for 3 or 4 years, without duly valuing your estimable qualities, your temper, and manners and talents and acquirements: and I feel certain that your recent disappointment will eventually lead to an increase of your worth and I trust that, in consideration of my age and long intimacy with your Father, I shall not be deemed impertinent in thus expressing my sentiments.'[23]

On Friday, May 12, 1848, the Public Examinations commenced, and on Monday, May 15, he passed his degree *viva voce* and almost at once travelled to London to begin studying surgery.

CHAPTER FOUR

Surgical Training

DR BUCKLAND BEGAN to seek advice from some of his knowledgeable and influential friends about the best training for surgeons before Frank left school. He approached Sir Benjamin Brodie and Richard Owen (later Sir Richard Owen) early in 1844; both were well qualified to give advice.[23]

Brodie (1783–1862) was one of the great surgeons of the day with a large and fashionable practice. He had been present at the removal of a sebaceous cyst from the scalp of George IV, and when the king was dying Brodie slept every night at Windsor Castle and arose at 6 a.m. to converse with his patient for an hour or two, before returning to his work in London. Both William IV and Queen Victoria appointed him their Serjeant-Surgeon, a post, now abolished, which at that time still survived from the days when the monarch took the field with his army. When the great engineer Isambard Kingdom Brunel inhaled a half-sovereign whilst entertaining a party of children with conjuring tricks, it was Brodie who was summoned.

He had trained at St George's Hospital under Sir Everard Home, and served the Hospital first as Assistant Surgeon and then as Surgeon from 1808 until 1840. He was not especially skilful in performing operations, but he was outstandingly good at making a quick and accurate diagnosis. He also insisted upon the need for making detailed notes of his patients, but perhaps his greatest contribution to surgery of the period was his introduction of conservative methods in treating diseases of the joints. Many who walked the streets of London were indebted to Brodie for the possession of all their limbs, and probably their lives as well.

It was Brodie also who had taken an active part in the

development of St George's as a teaching hospital. He was for many years an examiner and member of the Council of the Royal College of Surgeons and he became its President in 1844. Brodie was also first President of the General Medical Council which was set up under the Medical Act of 1858.[43]

Richard Owen (1804-1892), described by his admirers as 'The British Cuvier', was the first Hunterian Professor of Comparative Anatomy and Physiology at the Royal College of Surgeons (Plate v). Although he had trained as a surgeon, and had practised in Lincoln's Inn Fields in his younger days, his main contribution to science was in comparative anatomy. He was a meticulous worker and careful observer, at his best in detailed descriptive anatomy but lacking Darwin's far-seeing genius; when Owen attempted to produce general biological theories, these verged on the fanciful.[19]

He was distrusted and disliked by many of his contemporaries, partly because of his vindictiveness which he combined with somewhat sinister good manners: 'he is so frightfully polite', wrote T. H. Huxley, 'that I never feel thoroughly at home with him.'[44] Darwin, in his autobiography, mentions that Owen's power of hatred was unsurpassed and that he believed Owen became his bitter enemy after the publication of the *Origin of Species*, not because of any quarrel, but out of jealousy for its success.[18] He was undoubtedly a very able man, however, who was largely responsible for the setting up of the British Museum of Natural History. He had a great respect for Dr Buckland, and they had once collaborated in trying to find out how the pearly nautilus rises and sinks in the water.[19]

Owen and Brodie concurred in the view that Frank would be better advised to begin his surgical studies at the age of 21, rather than continue his academic studies at Oxford until he was 22 years old. Owen added: 'The difference of a year would not counterbalance any advantage which he might derive from prolonging his academical studies to 1849. A great point would be gained if any friend of yours who is a Surgeon in an Hospital would consent to your son's being articled as an Hospital Pupil at the age of 18 or 19, and to pursue for the first three years his studies for the academical degree. Such a connection would have great influence in a subsequent election as Surgeon to such hospital which is the surest basis for the honours and emoluments of a London surgical career.' Brodie merely commented that the opportunities of learning anatomy at Oxford were smaller than those in London '. . . but if he could learn a little and get accustomed to the sight of dissection at an early period and before he enters here on regular professional studies it would be of some advantage to him.'[23]

Brodie invited Dr Buckland and Frank to his country estate of 450 acres at Broome Park, Betchworth, Surrey, over Christmas, 1844. 'I wish very much to secure your son's acquaintance', he wrote, 'and I am not without hopes that I may give you a few suggestions which will be useful to him on his course.' Brodie, almost until his death, continued to help Frank in numerous ways, and was always concerned to see that his career as a surgeon was proceeding smoothly. 'My dear Mr Dean,' he wrote in 1846, while Frank was still at Christ Church, 'I would strongly advise your son to be at once put down as a candidate for the Athenaeum. It will give me great pleasure to be his proposer or seconder as you may think best.' A month or two earlier he had asked Dr Buckland to be present to vote at his son Benjamin's election for membership.[3] Frank Buckland was proposed by Brodie and seconded by Sir Roderick Murchison; he was elected eight years later.[45]

Brodie personally conducted Frank to St George's Hospital in January, 1847, and his name was enrolled as a student under Mr Caesar Hawkins, F.R.S.,[46] Surgeon to the hospital from 1829 to 1861 and known affectionately as 'The Emperor'. The plan was clearly for Frank to commence his training in the autumn of 1847, after taking his B.A. at Oxford, but his failure in the examination in the autumn of that year forced him to postpone his surgical studies until May, 1848.

It is not clear why St George's Hospital was chosen in preference, for example, to the Westminster Hospital, which would have been more convenient for Frank who lived in the Deanery at Westminster throughout most of his period of surgical training. Perhaps one reason was the influence of Brodie; perhaps another was the high reputation the hospital had achieved in the first century of its existence. Of the famous physicians and surgeons of the eighteenth century, none could compare with John Hunter, surgeon to St George's from 1756 until his death in 1793. Although it has been truly said by

Blomfield, the historian of St George's, that Hunter '. . . found surgery a narrow craft and left it a science . . .'[47] he is now chiefly remembered for his major contribution to biological science which posterity has judged to be of even greater importance than his surgical work. William Buckland had an enormous respect for John Hunter and Frank was brought up to regard his memory '. . . with a respect approaching almost to veneration'.[48]

Medical and surgical training in the middle years of the last century was still badly organized and somewhat haphazard, although the need for reform was beginning to be widely recognized. Owen, in a letter to Dr Buckland written in 1845, described the training of a surgeon: 'The College of Surgeons require three years of attendance on the practice of surgery at a recognized Hospital, and they judge of such by the Certificates of the Surgeons of such Hospitals which are only given on actual attendance. They require also 1 year's attendance on the practice of physic at a recognized Hospital.'[23] The student became an in-patient dresser, and usually assisted a number of surgeons in turn, each for a period of six months; he thus had ample opportunity of watching the surgeons at work, and of noting the progress of patients until they died or were discharged.

A medical school within the walls of St George's was set up in 1831, but no space could be found for dissecting rooms and lecture theatre, and students therefore still had to seek instruction in anatomy elsewhere. Before the establishment of the medical school, students attended lectures in a number of different places, wherever suitable instruction could be obtained, and they continued to learn anatomy at one of the two rival establishments close to the hospital. One of these, at No. 1, Grosvenor Place, was set up by Samuel Lane, who had been House Surgeon at St George's, and was run by him together with James Arthur Wilson, Physician to the hospital. The other school of anatomy was run by staff of the hospital in premises purchased by Brodie in Kinnerton Street; Brodie, of course, was repaid for his outlay from fees paid by students. Lane's school, one of the last of the private medical schools, finally closed in 1863, and the school in Kinnerton Street moved into buildings attached to the hospital itself in 1868.[47]

One problem of anatomical training at this time was to obtain sufficient human bodies for dissection. What were available came mostly from the workhouse, and cost as much as £10 apiece. It was perhaps partly to gain further experience in dissection that Frank went to Paris in August, 1849. Here, corpses were cheap and the supply more than adequate, especially since Paris was in the grip of a cholera epidemic. More important, however, was that Paris was recognized as one of the leading centres of medical training and research. The French Revolution had swept away many of the conservative restraints in medicine. The importance of relating physical signs observed in life to the conditions found on autopsy was established, and students flocked to Paris to learn from the leaders of the new schools of thought.[49] Frank left home on August 1, and travelled through Winchester, Le Havre and Rouen. He wrote home on August 6, '. . . I have been this morning round the wards of La Charité, and have begun a course of operations on the dead body, yet I have hardly been here twenty-four hours. Only think, we have a fresh subject every day, and may perform any operation we like.'[23]

He wrote home again on August 21:

> I found going to the Hospitals in the morning tired me too much and made me feel uncomfortable for the day, although I had something to eat before I went to them so I have not been there for several days. I feel the better for it. My time is fully occupied without them, and I don't wish to get below par again. I am attending a course of bandaging every day at 11. The french have many pretty little bandages which are not known in England nor is there a course to teach this science in any of the schools in London. We bandage a stuffed figure which turns in all possible directions. At 12 the operations. There is a large horrid looking cart which goes round to the Hospitals in the morning and brings in the dead people. I have seen as many as 10 at one time. They are sewn up in coarse cloth. The man pulls them out and the professor chooses one to dissect for which he pays 4 francs. The *teeth* of these poor creatures are the perquisite of the porter and he pulls them all out to sell to the dentists. Last week I performed all the amputations and am beginning to feel confident and get my hand into the work. When I have done with the Professor I go over those operations I have done before and

generally all that remains of the body is the trunk (*à la* Greenacre).* The subjects are principally old men and women but we have some fine men and pretty women. The thinner they are the better.

He also remarked: 'the french students are intelligent for the most part but don't work like the Germans. There are great quantities in Paris, although the vacation has commenced.'

Frank no doubt still relied largely on his parents for financial support, although he was receiving an income of about £80 a year as a Student of Christ Church.

> Thank you very much for the 4 halfs of the notes which have arrived here quite safe this morning [he wrote to his father in September]. There is a book on bandaging which I shall now buy which will be very useful and which contains many new and good manners of supporting fractures, etc.[23]
>
> The operations are still going on, I have tied all the arteries several times and performed all the amputations and resections of the bones the most difficult of all. I feel great confidence such as before I had not experienced. I have bought a little book called *Medicine Operative.* We have not a parallel work in England it is excellent. I understand now enough french to read it without much difficulty. . . . I frequently go round the wards of La Charité – the French surgeons can make a good diagnosis, but they seem to be very far behind in treatment. They seem to look on calomel as a sort of poison and never give it except when obliged for specific cases. Velpeau and Cruvellier† are the two great surgeons there. They both have published standard medical works.

Not all his time was spent in work, however. He visited the Jardin des Plantes and reported that '. . . the things seem to be

* James Greenacre was hanged at Newgate in 1837 for the murder of his intended, Hannah Brown, a penniless girl who had made him believe she possessed a large fortune. He cut up the body and hid portions of it in various parts of London. The trunk, wrapped in a sack, was hidden behind some flagstones near the 'Pine Apple' toll bar in Edgware Road.[50]

† Alfred-Louis-Armand-Marie Velpeau (1798–1867), Professor of surgical chemistry in the University of Paris.

Jean Cruveilhier (1791–1874) occupied a chair of pathological anatomy specially created for him in the University of Paris. He was the first to describe disseminated sclerosis.

rather neglected in the Zoological department'. He also went '. . . to Montmartre and found several good crystals there. They do not work the quarries now, but the view from the wind mills is magnificent. I have two more weeks to stay here and I intend to take a little holiday and see Grenelle, more museums, etc. I shall try hard to get into the Catacombs, but this is difficult. One day I must go to Alfort to see the Hospital for animals, Horses, Dogs, etc.* and another day to the horse slaughter house.' He mentioned also a visit to Montmartre Abattoir where he had learnt a new way to kill sheep '. . . very merciful and quick'.

He also commented: 'The other 3 Englishmen went to Fontainbleau but I declined going, for two of them are too lazy for sight seeing, or are grumblers. I shall go if I have time, but I take Dr Burchell's advice which he gave me about travelling i.e. to follow up one subject in sight seeing. Museums must be my line and if I have time for other things so much the better, but my own trade first. I will procure the maps you wanted and bring them home with me.'[23] Burchell, the great African explorer, was a family friend.

Dr Buckland sent Frank's letters as they arrived to his friend Brodie who replied: 'My friend Frank has many of those qualities which ought to lead to success. He has a great turn for original observation and he seems to have his heart engaged in his pursuits which, I understand, that he follows steadily, neither looking to his right or his left. Then he is kind and good-natured, and makes friends, without it causing him any particular trouble to do so.'

In reply to a subsequent letter, Brodie wrote: 'Frank's letter is excellent. It is a great satisfaction to me and it must be a *very great* one to you to find that he is going on so well. His observations on Parisian surgery are, I doubt not, very accurate at least in agreement with all that I have seen and heard myself.'[23]

Frank returned to England at the end of September, and continued his training at St George's. Conditions in hospitals at this period, before Florence Nightingale's influence became

* Maisons-Alfort, a suburb to the S.E. of Paris. Claude Bourgelat (1712–1779) established a famous veterinary school here in 1765.

felt, were still primitive. Anaesthetics began to be introduced into general surgical and obstetrical practice in 1847, but their use was not widespread for some years; anaesthetics became popular after Queen Victoria was given chloroform at the birth of Prince Leopold, Duke of Albany, in 1853.[47] Antiseptics were unknown. Surgeons operated in ancient blood-encrusted garments, and the dresser or house-surgeon, when he was first appointed, generally used the oldest coat he could find, and carried a wisp of ordinary whipcord in his lapel for tying off arteries. Surgery still depended to a great extent upon the strength of wrist, and the speed and accuracy of the surgeon. Operations on certain parts of the body, for example the thorax and abdomen, were generally held to be so dangerous as to be attempted only as a last desperate expedient.[51]

Those patients who survived the brutalities of the operating theatre, however, had at best only a moderate hope of survival. Inflammations and suppurations were accepted as unavoidable companions of the healing knife, and even the most fortunate generally endured a long period of sepsis of the wound following the operation. The surgeon was perhaps mainly occupied in amputating limbs, since more conservative techniques, aimed at saving them, would have involved even more terrible risks to life. The microscope had not yet been accepted as an instrument capable of helping in diagnosis, and erroneous theories as to the causes of disease encouraged the use of leeches and of 'cupping' of patients to remove what was believed to be an excess of blood.[51]

Conditions in the hospital wards themselves were not good, and the characteristic 'hospital smell', which was sometimes so powerful that it nauseated those unaccustomed to it, was caused by a combination of dirt, inadequate sanitation and gangrenous wounds. Florence Nightingale wrote that: 'The floors were made of ordinary wood which, owing to lack of cleaning and lack of sanitary conveniences for the patients' use, had become saturated with organic matter, which when washed gave off the smell of something quite other than soap and water.'[52]

The senior nurses at St George's were good, although perhaps not always literate. The assistant and night nurses were, according to an historian of the hospital, mostly '. . . rough, dull, unobservant and untaught women'. The head nurses had their own rooms in which they could take their meals but the others '. . . fed as they could, cooking what they wanted, toasting their bacon on bits of wood at the ward fires, and eating in the ward or scullery'. Sometimes they would bivouack and eat their dinners in the corridors. They had no training and no uniforms, and the medical staff perhaps regarded them more as charwomen than as assistants in helping to restore patients to health.[47]

In some institutions, nurses smuggled drink into the wards, and scenes occurred which were reminiscent of a pot-house, or worse. Since they were mostly illiterate and quite untrained, even when sober their value at the best can have been but small. An inquiry into the treatment of the sick at the Strand Workhouse as late as 1866 revealed that of fifteen pauper nurses, only two were below sixty, four were above seventy and one seventy-eight. Only three could read adequately and one nurse, who said she could read, was tested with a label inscribed 'This lotion to be applied externally only'; she read it as 'Two spoonfuls to be taken four times a day'.[53]

Frank Buckland was apparently a popular student, who mixed well with his fellows and with the staff. Most of his contemporaries became surgeons, some achieving fame in their profession; these included John William Ogle, who treated Buckland in his last illness, and Henry Pollock. Both were prizemen of the hospital. Henry Gray (1827–1861), author of *Anatomy Descriptive and Surgical*, and destined to be cut off by smallpox almost at the beginning of a brilliant career, was lecturer in Anatomy in the Medical School in 1849 and House Surgeon in 1850.[46] Francis Galton (1822–1911), Charles Darwin's cousin and the founder of eugenics, entered the Medical School in 1844, but had probably left before Buckland began his studies. Bompas implies that Professor T. H. Huxley was at St George's with Frank, but this is clearly wrong. The Pupil's Register shows a Charles Rodney Huxley, who registered in 1849.

One of the most interesting of Frank's contemporaries, however, was Francis Day, one of the best known ichthyologists that Britain has produced. He was born in 1827, educated at Shrewsbury, and enrolled as a surgical student in September,

1848. After taking his M.R.C.S. in 1851, he entered the Honourable East India Company Service as an assistant surgeon and was involved in the Burma War of 1852–1853. He was eventually appointed Principal Medical Officer of the Madras Presidency and Professor of Materia Medica at Madras University, posts he held together with the Inspectorate of Fisheries in India. He retired in 1877. He was the author of a standard work, *The Fishes of British India,* recently reprinted, and, after returning to Britain, he wrote his classic *Fishes of Great Britain and Ireland,* which is still employed as a reference work today. He died in 1889, at the age of 61.

Buckland took his M.R.C.S. in May, 1851; he was appointed House Surgeon at St George's on June 24, 1852, and resigned exactly one year later. A colleague of later years wrote:

> He used to say that the cases which were brought into the accident ward grouped themselves into classes according to the hours of the day. The suicides came at an early hour of the morning; the scaffold accidents next, since a scaffold, if it gave way at all, gave way early in the day; the street accidents afterwards, and so on. At St George's he collected a fund of good stories, with which he used to amuse his friends to the last days of his life. One of the best of them told, as he never minded his stories telling, against himself. An old woman came to the hospital with a cough, which she declared nothing would alleviate except some sweet, luscious mixture which another out-patient, a friend of hers, had received. The old woman was given a bottleful of the mixture, and returned again and again for more, though her cough got little better. At last Mr Buckland's suspicions were aroused, and he desired that his patient should be watched. She was watched, and was found out-side Chelsea Hospital selling the mixture in halfpenny tarts.[26]

Although Buckland was a keen and conscientious student, it appears that he did not possess some of those qualities which were necessary for success in surgery. He may have lacked some manual dexterity. He may even have been revolted by the squalor, the filth and the inhumanity of the profession that had been chosen for him. Throughout his stay at St George's he continued his rather diffuse studies of the animal kingdom as a whole, and perhaps also he found it difficult to concentrate his attention sufficiently on the study of surgery. At all events, he maintained a small menagerie in the Deanery at Westminster, where he met many of the foremost scientists of the period.

CHAPTER FIVE

Social Life

DR BUCKLAND WROTE to his friend Liebig in December, 1845, soon after he knew for certain that he was to be made Dean of Westminster: 'I have a splendid House in which I shall hope to assemble my scientific friends of all nations that visit the Metropolis of England. . . .'[37] He set about his self-appointed task with characteristic briskness, and for the next four years the Deanery was one of the centres of London's intellectual life. The witty and intelligent geologist and his cultured wife (Plate v) had an extraordinarily wide circle of friends and acquaintances and these they entertained at breakfast or luncheon. Frank, who was nineteen when his father became Dean, began to play his part in this social activity during his vacations from Oxford, and he shared in it more fully when he himself moved to London in May, 1848, to commence his surgical training. He became known to many of the famous and influential men of the period, and established close friendships with some of them.

In later years these social contacts were of considerable help to him, and the fame of his illustrious father always ensured him a sympathetic hearing even from those who did not know him personally. The opportunity of meeting such a large number of the famous men in every profession can surely come to very few young men in their early twenties in any age. Michael Faraday, Sir John Herschel and Sir George Airy; I. K. Brunel and Robert Stephenson; Edward Forbes and Louis Agassiz; Sir Charles Lyell and Adam Sedgwick; and François Guizot and John Ruskin are only a few of those who visited or stayed at the Deanery during this period. Politicians and poets, scientists and soldiers, explorers and engineers, all met and talked about their findings and their ideas under the mellowing influence of the Dean and his family.

The rambling old building with its sixteen staircases must also have proved irresistably fascinating to Frank and his brother Edward, as they roamed from the cellars to the leads of the roof, where their young sisters grew mustard and cress in boxes. The wainscoting in a narrow passage in the Deanery crashed to the ground during a gale one night to reveal what was thought to be one of Dean Atterbury's hiding places. The two young men were delighted and one of them was lowered on a rope into the small room which contained a crumbling worm-eaten table and bedstead.[8] Furthermore, Westminster Abbey was a constant source of interest, and there was always something to see, something to investigate, in the ancient building which enshrines so much of English history. Frank discovered, for example, the place where Isaac Walton had scratched his initials on the marble of the tomb of his friend, the great classical scholar Isaac Casaubon; they are still to be seen there today.[54]

Frank, assisted by the son of Lord Chief Justice Baron Pollock, Lord Chief Baron of the Exchequer Court, a medieval institution now abolished, on one occasion suspended a long, heavy pendulum from the roof of the nave of the Abbey, in order to demonstrate the effect of the rotation of the earth.[13] Foucault first carried out this experiment, which now bears his name, in 1845; it is today one of the permanent demonstrations at the Science Museum in South Kensington, London. On another occasion, when he was showing a number of visitors round the Abbey, Buckland and his party were inadvertently locked in. He obtained their release by tolling one of the bells.[13] He also succeeded in diagnosing what was wrong with one of the large organ pipes which began to play flat. He extracted the corpse of a cat by fishing for it from above with a rod and line.[8]

When he moved from Oxford he brought many of his animals with him. Tiglath-Pileser, his baby bear, had died in the Zoological Gardens, and now stood, a monument to the taxidermist's art, on the staircase at the Deanery. His white-tailed sea-eagle, which he had kept outside his rooms in Fell's Buildings, was banished from Christ Church after escaping into the College chapel and lived with Mr Osman, a bird stuffer in St Aldate's Street, Oxford, during the remainder of Buckland's college career. It was moved to the Deanery and shortly afterwards celebrated the fact by escaping. It made its escape on April 9, 1848, the day before that chosen for a big Chartist demonstration and when large numbers of special constables, especially sworn in to deal with the expected riots, were in Parliament Square and, indeed, in the Deanery itself. It must have made a magnificent spectacle as it soared up into the air and perched on one of the pinnacles of the Abbey. The Chartist demonstration ended in a downpour of rain and was a fiasco; the eagle was finally captured with a live chicken tied to a pole, and was shortly afterwards taken to the Zoological Gardens.[15]

The Deanery housed a small menagerie of animals, including various birds, chameleons, newts, hedgehogs, tortoises, dogs, cats and snakes which, according to Frank's brother-in-law, '. . . sometimes strayed, and were met casually on the stairs, to the alarm of those visitors whose department of science did not enable them readily to distinguish between the venomous and harmless species'.[13] The monkeys, Jacko and Jenny, were also sometimes the cause of trouble amongst the domestic staff. Jacko was purchased by Frank from an innkeeper in Bayeux and brought back to London by way of Southampton. As Frank was buying a ticket at the railway station, Jacko popped out his head from the bag in which he was carried, much to the surprise of the booking clerk, who rapidly regained his presence of mind, however, and reminded Frank that a ticket was required for a dog. No amount of remonstrance, no display of the entire animal, would convince the clerk that it was a monkey and not a dog. At last, in good humoured exasperation, Frank produced a tortoise from another pocket, and asked what he proposed to charge for that. After consulting his superior the man replied with a grave but determined manner: 'No charge for them, sir; them be insects.'[14]

Jenny, his other monkey, had been brought when young from Gibraltar. She also escaped from the Deanery one day, and a thrilling chase ensued over the housetops of London. She lived to an old age in Clapham, where Frank had a friend who looked after her, and she did not die until 1869.[23]

The Deanery housed also large numbers of rats; indeed,

they invaded the building when the scholars of Westminster school went home for their holidays. When the house was quiet, the rats could be heard scampering about beneath the floor of the drawing room, to the alarm of the servants. Frank began to keep some as pets, and they became extremely tame. They also bred, and Frank would periodically take a sackful to the Zoological Gardens to feed to the snakes. Afterwards, whenever it was possible, he always had one or two tame rats in his house;[14] his nephew recalled in later life calling on his uncle not long before he died, and being presented with one of his tame rats.[55]

It was probably also during this period at the Deanery that Frank began to make contact with a fascinating and motley collection of people who were involved in some way with the collection or sale of animals. Ratcatchers, birdcatchers, bug destroyers, they were all welcomed as friends. He had learned the lesson well from his father, that the people who actually did a job had knowledge and experience that was interesting and usually worth acquiring. At the head of this group must undoubtedly be placed Abraham Dee Bartlett, whom Dr Buckland had met at least by early 1846. Bartlett was originally a supplier of birds and small mammals and a taxidermist, but he was something more than a mere dealer and contributed to the Proceedings of the Zoological Society.[56]

Bartlett was appointed resident Superintendent of the Zoological Gardens in Regent's Park in 1851, and retained this post until he died in 1897 in his eighty-fifth year. He achieved a considerable reputation. When a cask arrived from Africa in 1858 containing the body of a gorilla, at this time new to science, Professor Owen invited Bartlett to be present. When the cask was opened, the stench was so strong that it was immediately closed again and it seemed unlikely that anything more than the skeleton could be saved, but Bartlett had the cask taken to the middle of a large field in Norwood. After working on the corpse for several weeks, he and his assistant succeeded in stuffing it.[57] He was not scientific in his methods, but he was not unlike Frank himself in having an intuitive gift of sympathy with, and understanding of, animals that often enabled him to rear them and keep them alive where others would have failed. The two became fast friends and together would visit booths and sideshows at fairgrounds, and afterwards would compare notes on all they saw. But Frank had many other friends such as Charles R. Davy, the birdcatcher, and he added to them year by year.

He began to haunt the dockside areas. Here, at the heart of a great commercial empire, were constantly arriving craft from every port in every continent, carrying not only their lawful cargoes, but also a rare collection of sailors' pets. On one occasion he was offered a seal for ten shillings, but it looked so moribund that he doubted whether he could get it back to the Deanery alive; he heard afterwards that a Jew purchased it for five shillings and, having cured it, sold it at a considerable profit.[14] He also became friendly with Mr Charles Jamrach, and later he wrote about him and his shop on many occasions.

Jamrach, a naturalized British subject, was the son of the chief of Hamburg's River Police. He inherited both a love of natural history from his father, who, through boarding foreign vessels became interested in the sailors' strange pets, and also a knack for making it pay. Jamrach's shop at No. 164, Ratcliffe Highway (now St George Street) was well known in Victorian London. He had 'runners' who boarded vessels at Gravesend and all the London docks in order to buy any animals the sailors might have to offer. He also had agents at some of the major British ports and abroad, for example at Bordeaux, Marseilles and Hamburg. Sometimes, masters of merchantmen would call upon Jamrach before they sailed, in order to obtain a list of what animals he wanted and how much he would pay for them. He supplied animals to the Zoological Gardens and also to private buyers.[58] One visitor commented: 'A kangaroo was recommended to me as a very pretty pet (one had just been sold at Mr Jamrach's for fifty shillings). . . .'[59]

Even Mr Jamrach's animals occasionally escaped. Once a tigress walked out into the Ratcliffe Highway and seized a boy of about nine by the shoulder. Jamrach ran up and seized the animal by the loose skin of the neck but she began to run down the street. He then succeeded in slipping the animal's leg from under her so that she fell and they all lay there in a heap, the boy in the beast's mouth, and Jamrach slowly throttling her, until one of the attendants came up and hit the animal on the nose with a crowbar. The child was not greatly hurt, the bite on the shoulder healing in eight days, but he was so frightened that he did not speak for four hours.[60]

During the summer and autumn months, the Buckland family usually moved to the Rectory at Islip, and Frank would join them at week-ends when he was able to do so. He was very friendly with the parish doctor, Mr Blick, who also seems to have had an interest in natural history. According to Mrs Gordon he '... was a most kind old gentleman, who took almost as great an interest in Frank Buckland's hospital progress as his father himself. On most Saturdays, when the young medical student came down from town, the big old Rectory kitchen would be filled with lame, halt and blind, sent up by the doctor for Frank to report upon and treat in the most approved modern way. One of his sisters [Mrs Gordon herself] had to go round with him, and take down his directions, which she would see carried out during the week – training, or rather experience, that has proved of the greatest value to her during a lifetime spent in a country parish.'[8]

The mid-1840s saw a remarkable growth in demand for education from the masses of labouring poor in the towns and cities; Samuel Smiles was stimulated to write *Self Help*, a book which characterizes well the spirit of the period, after being invited to address a group of working lads in Leeds who had come together for their mutual education and improvement. Interest in adult education for working men was also stimulated by men like Charles Kingsley, F. D. Maurice and Thomas Hughes.[16] Educated professional men like Samuel Smiles gave up their time to give lectures and demonstrations to groups of working men who met together after work. Dr Buckland, who throughout his life took a great interest in popular education, was no doubt delighted to note this trend, and he encouraged the establishment of a night school at Islip. He built a cottage at one end of the tithe barn and fitted up one room as a recreation room for the village lads. The night school was held there three times a week, and it was a duty of some member of the family to be present to give a talk, for example about a coal or salt mine. The Dean insisted that if possible these talks should be illustrated by pictures or specimens, partly for their intrinsic interest but also for 'making them remember'.[8] It was here that Frank had his first experience as a popular educator. He could not have had a better teacher than his own father, whose abilities as a lecturer were outstanding.

The Dean was now working very hard, probably harder than he had done at any time previously in his whole life. He found the fabric of the Abbey in need of considerable repair, and his geological knowledge enabled him to choose the right stones and reject faulty ones and to superintend the work in a way which would have been beyond the competence even of most skilled architects. Westminster School was sadly neglected; the buildings were in an appalling state and the standard of teaching had fallen. He introduced Dr Liddell, the lexicographer, as the new Headmaster and set about renovating the buildings. In particular, he was concerned in improving the drainage system of the school. 'A ditch filled with black mud – a creek of the Thames it was said to be – came up as far as these buildings; but apparently no tide ever succeeded in washing back into the river any of its murky contents.' He would rise soon after 7 a.m. and work incessantly until 2 or 3 a.m. the following morning. At length, at Christmas, 1849 his mind and body, strong as they were, began to prove unequal to the demands made upon them; he found his papers in confusion and could not get through his work. He retired to Islip and spent most of his time there until he died in 1856.[8]

His father's illness must have proved a considerable additional burden to Frank, who now, at 23 years of age, found himself largely responsible for the care of his father, mother, brother and sisters. His father was mentally afflicted and incapable of making decisions for himself. He was sometimes rational, and would sit for hours in a chair, perhaps occasionally glancing at the pictures in a popular magazine. At Richard Owen's advice, objects of natural history were left in his room, but the Dean requested that they should be removed. Frank wrote to Owen in 1851 that when one of his uncles called, 'The Dean would not speak . . . and looked another way. He would answer no questions and make no remarks and seemed glad when he took his leave.'[61] Dr Buckland's illness was a trial for the family, however. Mrs Buckland, writing to a close friend, said, '. . . suddenly he will use the most despairing language and expressions that are horrifying – as to his spiritual condition he never uses improper language *in my presence* thus showing remarkable self-constraint and, it is most strange that he seems to be aware that he is uttering what he ought not and it would seem that it is involuntary'.[3]

Frank, in company with Charles Rodney Huxley, one of his medical colleagues at the Hospital, took the Dean to Guernsey in 1850 for a brief holiday, but to no avail.[23] Medical science could do no more for him. Frank probably continued to live at the Deanery until he took up residence at St George's on appointment as House Surgeon. He entertained his father's friends as well as he could when the necessity arose.

It was probably in 1850 that he first met Hannah Papps, perhaps a coachman's daughter, who was later to become his wife. Marriage at that time was out of the question, for his only source of income was probably what he received as a Student of Christ Church, perhaps £80 a year in all, and this would have ceased on marriage.[32] A son, Francis John, was born to them on August 23, 1851, at 18, Pulford Street, Pimlico,[62] a street running down to the river between the gasworks and the builder's yard of Mr Thomas Cubitt. The knowledge that Hannah was bearing his child, and his father's illness, must have added considerably to the strain of taking his examinations for Membership of the Royal College of Surgeons which, however, he passed on May 9, 1851.

His sunny temperament nevertheless enabled him to overcome this mental stress without much difficulty; he was already attempting authorship and in June, 1851, began unsuccessfully to try to find a publisher for some notes on the '. . . arterial and nervous supply of the upper extremities . . .' which Professor Owen, with a characteristically double-edged compliment, described as '. . . very ingeniously drawn up with a view to give a kind of information much needed by students preparing for their examinations'.[23] A year later, on

June 24, 1852, he was appointed House Surgeon at St George's, a post which brought him some additional, and no doubt much needed, income.

He was now enjoying a social life of his own. His father's friends, aware of the Dean's illness, perhaps put themselves out to entertain the cheerful young man who had such wide interests and such peculiar pets. Sir Robert Inglis, President of the Literary Society, and one of the leaders of London's social life, invited him to breakfast, Professor Owen gave him an open invitation to stay over the week-end at his home in Richmond Park, and Sir Roderick Murchison invited him to dinner. One of his colleagues from the hospital, Charles Lloyd, seems to have lived with him in the Deanery at this period, and he wrote an amusing sketch of Frank, which gives a very good idea of what he was like at this time.

> In a room not many yards distant from Westminster Abbey sat two young men. The night was a cold one in April, 1852. One of them was sitting thoughtfully by the fire, and, if the truth must be told, was smoking – the other sitting, by no means thoughtfully, at a table, and with equal truth might be said to be eating marvellously – A good appetite had been sharpened by a day spent in dissection and potatoes, pig's-flesh, pickles, and pudding succeeded each other in indistinguishable haste – Yet between while he read, or thought he read, a new book, containing a lively Dissertation on Inflammation of the Bowels – sometimes dropping an occasional and pleasant remark on the Intestines, sometimes interrupting his eating to drink a long draught of beer.
>
> As nearly as might be judged at a glance, he was four feet and a half in height and rather more in breadth - what he measured round the chest is not known to mortal man.
>
> His chief passion was surgery – elderly maidens called their cats indoors as he passed by and young mothers who lived in the neighbourhood of St George's Hospital gave their nurses more than ordinarily strict injunctions as to their babies. To a lover of Natural History it was a pleasant sight to see him at dinner with a chicken before him – to watch the scrupulous delicacy with which he removed the leg out of the socket, or examined, after very careful picking, the numerous troublesome little bones which constitute the pinion, and finally to hang over him as he performed a Post Prandium

examination of the head – and then to see how, undeterred by foolish prejudices, he devoured the brain.[23]

William White Cooper, the Queen's oculist, when calling at the Deanery in the spring of 1852, was introduced to the tame rats, kept in a sort of cloister below the house, and prevailed upon Frank to write an article about his pets.[13] This was subsequently published by Richard Bentley (1794–1871) in *Bentley's Miscellany* for August of that year, and so began a very profitable association with one of the most successful of Victorian publishers. Bentley incurred the displeasure of *Frazer's* and the *Athenaeum* magazines for his use of advertising to help to sell his works, but his methods were successful and he undoubtedly benefited the public in issuing 127 volumes of 'standard novels' at a low price. Many well-known novelists owed their first introduction to the public to Richard Bentley, amongst them Wilkie Collins and Mrs Henry Wood. *Bentley's Miscellany* was a popular journal begun in 1837 with Charles Dickens as editor.[63] Frank's success probably owed much to his first publisher.

The article on rats was subsequently enlarged by Frank and republished in his first book (*Curiosities of Natural History*, London: Bentley, 1857) but in its original form it gives a good idea of his wide circle of friends and his catholic taste in reading even at that time. Apart from quoting from Horace, he drew information from the *Historia Animalium* of the great sixteenth century anatomist Conrad von Gesner; from Henry Mayhew's newly published *London Labour and the London Poor*; from Wormius, the seventeenth-century Danish historian and antiquary; from a little book on the rat by 'Mr Shaw of rat-catching notoriety'; from Cuvier, the great French anatomist; from Thomas Pennant, the celebrated English eighteenth-century naturalist; and from a book by the Rev B. Vernon, entitled *Early Recollections of Jamaica*, besides describing his own experiences, and those of his friends including 'Mr Gibbons, a most intelligent and civil rat-catcher, residing in the Broadway, Westminster . . .'

He wrote articles also about frogs, published in *Bentley's Miscellany* in 1852, the cobra de capello (1853), his monkey Jacko (1853) and probably also the ant-eater (1854), although since he wrote anonymously at this time, it is not always possible to be certain of the authorship. He also wrote for Dickens's journal *Household Words*. Nevertheless, the income derived from this desultory work cannot have been very great. He gave up his post as House Surgeon at St George's in June, 1853, and seems to have had no regular employment until he joined the Life Guards in August of the following year. Had his father been able, no doubt he would have secured for his first-born a post where advancement was reasonably certain; Frank was now fully trained, although he lacked experience, but his main requirement was perhaps an influential friend.

In July, 1853, Frank approached Lord John Thynne, the Sub-Dean of the Abbey, asking for his help in obtaining an appointment as surgeon to one of the prison establishments. Lord John wrote to the Prime Minister, the Earl of Aberdeen, who replied: 'The situation of poor Buckland must naturally call for sympathy of all who knew him. On behalf of his family I should be glad to do anything in my power for his son, but his profession removes him very much from the sphere of my interference. I imagine the office you describe must be at the disposal of Lord Palmerston, who probably for the sake of his father, and in consequence of the good report you make of his son, would be well disposed to attend to any such request as you have made to me.' Lord John wrote thereupon to Lord Palmerston, Home Secretary in Lord Aberdeen's government, who asked his secretary '. . . . to place the name of Mr Buckland on the list of candidates. . . .' It was pointed out that '. . . it is very seldom, however, that such vacancies occur, and I believe in all cases the medical officer is compelled to devote his whole time to the duties of his office'.[23]

Nothing came of this attempt to find a suitable post, and no doubt there were others. Perhaps hitherto Frank Buckland had acted mainly in response to spurring by his father and he may now have been content for a period to lead a life of comparative leisure. There was keen competition for medical posts in and around the Metropolis, but nevertheless he probably wanted to remain near London in order to be able to help his brother and sisters and especially his mother, who was apparently still engaged in parochial work in Westminster in spite of her husband's illness. She was, for example, attempting to establish a Working Men's Coffee House and Institute in Westminster. 'I hope your "(Tea) Pot House" will succeed', Lord John Thynne wrote to her. It was here, in December, 1853, that Frank first gave his lecture entitled 'The House We Live In', which he gave on a number of occasions subsequently. The syllabus of this lecture, as published on another occasion, included such topics as 'The Human Frame the House. The Soul the Tenant', 'Bone-Use, Structure – Design of Creator evinced by Variety of its Form' and 'Solomon's Portraiture of Old Age (Ecclesiastes) Explained'.[23]

His time was no doubt fully occupied in visiting his friends, attending lectures, in examining animals, alive and dead, and in fact taking an interest in almost anything. He sought an interview with Professor Michael Faraday to find out his opinion of 'Lord Mount Edgecumbe's apparatus for ventilating with an Archimedes screw'.[23] But as time went on he must have realized that something would have to be done to continue his career, for he was now in his twenty-eighth year. It was perhaps this consideration, as much as any other, that led him to seek a commission in the Household Cavalry.

CHAPTER SIX

The Life Guards

FRANK BUCKLAND was elected to membership of the Athenaeum in February, 1854, almost eight years after his name had been put forward by Sir Benjamin Brodie. Such a delay between proposal and election was not in those days unusual. The names of some of his supporters recorded on his ballot sheet indicate the high esteem in which Dr Buckland was held. They included, for example, Viscount Mahon (Earl Stanhope) the historian, Robert Brown the botanist, Thomas Sopwith the engineer, Caesar Hawkins the surgeon, Dean Milman of St Paul's, Edward Forbes the zoologist, and Richard Hutton, editor of *The Spectator*. His election by 158 votes for to 5 votes against was unusual both for the total number of votes and the small number against him.[45] Frank Buckland actually joined the club in August, 1854. Old W. J. Broderip, Dr Buckland's lifelong friend, wrote to Mrs Buckland:

> I must confess that I could not understand your indifference and determination to stand aloof with regard to Frank's admission into the Athenaeum. I thought it of great consequence to him, exerted myself accordingly, and attended at the ballot notwithstanding an inflamed eye and that it would have been better for me to be in bed. Brodie was there doing his duty manfully like a good man and true as he is.
>
> Permit me in reply to your observation to remind you that in order to get employment your son must be known. It is something to have his name, education and profession suspended for a week in the meeting room of such a club as the Athenaeum with an overflow of some of the best names in London to answer for him. It is something more to be elected at a season when there has been more black-balling going on than ever I remember – nay on the very night of his election when one candidate was certainly so excluded and another I believe withdrawn.

> I hope and expect that Frank is made of the stuff that is *not* fit for ledger work and I should be very sorry to see him in partnership with anyone. Others as well as myself will be very much out if he does not eventually occupy a high position in his profession and it is better that he should bide his time. I should not object to a surgeoncy in the Guards to begin with.[23]

Frank Buckland was gazetted Assistant Surgeon to the Second Life Guards on August 14, 1854, and joined his regiment the following day. He probably never intended to make the Army his career but, as suggested by Broderip's letter, felt he could 'bide his time' while he acquired further experience and became known in the proper quarters. He regarded himself primarily as a surgeon, not as an officer in the Guards, and the fact that he was a member of the learned professions distinguished him from most of his brother officers. Nevertheless, an officer's life in the Guards, the *élite* of the British Army, was undoubtedly a pleasant one at the middle of the last century. The duties were not generally onerous, and allowed ample leisure for a man to pursue his own interests whilst at the same time providing him with a reasonable income and affording him an opportunity of exercising the social graces amongst congenial companions. In other circumstances, therefore, Frank Buckland might have been tempted to remain until he could retire on half pay, instead of resigning his commission, as he did eight and a half years later.

The Life Guards appear to have been more favourably treated even than the Royal Horse Guards (The Blues), for in Buckland's time a private in the Life Guards was paid threepence a day more than a private in the Blues. Officers' pay had been equalized in the 1830s.[64] The Household Cavalry had a special allowance for the mess table, which was charged on the Civil Estimates. It is perhaps not surprising, therefore, that the Household Cavalry were sharply criticized by parliamentary radicals on more than one occasion, and that attempts were made to take away some of their privileges and to reduce the size of the establishment. It was felt, probably rightly, that heavy cavalry were unsuitable for most of the wars waged after mid-century and as one M.P. remarked in 1871, 'The men are too tall. The accoutrements are too heavy. With modern rifles the regiments would be destroyed before they could execute a charge.'[65]

The Household Cavalry were not in fact involved in any foreign service from the Battle of Waterloo in 1815 until the Battle of Tel-el-Kebir in 1882.[64] The Crimean War, which began in March, 1854, five months before Frank joined, had no effect on the Guards, except that occasionally officers were deputed to superintend '. . . the packing of hay for the seat of war'.[66] Their duties were mainly concerned with the mounting of guards at the royal residences at Windsor and in the capital, and in providing escorts at ceremonies concerned with royal deaths and marriages and visits of foreign heads of state. They were also invariably required for the numerous grand military reviews which were a feature of the period, and where the splendid figures of the Guardsmen, clad in their scarlet tunics, made an impressive show.[64]

The duties of the surgeon and assistant surgeon were primarily to attend the sick and injured; they were expected to be present whenever the Regiment marched out of barracks, whether to reviews, inspections or field days at all corporal punishments and, ominously, at target practice.[67] Field days often took place on Wormwood Scrubs, no doubt already well known to Frank, whose friend, Charles R. Davy, a professional bird catcher, caught starlings there and sold them for shooting matches at 4*s* to 6*s* a dozen. Frank used to enjoy these excursions, and he observed how rooks were nowhere to be seen when the men first arrived, but soon appeared to eat whatever scraps of bread fell from the men's sandwich papers.[14]

The surgeon or his assistant every morning held sick parades in the hospital to which, if they were able, the sick N.C.O.s and men were marched in charge of the N.C.O. on stable duty. Treatment was also provided for the officers, their wives, families and servants, and the wives and families of the men, and it was the surgeon's duty to make certain that everyone bore '. . . unequivocal marks of either small or cow-pox'. Apart from these duties, and visits to those who were sick or in the cells, the surgeons do not appear to have had much else to do. They had some other tasks, such as occasionally inspecting the men's barracks and quarters, and certifying that those patients in the hospital who wished to make wills were in a fit state of mind to do so, but even the most conscientious of men cannot have found this job a full time occupation.[67] The strength of the regiment was 439 all ranks, and nowadays this would warrant the employment of only one surgeon, not two. Nevertheless, the situation is not entirely comparable, for at that time the surgeon would have undertaken major operations which nowadays would be performed in a hospital elsewhere.

When Buckland joined his regiment it was stationed at the old Knightsbridge Barracks, which were dilapidated and were finally pulled down in 1876. The other regiments of the Household Cavalry, the First Life Guards and the Royal Horse Guards, were stationed in the Cavalry Barracks at Windsor and the Regent's Park Barracks in Albany Street. Once a year, on a day in early April, the three regiments exchanged their quarters, two of them passing on the road between Windsor and London. In April, 1855, the Second Life Guards moved to Windsor and in April, 1856, they moved to Regent's Park Barracks, returning again to Knightsbridge in 1857.[66]

Although Frank was apparently strict as to discipline, he was a popular officer. Once, when the regiment was stationed at Windsor, his batman brought him a box which contained a strange looking and weird skeleton, claimed to be the 'Skeleton of King Charles the First's favourite parrot'. It was in fact the skeleton of a rabbit which some troopers had cleverly arranged to give the superficial appearance of a bird's skeleton in order to trap 'the Doctor'. It was the type of humour that appealed to Buckland; he saved the worthless object and put it into his private museum.[1] It was also typical of his humour to have his little capuchin monkey, Jack, dressed in the coat of a Troop Corporal Major of the Life Guards. The garment was made by the regimental tailor, who had repeatedly to repair it, as the mischievous animal tore off the crown and three stripes. Eventually, the monkey was reduced to a Private, with disgrace.[60]

Frank Buckland's financial position after he had joined the Life Guards was a not unenviable one for, at a time when agricultural labourers in the south of England were earning about 9*s* a week, and skilled factory workers in the north were earning only twice as much, he was receiving pay of 7*s* 6*d* a day plus 1*s* a day forage.[67] In addition, he still received his income as a Student of Christ Church and possibly an allowance from his father as well. Nevertheless, he had to pay for his mess bills, his uniform and for all those other expenses which were an unavoidable part of the life of an officer and a gentleman. Most of his brother officers came from wealthy families and were no doubt able to spend money on a lavish scale. Moreover, he was supporting Hannah Papps and his small son Francis John, whom he nicknamed 'Physie'.

On February 9, 1856, 'Physie', who had been ailing for about two years, died probably of tubercular meningitis. Hannah Papps was living at Clewer, no doubt to be near Frank who was stationed in the Cavalry Barracks at Windsor a mile or two away. The boy's death was a sad blow to Frank, who was much attached to 'poor little Physie'.[68] The child was buried a week later in a grave purchased by Frank in Brompton Cemetery, London.

Less unexpected, but as much of a shock, was the death of Dean Buckland at Islip on August 14 of the same year.* He had been unable to carry out his duties for over six years, and the family seem to have entertained little hope of his eventual recovery. 'You will grieve to hear of our sad bereavement,' wrote Frank's sister Elizabeth (later Mrs Gordon) to a friend of the family; 'My dearest father is at Rest. He died in Frank's arms yesterday at 3.15 p.m., most peacefully and apparently asleep.'[3] It would perhaps have pleased the pawky humour of the geologist who had spent his life in studying the rocks, to have known that his grave had to be blasted out of the limestone in the cemetery at Islip.

* He was suffering from a tubercular infection of the upper cervical vertebrae which eventually spread to his brain and destroyed his reason. Frank had a *post mortem* examination of his father carried out: 'My dear Mr Cooper,' he wrote to William White Cooper, 'You can guess from the paper what has happened. The poor Dean died yesterday at 3.35 p.m. We are going to make a post mortem today. Dr Ogle is going to do it. . . . It has just occurred to me that you might like to be present. . . . Edward has just come in he says my mother also thought that you might like to be present.'[69]

Frank Buckland subsequently gave the affected vertebrae to the Hunterian Museum. It is apparently unusual for tubercular infection to occur so high in the vertebral column. The Museum Catalogue states that: 'No other symptoms manifested themselves during life but those attributed to melancholia.'

Much of the responsibility of selling off his father's estate fell on Frank who, however, had the able assistance of his uncle George Bowes Morland (1807–1873), Clerk to the Berkshire Justices of the Peace, who was principal of the family firm of solicitors in Abingdon.[23] The Dean left most of his geological specimens and associated documents to the University of Oxford; his private collection of minerals, fossils, casts, medallions and '. . . a variety of Miscellanies . . .' was sold on January 30, 1857, at Steven's Auction Rooms, King Street, Covent Garden, London. The miscellanies included 'A stuffed Hyaena on stand, twenty-four years in the Surrey Zoological Gardens.' This was Billy, which had originally been sent by Burchell the explorer to Dr Buckland, who at the time was doing his work on the bones found in the Kirkdale cave in Yorkshire. Frank had been taken to feed the animal with cake when he was a small boy. It must have caused him great pain and sorrow to see his father's valuable collection, the work of a lifetime, being dispersed to dealers and collectors who could not know, as he did, the personal history of each specimen. The total value of the Dean's estate, which included various small holdings and shares in companies, including the Oxford Gas Company, amounted to over £14,500, of which Frank received about £2,650.[22] This was enough to give him some feeling of security; he was not wealthy, but now had a certain measure of independence.

He was also beginning to become known as a writer of articles on subjects of popular natural history. It was perhaps the need for more money which initially drove him to write these articles. His training was very similar to that of some of the great biologists of the nineteenth century, including Richard Owen, T. H. Huxley and Charles Darwin, in that they all received some form of medical apprenticeship before devoting their lives to the study of animals. As T. H. Huxley commented in 1852, however, 'Science does everything in England – but *pay*. You may earn praise but not pudding';[44] and there is evidence that Frank was both ambitious and in need of money when he first joined the Guards. He had begun his training with such high hopes. 'My object in studying medicine (and may God prosper it!)', he had written in his private journal in 1846, while still an undergraduate at Oxford, 'is not to gain a

PLATE V

William Buckland, D.D., F.R.S.; probably taken about 1845.
From an engraving in his Bridgewater Treatise, Ref. 2.

Sir Richard Owen, F.R.S.
From an original photograph by Elliott & Fry.

Mary Buckland, from an original photograph in the possession of Mrs. Phyllis Cursham.

PLATE VI

(*top*) An artist's impression of the finding of John Hunter's coffin. 1859.

From *Illustrated News of the World*, April 2, 1859.

From a copy in the Library of the Royal College of Surgeons of England.

(*bottom*) Another illustration possibly of the same event, published in Reynolds Miscellany in 1868. Buckland's note 'This gives a good idea of my work' may only indicate the similarity to his work rather than be a direct reference to Hunter.

name, money and high practice, but to do good to my fellow creatures and assist them in the hour of need.' Another entry in the same year was 'My object in life, to be a great high priest of nature, and a great benefactor of mankind'.[13] By the time he joined the Guards, his youthful enthusiasm was beginning to be blunted; as a surgeon, he could not do good to his fellow men without the opportunity of a post suitable to his social station, and he lacked the mental discipline and singleness of purpose which is so clearly to be seen in the early professional careers of biologists like Owen, Huxley and Darwin. Furthermore, his attitude to animals was a highly personal one. He was interested in them because they were interesting pets rather than for any scientific reason and in this respect he differed from his father and more nearly resembled his artistic mother. Perhaps he saw in his popular writing an opportunity to make a name and quickly to become widely known. Whatever the reasons, by 1856 he was well on the road to becoming a successful and well-known journalist, but not a famous scientist or surgeon.

Fate dealt Frank Buckland another severe blow in 1857, for his mother died on November 30. She was buried beside her husband in Islip on December 8. After her husband's death, she had moved with her three daughters to No. 2, East Ascent, St Leonard's. She was in poor health, but continued to derive pleasure from studying marine life, in which she had long been interested. Only the day before her death, she was looking at marine sponges under the microscope, with the aid of Dr James Scott Bowerbank, F.R.S. (1797–1877), a distinguished authority on this group of animals and whose monograph on them is still of value. Frank felt her death most keenly; he had greatly respected his father, but he had been much closer to his mother. His father had perhaps been slightly remote from his family, for he was an extremely busy man with many interests, and the upbringing of the children had rested very largely with Mrs Buckland.

On the same day as his mother died, he finished the preface to his first book, *Curiosities of Natural History*. It was published by Richard Bentley and consisted of a series of articles, some of which were rewritten, which had originally appeared in *Bentley's Miscellany* and the *St James's Medley*. He dedicated the volume to the memory of his father '. . . to whose example and instruction I owe that taste for natural history which has furnished me with agreeable occupation during the leisure hours of my profession'.[14] The book was generally well received. 'We trust young Buckland,' one reviewer said, 'having broken the ice of literature, will follow in the footsteps of his illustrious and talented father, and thereby become an ornament to the profession he has chosen.'[23] Even the *Literary Gazette* gave a very favourable review, whilst taking the author to task for such obvious grammatical errors as 'I have never tried the experiment, nor do I intend to do' and 'a tertiary strata at Oeningen'.[70]

With the publication of the *Curiosities of Natural History*, Frank Buckland's success as an author was assured. Shortly after the book's appearance, he received on December 15,1857, an invitation to answer questions on natural history for *The Field*, the country gentleman's newspaper, which was first published in 1853. He entered into formal contract with the paper in May, 1859. The paper had already passed through the hands of two proprietors, and was now in the hands of the third, William Edward Cox, later Serjeant Cox, who had founded the *Law Times* in 1843. Under Cox the paper became very successful. The manager of *The Field*, until his sudden and unexpected death in 1865, was John Crockford, founder of the Clerical Directory, who became one of Buckland's personal friends.[21]

Dr Buckland had encouraged his son to note down everything that might subsequently be of interest, and since Frank's interests were very wide, he had accumulated in the course of the first thirty-one years of life an extraordinary rag-bag of miscellaneous information into which he now dipped whenever called upon to write an article or give a lecture. Writing for *The Field* was good experience for him, because it brought him into contact with professional journalists and with other naturalists. The discipline of having to write regularly, and to a specified length and by a specified date, was useful, although he found it irksome to have his contributions edited by those who knew less about his subject than he did. He wrote rapidly and although what he produced was occasionally slipshod and showed inadequate revision, it was always worth reading for its lively imagery as well as for its original information, often based on his own observations.

During the next few years he developed a quite distinctive style and it might even be claimed that he initiated a new mode of popular writing on natural history, one which was fresh, vigorous and direct without being inaccurate or condescending. He transmitted his own personal love of animals and his breezy good humour through the printed word. Here, for example, is Frank Buckland's description of a bat asleep, taken from an article published in 1861.

> When the bird goes to roost, he tucks his head under his wing; so does the bat; but how is this possible as he is suspended by the heels? The operation is most interesting. The bat first folds up one wing across his body, and then the other, as an indignant cavalier on the stage folds his military cloak when 'resolved to revenge the insult'. Imagine the indignant biped at this moment to be hung up by the heels, and to dip his head into the collar of the cloak, and you will see the manner adopted by the bat for putting on his nightcap. When the beast is thus taking his siesta, he reminds one of half a pound of brown sugar done up in brown paper and hung up by the small end.[71]

At the time of his mother's death, and certainly with her encouragement, Frank was also preparing a revised version of Dr Buckland's *Bridgewater Treatise*. He wrote a memoir of his father's life which was printed at the beginning of the work. He wisely asked some of his father's old friends, including Professors Richard Owen, John Quekett and John Phillips, to revise portions of the text, which was first published in 1836. Quekett had replaced Owen as the Curator of the Hunterian Museum at the Royal College of Surgeons on Owen's appointment in May, 1856, as Superintendent of the Natural History Department of the British Museum. Phillips, nephew of the pioneer geologist William Smith, succeeded Dr Buckland as Professor of Geology and Mineralogy in the University of Oxford. Frank wrote to Professor Phillips on December 9, 1857, thanking him for the final revised portion of the book. 'I could have wished that Mother saw the new edition of *Bridgewater*,' he wrote, 'but this was not permitted. I am in communication with two booksellers about bringing it out. I find it necessary to use great caution about what terms I make. Nothing is yet decided.'[72] Even after a publisher was decided upon, his difficulties were not over, for he had to see to the illustrations, in which he was helped by Owen, and to watch the progress of the work through the printer's hands. 'Clay the printer of the Bridgewater', he wrote to Owen in June, 1858, 'belongs to the Class of cold blooded and slow moving animals; and like them is tremendously active for a while and then lethargic for a long period. However, the first part is printed all but the Botany. Poor Mr Brown* looked over the Botany but left unaltered two statements one as regards Stigmaria the other as regards Pandanus and I have been obliged to put these into other hands to get corrected. Quekett said he would get this done for me, I believe by Rupert Jones. I was afraid of asking Dr Lindley as I heard that he was dreadfully dilatory; and I don't know him, which is another good reason.' Frank added as a postscript, 'What with Field days, the Hospital, etc., I have as much as I can well manage to do.'[61] In the event, the work was very successful. It was published in 1858 by George Routledge and Co. and the demand for it was so great that the 5,000 copies of the first printing were all sold within three days of publication.[23]

Frank Buckland began also to be in demand as a lecturer. As his articles, and later his books, became more widely read, so more and more people flocked to hear him lecture. He was at his best when talking to laymen, especially working men with little formal education. He was less comfortable, and less successful, when talking to educated people, particularly scientists. It was not that he talked in simple terms and refused to use the long words with Greek or Latin roots which tripped so readily from the tongues of many scientists of the period. It was perhaps

* Dr Robert Brown (1773–1858), botanist. He was librarian to Sir Joseph Banks and subsequently Keeper of Botanical Collections at the British Museum until his death. He was well known for his gentlemanly and kindly manner. Mrs Buckland appears to have played some part in getting the Bridgewater Treatise revised. 'I have seen Mr Robert Brown', she wrote to Professor Owen on April 15 (year uncertain), 'and have asked him as urgently as I dared to give his view at least of what was necessary to be done to the Botany of the Bridgewater – He was very kind but I see clearly it is not easy for him to exert himself.'[61]

mainly that his style was too diffuse, and he tried too hard to amuse rather than instruct his audience, for him to be accepted as a serious scientific investigator. Dr Buckland once said that he felt very nervous in addressing large assemblies until he had once made them laugh, and then he was entirely at his ease. Frank carried this excellent practice one stage further, and had his audience laughing much of the time. He had acquired his father's ability to talk entertainingly, but he had not inherited his father's logical mind, and he tended to flit from one topic to the next, according to whatever peculiar specimens he had managed to assemble and to whatever amusing tales he had contrived to collect. This technique was very successful with those who came to be entertained, especially those who were unaccustomed to listening to lectures, but those who came for instruction often regarded him as superficial. The report from the *Windsor and Eton Express* of his lecture on 'The House I Live In', given in February, 1859, to the Working Men's Association at Windsor, gives a good idea of the bizarre assemblage of objects with which he often illustrated his lectures: 'Among the specimens a New Zealander's head with the face tattooed, a large shell from the China Seas, a rat with overgrown teeth, the vertebrae of a boa constrictor, a bone tied in a knot, a lion's thigh bone, a monkey's skeleton, a model of an etruscan tomb attracted much attention. The lecture was listened to with marked attention, and was frequently applauded throughout.'[23]

During his career in the Guards, he lectured on many occasions, mainly in the south of England, and generally to groups of working men. He found all too often that in the time available he had too much to say, and too many objects to show. It said much for the mental and physical stamina of his audience, as well as his powers as a raconteur, that he would talk for two hours and more, and still retain their attention. The wide experience of public speaking that he gained at this time stood him in good stead in later years.

An invitation to address a group of working men at the South Kensington Museum, early in 1858, probably came from Professor Owen. The lecture was one of six '. . . intended to explain the Collections of the Animal Kingdom . . .' and given in the new lecture theatre. Other speakers in the series included Owen himself, on 'The Animal Kingdom and its Economic Uses', Lyon Playfair on 'The Use of Refuse Animal Matter' and T. H. Huxley on 'Fish and their Industrial Uses'. 'The Lecture Theatre will hold 450 persons', announced the handbill advertising the course, '350 seats will be reserved exclusively for Working Men, their Wives, and Children above fifteen years of age, who upon registering their names will obtain tickets at 6*d* each for the whole course. Tickets for the remaining 100 seats will be issued at 5*s* each for the course, or 1*s* each lecture, when there may happen to be room.' Frank's subject was 'Horn, Hair and Bristles' and during the lecture he '. . . exhibited a sample of the hair of the celebrated prize-fighter, Dutch Sam'. He also showed the skin and hair of the Siberian mammoth '. . . mounted in a silver box of ingenious construction.'[23]*

His sister Mary (Mit), later Mrs Bompas, wrote to a family friend: 'Frank is at Knightsbridge Barracks till April; we went to his Lecture at the South Kensington Museum while we were in London and very amusing it was and reminded me so very much of my dear Father's amusing way of relating everything that was connected with his subject.'[3]

In November, 1858, Frank was invited to go to Egypt with

* This box was made to the instruction of Dr Buckland who had received the specimen as a gift from the Bishop of Durham, Shute Barrington, to whom the geologist had dedicated his *Reliquiae Diluvianiae*. The mammoth itself was found in 1799 by a native fisherman in the delta region of the River Lena. It was a shapeless mass, almost enveloped in ice, but towards the end of the following summer one of the tusks and one side of the animal became visible. It was not until five years after it was originally found that it became completely detached from the frozen mud bank in which it lay. In March, 1804, the fisherman extracted and sold the tusks which were 9 ft 6 in long and weighed 360 lb altogether. Two years later, an English merchant named Adams was in the area, and was shown the mammoth's skeleton and a large quantity of skin covered with long hair and reddish wool. The natives had fed some of the flesh to their dogs and the remainder had been eaten by wild animals, but so much skin and hair remained that ten men could scarcely carry it. Adams took great pains to collect as much as possible of the carcass, and to recover the tusks which had been sold. The skeleton was purchased by the Tsar for the Museum of the Academy of St Petersburg. Portions of the skin were presented to many continental and English museums.

the great engineer I. K. Brunel, as his medical attendant. Brunel's health was broken by the years of strenuous effort and exposure that he had endured in designing and superintending the building of some of the railways of Victorian England. He was suffering from Bright's disease, and was being attended by a number of specialists, including Brodie, who may have suggested that Frank might accompany his patient on his voyage to the sun in search of better health. Brunel, in any event, had been acquainted with the Bucklands for some years, and no doubt had met Frank on a number of occasions. The terms offered were a guinea a day and all expenses paid; the journey was to last from December 4 until the succeeding March.

In spite of his illness, Brunel remained cheerful; he clearly knew the type of man he wanted to have about him, and felt that a good companion, rather than a first-class doctor, was the prime requirement. He and his sister, Lady Hawes, had decided, he wrote to Frank on November 17, that '. . . whoever accompanied me should not be a *mere* medical man – excuse my speaking so of a professional man, but I should say the same of a *mere* engineer . . .' They wanted someone who should have some other pursuits, such as chemistry, geology or botany, besides his professional interests, first because he would be a more intelligent companion, '. . . secondly because without it he would be a bore – and thirdly because my son who is accompanying us would profit by it'. Brunel further said: '. . . I hope and believe you have all sorts of hobbies', and with wry humour added: 'As to *medical* analysis, the analysis of urine I fear will be your only amusement if as I hope you go with us.'[23]

The opportunity of going on such a journey was clearly too good to miss, and Frank began to make enquiries to find out whether it might be managed. Both Lieutenant-Colonel Francis Martyn and Lieutenant-Colonel George Howard Vyse of the Second Life Guards agreed that he could be spared for the period, but his immediate superior, the Surgeon to the Regiment, Thomas Tardrew, said that it would put him to great inconvenience to lose his Assistant for so long a time, and Frank therefore wrote to Brunel to decline the invitation.[13]

Brunel replied understandingly and characteristically: 'A Doctor Scott Watson is going with me, a very *respectable* gentleman as compared with you – nearly old enough to be your father but still my junior.' He added: 'I will bring you home a small mummy if I can.' He was as good as his word, and gave Frank the mummy of an ibis, which was dissected out in Regent's Park Barracks.[73] Brunel also sent a mummy cat only a few days before his death, and Frank dissected this also. 'I have taken the bandages off it', he wrote, 'and find that it must have been a red-coloured cat. Its dried-up tongue projects from its mouth after the fashion of dead cats of our own period.'[15]

It was perhaps unfortunate for posterity that Frank did not go with Brunel to Egypt. It is very unlikely that the course of the engineer's disease would have been any different and that he would have lived any longer, but a keen and sensitive observer like Buckland, living on friendly and even intimate terms with him, would certainly have brought back reminiscences and impressions which might have thrown much light on Brunel's enigmatic personality. One of Frank's friends in the Life Guards, Augustus T. Boyse, evidently felt that the journey would be good for the surgeon as well as the patient. 'And so you refused the offer of an Egyptian Campaign;' he wrote to Frank from Piedmont on March 1, 1859, 'I think you were wrong, because it would have been a step towards the rupture of certain relations that you wot of, and which *must* sooner or later be broken off.' This, fairly certainly, was a reference to Hannah Papps, and was a view not, apparently, shared by Frank who does not seem to have tried to hide his relationship with her, at least from his immediate circle of friends.[23]

CHAPTER SEVEN

Steps to Fame

THE BUCKLANDS, father and son, had tastes in some respects similar to those of John Hunter, the great eighteenth-century surgeon, anatomist and physiologist who founded the study of surgical pathology. Hunter stands out amongst his contemporaries for his wide ranging and original genius. The Bucklands shared, for example, Hunter's interest in the peculiarities and variations of the human form; they shared also a robust insensitiveness, at times almost macabre, to the dead, whether animal or human. Hunter had no qualms in stealing the corpse of O'Brien, the Donegal Giant, and preparing his skeleton in a copper in the basement of his house in Earl's Court, then surrounded by fields. Under similar circumstances the Bucklands would probably have recoiled from body snatching, but would have been unperturbed at the prospect of boiling down a body in the kitchen, provided it was done in the name of science. Dr Buckland, indeed, is reputed to have eaten a portion of the embalmed heart of Louis XIV: 'I have eaten many strange things, but have never eaten the heart of a king before.'* Dr Buckland used to say that the worst thing he had ever eaten was a mole, but afterwards changed his mind and said that there was one thing even worse, and that was a bluebottle fly.

The Bucklands also, as has been mentioned, greatly respected Hunter. Dean Buckland had commented to Richard Owen in 1847 that Westminster Abbey contained no monument to Hunter and proposed that a fund should be started to

* Told by Augustus Hare in *The Story of My Life* quoted in [10]. The heart belonged to Lord Harcourt of Nuneham, near Oxford, who was in Paris during the French Revolution and had purchased it from the revolutionary who had been engaged in wrecking the Sun King's tomb. The Harcourts and Bucklands were close friends.

pay for one. A meeting took place at the Royal College of Surgeons, and the Dean offered to forgo his usual fees and to promote the matter in other ways, but nothing had come of it. Frank, of course, knew of this attempt to provide a memorial to his hero, whom he once described as '. . . in my opinion, one of the greatest men, if not the very greatest, England ever produced',[74] and in 1859 he searched for, and found, Hunter's body, which was then reinterred in Westminster Abbey.

Hunter died at the age of 64 years at a meeting of the Board of Governors of St George's Hospital, London, on October 16, 1793, and was interred in the crypt of St Martin-in-the-Fields at a private ceremony a few days later. His body would still be there today but for a change in the law, foreshadowed in the Public Health Act of 1848, respecting burial of the dead. Before this change, the dead were either buried in burial grounds, generally in the vicinity of churches, or in crypts or catacombs, but by the 1840s burial grounds in the towns and cities of industrial England were often no longer adequate. What had once been picturesque country churchyards had become sunless, undrained, festering wastes surrounded by factories and slum dwellings, and new graves were often dug over or through existing ones. Crypts, also, were crammed with coffins, often placed in a most unseemly manner, and in some instances the odour of sanctity in the church above must have been tempered by the effluvium rising from the dead below. The sanitary reformers, led by Edwin Chadwick, suspected that the dead, if not cared for adequately, might return to plague the health of the living.

Various changes in the manner of burying the dead were therefore introduced, especially after the Public Health Act of 1858, which gave powers to the Privy Council previously vested in the somewhat ineffectual General Board of Health. Numerous orders in Council were issued ordering that particular public crypts and catacombs were no longer to be used but were either to be sealed or the coffins removed and buried elsewhere.[75] A period of grace was allowed, however, after the announcement of the intended sealing of any crypt, for those who wished to remove particular bodies and make their own private arrangements for reburial. A notice in *The Times* referring to the sealing of the crypts and catacombs of St Martin-in-the-Fields appeared in January, 1859, and was seen by Frank Buckland, who was about to go on leave. He recalled that Hunter's body had been interred there, and immediately hurried up from Windsor to make his own investigation on the spot. Having identified the vault in which the coffin lay, and having informed the President of the Royal College of Surgeons, he began the self-appointed task of examining every coffin as it was removed to the catacombs outside the church. It was a most unpleasant task: '. . . this vault was a good-sized room, as full as ever it could hold with coffins, piled one over the other from the very top to the very bottom. Many coffins were even piled up crossways in front of the door, so that no entry could be obtained except by moving them, and others were jammed up together in all possible positions, without the least attempt at order, reminding one much of books packed in a box to be sent away.' Furthermore, the whole place had a faint and sickly smell, peculiarly offensive and overpowering; both Buckland and Mr R. K. Burstall, the vestry surveyor who assisted him, were afterwards stricken by a mysterious illness from which Mr Burstall did not fully recover for four months.

The vault contained over two hundred coffins and the total number in the whole crypt was well over three thousand, of which Buckland must have examined a considerable proportion. The search began on January 26 and ended on February 22. The coffin for which he was searching was almost the last to be brought out, and still in fairly good condition, the brass plate on it remaining bright and untarnished (Plate VI). The coffin was immediately locked in an empty crypt and Buckland hurried away to inform Professor John Quekett and the President and Council of the Royal College of Surgeons of the successful outcome of his search. Many eminent people came to examine the coffin during the next few days.[48]

Richard Owen, who greatly enjoyed moving in Society, had just returned from a levee when he was told of the discovery. He described the incident in the following words: 'After resuming ordinary costume, I went with Frank Buckland to the vaults beneath St Martin's Church, which are now being emptied, to see the coffin of John Hunter, which was found in a corner of one of them. It was in good preservation, and I have written to Dean Milman about getting it into St Paul's. But such a scene! A score of Irish labourers hauling along the coffins, higgledy-piggledy, from one dark recess to the other. The sexton, to show the conscience of undertakers, pointed to one large coffin, supposed to have included a leaden one, but never had. Putting his foot upon it, he pressed it down and drew back the top and one side, exposing to view the black shrivelled remains of the "Hon. Lady ———." A mask of the features had been taken by a mass of the chrysalises of the *Dermestes*, or darkling-beetles, an inch thick. Faugh! I quitted the scene, thinking that *it* and the Levee had been two of the greatest contrasts which London could have exhibited in the same afternoon.'[19]

Hunter's body was reinterred in Westminster Abbey on March 28, 1859,* after some initial difficulty which Buckland may have helped to overcome by calling on a few of the members of the Chapter known to him and telling them of his father's original interest in securing a monument to Hunter in the Abbey.[19,48] A fund was also started for the purpose of erecting a statue of Hunter in his museum at the Royal College of Surgeons and Buckland was invited to join the organizing committee. The life-sized statue of Hunter by Weekes, based on Reynolds's famous portrait, now standing in the entrance hall of the College, together with a scholarship in comparative anatomy, ultimately resulted from this fund.

Buckland's efforts were recognized by the Council of the Leeds School of Medicine, who presented him with a silver medal commemorating Hunter by Wyon, and by the Council of the Royal College of Surgeons who in 1864, somewhat tardily, gave him a set of the catalogues of the Museum.[48]

Although his action seems generally to have been applauded however, one or two dissentient voices were raised in protest,

* John Hunter was reinterred on the north side of the nave, near the grave of Ben Jonson. Ten years earlier, during the preparation of Sir Robert Thomas Wilson's grave in 1849, Buckland had acquired portions of Ben Jonson's coffin and a number of bones, including the poet's 'heel bone'. These, and other miscellaneous objects, were found in 1938 by chance in an old furniture shop by Mr Peter A. S. Slater of Helensburgh, Dumbartonshire.[220]

including that of the *Illustrated London News.* ' "So, good Mr Buckland," say we, "be content with this one removal, or we shall have anglers removing honest Isaak Walton from Winchester to Westminster, Quakers carrying Penn from a cemetery in Bucks to the sepulchre of English Kings, and poets removing Milton from Cripplegate to Poet's Corner." '[76]

The discovery of Hunter's coffin increased Buckland's prestige and added to his fame. He continued to be in demand as a lecturer sometimes, apparently, charging a fee for his services. He was also engaged in preparing another book, whose provisional title was 'Gossip on Natural History'. In the event, however, it was published as *Curiosities of Natural History, Second Series.* The preparation was delayed by the illness, lasting ten months, of Thomas Tardrew, Surgeon of the Regiment, who died on May 4, 1860. The second series appeared in June and the book was dedicated to his mother '. . . for whose early instruction and parental care I owe a debt of gratitude I can never repay'.[15] The work was generally favourably reviewed; the *Morning Post* said: 'By systematically sorting these materials he has produced a summary of natural facts equally scientific and entertaining.'[77] A second edition was printed in December, 1861, together with a second edition of the First Series, which had already been reprinted three times.

In general, however, Buckland's official duties do not appear to have interfered seriously with his other activities, about many of which he wrote in *The Field* or elsewhere. Anywhere where there was something of interest, something about which he might write, there he was sure to be found. In 1859, for example, he wrote articles, amongst many others, about the performing bull at the Alhambra Palace, the talking fish (which was actually a seal) and a whale washed up at Gravesend. Life was not so full, as it evidently became later, to prevent him spending an occasional day or two of leisure. A watercolour has survived, by W. Hyde Briscoe, an artist sometimes employed by *The Field,* entitled 'The staff of the 2nd Life Guards gudgeon fishing at Surley Hall, Windsor'. It shows Frank Buckland, Adjutant Robert Reid and the Riding Master (John Reid) fishing from a boat. The Riding Master is shown drinking from a large beer can;

Buckland, short, stocky and bearded, is seated smoking a cigar.[3]

He made numerous visits to one of the Londoners' playgrounds, the Cremorne Gardens, where he knew the secretary, E. M. Adams, and to whom he sometimes confided his problems. On at least one occasion he took Hannah Papps with him, and they had their fortunes told by the Wizard. 'The influences in your Nativity has been slightly untoward,' said the piece of paper handed to Frank. 'Contradictions to your will has happened when happier results were anticipated – the tokens however promises benefic tendencies respecting the future – many changes are at hand, and the one you are contemplating will be to your advantage. . . .' Hannah said hopefully, amongst much else: 'You will Marry one with Money, and a good and lucrative profession.'[23]

Frank Buckland was now writing regularly for *The Field*. His first contributions were in the form of unsolicited notes and letters to the editor. As already mentioned, he entered into more formal contract with John Crockford to answer questions in the natural history columns in 1859, and by 1863 was editor of this department of the newspaper. Relations with *The Field* were terminated in 1865, by which time Buckland's position as a popular writer on natural history was consolidated. His contributions undoubtedly added to the interest of the columns of *The Field*, and were sometimes reprinted by other journals, but it would be wrong to imagine that he was in any way unique, a herring amongst sprats, for *The Field* could claim to have on its staff or amongst its contributors some first-class men who were acknowledged experts in their own topics.

The paper was divided into a number of separate departments, each under its own editor who was ultimately responsible to the Editor-in-Chief, John Henry Walsh (1810–1888). Walsh was appointed in 1857 by the proprietor, Mr E. W. Cox; he steered the paper wisely and successfully for thirty years. He had trained as a surgeon, was a Fellow of the Royal College of Surgeons, and followed this profession for some years before he turned to journalism. He was a good naturalist, an all-round sportsman, leading authority on dogs, both for sport and show; his great work on shotguns and powders led to the development of the modern shotgun.[21]

In charge of the angling departments was Francis Francis, four years older than Buckland and from a very different background. Francis was the son of Captain Morgan, R.N., and was born at Seaton, at the mouth of the River Axe in Devon. On coming of age, he changed his surname to Francis in order to conform to stipulations in the will of his step-grandfather. He was trained as a civil engineer, but never obtained a living by this profession for on completing his articles he determined to devote his life to sport, particularly angling, and journalism. His early education was obtained at various private schools and from several tutors, but by his own application he contrived to acquire a good knowledge of English literature and to make himself a fair classical scholar. He was, moreover, a versatile man, musical, artistic and athletic, and he derived much pleasure from collecting together a good angling library. He wrote many books on the freshwater fisheries, including the *Practical Management of Fisheries*, which ran to six editions, and *Fish Culture* which ran to two. He died courageously a lingering death of cancer of the tongue in 1886.[7]

The Dictionary of National Biography says of him:

> Scrupulously fair in word and thought, his nervous temperament made him no respecter of persons, and at times caused him to be hasty both in temper and judgement, but he was always ready to own himself mistaken, and was quick to forgive as well as to forget.

The editor of the poultry department was William Bernhard Tegetmeier. He was born in 1816, the son of a Hanoverian surgeon who had enlisted in the Royal Navy and who had subsequently set up in practice in London, living in Bury Street, in a house owned by the famous naturalist William Yarrell. Yarrell took a liking to the young man, who through him acquired an interest in natural history. Tegetmeier studied medicine at University College but did not qualify, preferring to devote his life to science and journalism. He became well known as a naturalist and was a frequent contributor to the meetings of the Zoological Society of London. Yarrell introduced him to Charles Darwin, who obtained much information from him on various subjects, particularly the breeding of birds, which Darwin quoted in a number of his books, notably *The Variation of Animals and Plants*.[78]

Tegetmeier was a man of real ability with a good knowledge of developments in his own branch of biology; his approach to problems was that of a scientist concerned only with ascertaining the facts, rather than, like Buckland, that of a man more interested in telling a good story. The two men were also very different in their personalities, for whereas Buckland was good tempered and mixed easily with all kinds of men, Tegetmeier was readily moved to wrath and many of his colleagues had cause to remember his acid tongue.

No account of the staff of *The Field* at this time would be complete, however, without mention of that flamboyant character the Honourable George Charles Grantley F. Berkeley. Berkeley was the sixth son of the fifth Earl of Berkeley and was born in 1800. He joined the Coldstream Guards in his teens and after an uneventful military career devoted his life to sport, where his main interest was in hunting the deer and the fox. His book *Reminiscences of a Huntsman* (1854) is in some ways characteristic of the man, and consists largely of a series of pointless anecdotes of limited interest perhaps to those who knew the individuals concerned and to the social historian studying the habits of some of the impoverished nobility in mid-nineteenth century England. Berkeley himself confessed to a '. . . fondness for the most trivial sport . . .' and the impression left by his book is that of a man with a cantankerous disposition who regarded the whole of animated nature as provided solely for his amusement.

Berkeley began to write regularly for *The Field* in 1854 and continued to do so until his vituperative correspondence culminated in 1863 in a violent row with Walsh and Crockford. Berkeley was apparently without any sense of responsible behaviour; he would rush into print for the flimsiest of reasons and would argue vehemently in favour of some quite preposterous point of view. This undoubtedly enlivened the columns of the paper, especially since he was sure to give any correspondent a good run by continually shifting his ground, but unfortunately Berkeley proved incapable of distinguishing between the views and the character of his opponent. Walsh

PLATE VII

Frank Buckland dosing a porpoise with sal volatile and water in the Zoological Gardens, London. November, 1862. From *Curiosities of Natural History*, Third Series.

PLATE VIII

Lord Powerscourt's Deer Horns from Transylvania. An engraving from *The Field*, October 25, 1862.

must sometimes have been hard put to it to present Berkeley's contributions in a suitably edited form.[21]

With men of such diverse interests and character, it is not surprising that serious differences of opinion sometimes occurred. It was the general policy of the paper to allow free and open discussion of any matter in its columns; Walsh rarely exercised his editorial right of terminating a correspondence, and some topics were debated at length for months together. The staff engaged freely in these debates, and letters from one departmental editor were frequently contributed to the columns of another department. Wherever argument was most heated, there would be found letters from Berkeley. Both Buckland and Francis were frequently involved in lively correspondence, but both showed admirable skill in avoiding the situation from which they could not retreat, whilst Francis in particular was adept at administering verbal punches where his opponent's case was most vulnerable.

Buckland's contributions covered a much wider field than natural history as this term is understood today. He wrote on new exhibits as they appeared at the Zoo, on strange animals and on animal behaviour. He also wrote about giants and dwarfs, about scientific ballooning, about Charles Jamrach the animal dealer, indeed, about anything odd or strange that came to the notice of his observant eye. Some of his articles reached a wider public than the columns of *The Field*, for they were reprinted in *The Times* and other journals.

His friendship with A. D. Bartlett enabled him to obtain first-hand news of happenings in the Zoological Gardens which he retailed to the public. The two men were very anxious to obtain a live porpoise and Buckland spent much time and trouble in attempting to revive dying specimens which reached the Gardens (Plate VII) and in travelling to the coast to inspect and arrange for the transportation of porpoises caught by local fishermen. None of the animals which reached the Gardens alive survived for more than a few days. Buckland, however, maintained public interest in the attempts not only by his contributions to *The Field* but also by writing letters to *The Times* describing his most recent exploits and announcing the arrival of yet another specimen at the Zoo. People flocked to the Gardens, generally to discover that the newcomer had just died. Thackeray wrote a lengthy *Elegy on the Porpoise* by the Sturgeon which shared the same pond. It began:

> *Dead is he? Yes, and wasn't I glad when they*
> *carried away his corpus;*
> *A great black, oily, wallowing, plunging,*
> *ponderous porpus.*
> *What call had Mr Frank Buckland, which I*
> *don't deny his kindness,*
> *To take and shove into my basin a porpoise*
> *troubled with blindness?*

This elegy was first published in *Punch* but was reprinted in *The Times*.[60]

Buckland's contract with *The Field* did not prevent him from writing for many other papers, including *The Queen*, *Leisure Hour* and *All the Year Round*. He was also a prolific writer of letters to *The Times*; sometimes these would give advice on some medical matter, such as the treatment of burns or the bite of an adder, or would refer to some item of biological interest. He once drew attention to the dangerous nature of certain types of glass ornament then popular for ladies' hats. The effect of these letters, whatever their intention, was to keep his name continually before the public.

In 1859 he began to turn his attention to means of increasing the country's food supply, an interest which led him to devote the rest of his life to the fisheries.

CHAPTER EIGHT

Food for the People

THE GROWING TOWNS and cities of Britain, and the rise in the population as a whole, caused continual problems of food supply during the middle years of the nineteenth century. Meat was expensive and many people could afford it only once a week if at all. Britain was still almost entirely dependent for her meat on what she could produce at home, for the refrigerator had not reached the stage of technical development where it could be employed for bringing frozen or even chilled meat by sea from the other side of the globe. Furthermore, more intensive methods of cultivation allowed various pests and diseases to spread throughout the crops; in particular, the potato blight, which altered the course of history in the 1840s, continued to appear and although in some years its attacks were mild, in others the potato harvest was almost ruined.

It is against this background that one must examine the interest in acclimatization, defined by Frank Buckland as '. . . a term which may be said to comprehend the art of discovering animals, beasts, birds, fishes, insects, plants and other natural products, and utilizing them in places where they were unknown before'.[79] The idea of acclimatization was not by any means new in 1859. One of the original aims of the Zoological Society of London, of which Dr Buckland, Sir Benjamin Brodie and W. J. Broderip were founder members, had been to introduce new and useful animals to Britain. 'When it is considered', said a Prospectus of the Society in 1825, 'how few amongst the immense variety of animated beings have been hitherto applied to the uses of Man, and that most of those which have been domesticated or subdued belong to the early periods of society, and to the efforts of savage or uncultured nations, it is impossible not to hope for many new, brilliant and useful results in the same field, by the application of the wealth, ingenuity, and varied resources of a civilized people.'[56]

The Zoological Society, owing to shortage of funds, could not do much in its early years to encourage these aims, but in December, 1847, perhaps at the instigation of the new and energetic Secretary, David W. Mitchell, medals were presented to Sir Roderick Impey Murchison and M. Dimitri de Dalmatoff for the parts they had played in introducing to this country the European bison, sometimes inaccurately termed the Aurochs. Murchison had been employed by Tsar Nicholas I to carry out a geological survey in Russia and had induced the Tsar to gratify Queen Victoria's apparent desire to see bison in the London Gardens. A pair of young animals had been captured through the efforts of M. de Dalmatoff, Master of Imperial Forests in the Government of Grodno.[56] Unfortunately they died not long afterwards of 'a murrain' that swept through the bovine animals at the Zoo.[79]

Numerous private collectors, however, appear to have been interested in the possibility of introducing animals from abroad, either for pleasure or profit. Foremost amongst these men was Lord Stanley, afterwards Earl of Derby, who maintained a menagerie at Knowsley, referred to by one author as '. . . the largest private collection of modern times'. Lord Derby sent men to collect animals in Singapore, India, Central and North America, Norway and Lapland, and maintained an expedition in West Africa for fifteen years. He was President of the Zoological Society for more than twenty years until his death in 1851.[80]

Interest in acclimatization in this country was, however, quickened by the apparent success of the French Société Imperiale d'Acclimatation, founded in Paris in 1854 largely through the efforts of the biologist Isidore Geoffroy Saint-Hilaire (1805–1861). Geoffroy Saint-Hilaire preached that man had three duties: to preserve the useful animals; to make the most of the domesticated animals; and to add to the list of useful animals others, at present of little use, which could be turned to account in some way.[81] The new society was successful in obtaining royal support, and in 1858 the authorities of the city of Paris gave an area of about 40 acres in the

Bois de Boulogne as a vivarium and garden. By 1860 the membership was over 2,000 and included thirty-five royalty '. . . from the Emperor of the French to the King of Siam, from the Sovereign Pontiff to the Emperor of Brazil'. The Société offered a series of prizes for what at that time no doubt seemed worthy objectives; many of them appear strange today. A medal, worth £40, was, for example, offered for the '. . . complete domestication, application to agriculture, or employment in towns of the Kiang (*Equus hemionus*), a valuable beast of burden, of great power and swiftness, which belongs to Thibet, or the peetsi (*Asinus Burchelli*), a South African animal, nearly allied to the zebra, but much resembling the horse'. It would be interesting to know what further steps the Société intended to take after the lucky winner had collected his prize for having succeeded in the '. . . domestication and multiplication of some species of kangaroo . . .' or the '. . . introduction and domestication of the Australian emu'.[79]

When Lord Derby died in 1851 he bequeathed to the Zoological Society a choice of whichever group of his animals were thought to be most likely to become acclimatized in this country. At Mitchell's advice, the elands were chosen. The eland, an ox-like antelope formerly widely distributed throughout Africa, can be as much as six feet high and weigh twelve hundred pounds. It will breed fairly easily in captivity in this country, provided it is protected from the full rigours of an English winter, and the Society's herd began to increase in numbers so satisfactorily that it became possible to part with breeding pairs to landowners prepared to contemplate the prospect of this large beast roaming through their parks. One of the first to found a herd in this way was Viscount Hill, at Hawkstone, near Shrewsbury; other herds were started by the Marquis of Breadalbane at Taymouth and by Lord Egerton at Tatton.[79]

The columns of *The Field* contained many references to the French Société and to the progress of the herds of eland. Buckland's interest was apparently aroused when he was invited to attend a dinner at the London Tavern on January 19, 1859, when eland was the main dish on the menu. The beast came from Lord Hill's herd; it was a six-year-old male, anything but fat and not in season, but appears to have met with the approval of most of those present. Professor Owen wrote to *The Times* the following day sending the experiences of a ' "committee of taste", including three brother naturalists . . .', who had sat down at this truly zoological dinner which, besides eland, had included a large pike, American partridges and a wild goose. He praised the culinary properties of eland as '. . . the finest, closest, and masticable of any meat.' Its flavour was compared with veal and capon and '. . . finally, the suggestion that it was (mammalian) meat, with a soupçon of pheasant flavour, was generally accepted.'[82] He later wrote: 'It is not too much to expect that in twenty years eland venison will be at least an attainable article of food: and seeing the rapidity with which it arrives at maturity, its weight, and its capacity for feeding, it is quite possible that before the expiration of the century it may be removed from the category of animals of luxury to the more solid and useful list of the farm.'[80]

Although the prospect of herds of eland cropping the pastures of Britain nowadays seems slightly comic and ridiculous, many people at that time saw it only as an original idea requiring little to make it a commercial success. Frank Buckland, of course, was always prepared to try anything as an article of food, and Owen himself was not averse to tasting something new and unfamiliar. 'I have just received from a friend in Canada', he wrote to Frank on December 31, 1859, 'a steak cut from a fine Moose-deer which he had shot. Perhaps he wished me to compare it with "Eland". I would not do so without your notice . . . I mean to have the steak for luncheon; and if you could run down on the 1.30 p.m. train to Mortlake, you would find it on table, with collar'd brawn, etc., etc., about ½ past 2.' Owen was now living in a grace and favour residence, Sheen Lodge, in Richmond Park.[23]

Buckland took up the idea of acclimatization with characteristic energy and enthusiasm. He was not the man to take only an academic interest in a subject; whatever the subject, it had to have some obvious practical value. Buckland, Berkeley and John Crockford were probably the main founders of the Society for the Acclimatization of Animals in the United Kingdom, but it undoubtedly owed something to David W. Mitchell who died in November, 1859, in Paris where he had gone to take up the appointment of Director of the newly founded Jardin d'Acclimatation. An advertisement in *The Field* for April 21, 1860, announced the intention to form an Acclimatization Society, and all those interested in becoming members were invited to write to Buckland at *The Field* Offices. The list of patrons included the names of the Marquis of Breadalbane, Thomas Blackwell, Esq., Engineer of the Grand Trunk Railway of Canada, and Berkeley. Thomas Blackwell was the husband of Frank's cousin, Anne.

Meetings took place soon afterwards and the Marquis of Breadalbane was elected President and Berkeley Vice-President. Buckland became Secretary, to be joined in that office shortly afterwards by James Lowe, an accomplished linguist and occasional contributor to *The Field.* The accounts of the Society's doings make droll reading today, and fully justify Dr J. E. Gray's comments at the British Association meeting at Bath in 1864 '. . . that some of the schemes of the would-be acclimatizers are incapable of being carried out, and would never have been suggested if their promoters had been better acquainted with the habits and manners of the animals on which the experiments are proposed to be made'.[83]

It is difficult to know how much Buckland was responsible for some of the bizarre schemes bordering on fantasy which were seriously proposed by the Society, but his advice certainly carried considerable weight. He gave a lecture to the Society of Arts in November, 1860, and presumably the views he stated then were his own. It is difficult to feel much sympathy with his proposal to fill the parks of noblemen and rich proprietors not only with eland, but with wapiti deer, Barbary deer, Virginian deer, Persian deer, reindeer and elk, to say nothing of yaks and American bison of which Lord Breadalbane already had a herd on his estate at Taymouth. Furthermore, there is cause for relief that the proposal to introduce beaver to this country came to nothing. Buckland suggested that kangaroo might thrive in English parks and although it may be true that 'there are many places . . . in England where it would thrive admirably', it surely would not suit the rural scene, and, notwithstanding the excellence of 'kangaroo venison', its value might have been somewhat lessened by the reluctance of many people to eat it.[79]

Even less likely to be successful, one would have thought, was the acclimatization of the capybara, suggested by M. Geoffroy Saint-Hilaire. The capybara, '. . . . the largest rodent in the world, strongly tempts the domesticator . . .', wrote a contributor to *All the Year Round* in 1861. The capybara, resembling an hypertrophied guinea pig, '. . . swims like the beaver, and feeds on water weeds, thus converting into wholesome nutriment vegetable substances which are turned to no account. It is very prolific, and produces a great quantity of meat in a short space of time.' The writer admitted, however, that 'Mr Darwin's account of the capybara, or water-hog, is much less encouraging – except in respect to the size of the animal', and added that M. Geoffroy Saint-Hilaire '. . . and the English Acclimatization Society have one obstacle before them – popular prejudice – which we fear will, for a time at least, wall in and imprison many of their efforts.'[81]

The subscription to the new Society was two guineas annually, later reduced to one guinea, and a donation of £10 made the donor a life member of the Society. Miss Burdett Coutts '. . . with that generosity and kindness of heart which has gained for her the respect and esteem of all classes . . .' gave £500 together with a promise of a subscription of £50 a year for five years.[79] The Society flourished for about ten years, and after the death of Lord Breadalbane in 1862, the Duke of Newcastle became President, to be followed by His Royal Highness the Prince of Wales.

The Society attempted to cross some imported animals with native ones. Lord Breadalbane crossed a domestic bull with a cow bison and in the Second Annual Report of the Society it is stated that: '. . . the Council has to regret that unavoidable circumstances caused the failure of an attempt to obtain a hybrid between the common Cow and the Eland – an experiment which was thought desirable.'[84]

Chinese sheep were imported at considerable expense from Shanghai, but do not seem to have been as successful as had been hoped. Their advantage over the native varieties was thought to be that they bred twice yearly and sometimes had five lambs at a birth.

The Annual Reports possess a nightmarish quality which

it is difficult to convey without quoting in full. Here is a passage from the Third Annual Report: '. . . the Society has received through the kindness of Robert Marshall, Esq, of the Royal Mail Steam Packet Company, a pair of the *Psopheo Crepitans*, Agamia, or Trumpeter Birds, from Central America. These fine birds, which are expected to breed well in this country, are easily domesticated, and become attached to the human race in a most extraordinary manner. In their own country, they will trustily watch a house, like a dog, and they give warning of danger by an arrangement in the windpipe which enables them to give forth a trumpet-like sound – whence the name. The Trumpeter Bird may also, it is said, be trained to watch a flock of poultry, and even to shepherd a flock of sheep. It possesses great courage, and is beautiful in form and colour.'[85]

It is small wonder that the Society was ridiculed. Someone even printed a fake Annual Report of the Society which hoodwinked the editor of the *Gardener's Chronicle*, who believed it to be genuine. 'In Birds a great success has been obtained by the Hon. Grantley Berkeley', it read, 'who has succeeded in producing a hybrid between his celebrated Pintail Drake and a Thames Rat; and the Council consider that this great success alone entitles them to the everlasting gratitude of their countrymen, as this hybrid, both from peculiarity of form and delicacy of flavour (which partakes strongly of the maternal parent), is entirely unique.'[23]

Relatively few people, however, appear to have found the ideas of the Society absurd, and even the Admiralty issued an order to all commanding officers in H.M. ships directing them to afford every facility in their power to accredited agents of the Society in the transmission of specimens from any part of the globe. Acclimatization societies were also founded elsewhere, particularly in Australia, where the rabbit and the prickly pear had not yet become major problems, thus providing an awful warning to would-be meddlers with the pattern of nature. There was some exchange of animals and plants between different societies, and on one occasion a consignment from Queensland destined for the Acclimatization Society found its way instead to the Zoological Gardens. The consignment consisted of an emu, a cock scrub-turkey, a dingo and some Australian hawks; the mistake was surely an excusable one.[86]

Following the receipt of reports that the Australian Society had held a very successful dinner, it was decided to arrange a similar event in London on July 12, 1862. A sub-committee consisting, amongst others, of Viscount Powerscourt, Berkeley, Crockford, James Lowe and Buckland, was set up; the menu showed without doubt that the Buckland genius had been at work. Over one hundred guests sat down to the meal in Willis's Rooms, with Buckland and Lowe at a side table serving those foods in short supply. It was, for example, difficult to make a mere quart of birds' nest soup go round.[87]

The tripang, a dried holothurian echinoderm popular in south-east Asia and described by one Victorian traveller as '. . . almost as tough as caoutchouc . . .' caused some difficulty in the cooking, and Frank borrowed the cook of the 2nd Life Guards to carry out this operation. The shrivelled objects, resembling pieces of horse's hoof, were soaked all day and boiled all night, by which time they looked like large black garden slugs and were cut up *instantly* by Buckland. After continued simmering for a long time they eventually became tender. The reports in *The Field* on the 'Japanese sea-slug' said that it was '. . . strong in flavour, and excited a divided opinion. Some said it was very unpalatable; others ate it with delight. We partook of a saucerful and much enjoyed it. Mr Willis (no mean judge) said it was nearly equal to turtle.'[87]

The intrepid company sat down shortly before eight o'clock and stolidly champed its way through dish after dish until it reached the end at nearly half past ten. Kangaroo steamer ('too highly salted, and not cooked properly'), Chinese lamb, Kangaroo ham ('too salt and not very tender'), wild boar ham, Syrian pig (a cross between the Syrian pig and a Yorkshire pig), the Hon. Grantley Berkeley's Pintail Ducks (a cross between the wild pintail and the common duck), Curassow, leporines (actually a rabbit, but claimed to be a cross between rabbit and hare), Chinese yams, and botargo appeared amidst a vast number of more common dishes. The occasion must surely have been one to remember. The report in *The Field* said: 'The room was decorated with a variety of interesting objects illustrative of the objects of the society. The most remarkable of these were the enormous horns belonging to Lord Powerscourt . . .' (Plate VIII). The meeting broke up well after midnight.[87] The annual dinner the following year took place in St James's Hall, when the menu seems to have been rather less exciting, although it did include ostrich eggs. As before, the room was decorated with various objects, 'spirited models of the head of the North American bison, and other animals, especially a case of Californian quails, and birds mounted as fire-screens'.[88]

One of the expressed objects of the Acclimatization Society was to improve Britain's freshwater fisheries and to introduce new species of fish to this country. Buckland threw himself wholeheartedly into this aspect of the work, especially into the various attempts at fish hatching.

The practice of collecting the fertilized eggs of fish and allowing them to hatch in a protected pool was known to the ancients, but there is apparently no evidence that they knew how to manipulate ripe fish so that they would give up their milt and ova and could thus be spawned artificially. Although the art of fish spawning is said to have been known to Dom Pinchon, a fourteenth-century French monk, and was presumably practised in some areas, the knowledge was not widespread and was probably lost again. It was a Westphalian landowner, Stephan Ludwig Jacobi, living at Hohenhausen, who rediscovered the artificial spawning of trout in the first half of the eighteenth century. By stroking the abdomens of ripe fish he found he could obtain eggs or milt, which he mixed together in a bowl so that fertilization occurred. He spread the fertilized eggs thinly on a bed of gravel at the bottom of oak boxes, about 12 feet long, 6 inches deep and 1 foot 6 inches wide, through which water was allowed to run continuously. The tops of the boxes were closed, and the water entered and left through fine brass meshes in order to keep out possible predators. After a period the eggs hatched and could be released to restock fresh waters. It is said that Jacobi received a pension from the British Government for his work.[89]

Sir Humphry Davy, in his famous book *Salmonia; or, Days of Fly Fishing*, referred to Jacobi's work, saying that it '. . . offers a very good mode of increasing to any extent the quantity of trout in rivers or lakes: for the young ones are preserved from the attacks of fishes, and other voracious animals or insects, at the time when they are most easily destroyed, and perfectly helpless. The same plan, I have no doubt, would answer equally well with grayling or other varieties of the salmo genus.' He also commented pertinently that this technique could be used for breeding hybrids.[90]

Davy's book was read by John Shaw, head keeper of the Duke of Buccleuch at Drumlanrig Castle by the River Nith, and a born experimentalist. Shaw began in 1833 to study the life history of the parr, or young salmon, at that time widely believed to be a distinct and separate species. He made special experimental ponds in which he succeeded in rearing parr from salmon eggs; he showed that the young salmon does not migrate to the sea the same year it is hatched, as had previously been thought. He found also that the time taken for fertilized eggs to hatch could be shortened by raising the temperature. He took fertilized eggs from a salmon; some he placed in a stream of water in the open, others he put into a tumbler of water in his bedroom window. He constantly replenished the water in the tumbler by directing into it a jet from a large earthen jar. 'The waste-water was carried out at the window along a wooden channel fitted up for the purpose.'

Shaw reported his results in a series of papers to the Royal Society of Edinburgh from 1836 to 1843. They aroused considerable interest and controversy.[91] Dr William Buckland, in company with his friend Professor Louis Agassiz (1807–1873), the famous Swiss ichthyologist, visited the experimental ponds at Drumlanrig Castle in 1844. Agassiz was particularly interested in Shaw's work, because he was carrying out similar experiments on lake trout at Neuchâtel.

Meanwhile, interest in fish hatching in France was stimulated by reports that two fishermen of Bresse in the Vosges Valley had discovered for themselves the possibility of artificial spawning and subsequent rearing of the fry and they began operations on their own account in 1842. M. de Quatrefages (1810–1892), the distinguished naturalist, drew attention to the potential value of artificial propagation at a meeting of the Academy of Science in Paris in 1848, and shortly afterwards the French Government set up at Huningue near the Rhine an establishment for the artificial spawning of fish. Fertilized ova were sent all over Europe and to Britain from Huningue, but comparatively few fish were hatched on the premises.[89] The Huningue (Huningen) establishment passed into German hands at the conclusion of the Franco-Prussian War.

It is very probable that experiments were being carried out in many other areas. Gottlieb Boccius, the author of a treatise on fish management, was apparently rearing young trout at Chatsworth and Uxbridge as early as 1841,[92] and he claimed 'the principle of artificial spawning I have been acquainted with as far back as 1815. . . .'[93] Some attempt was made to reap the commercial rewards of fish hatching by Thomas and Edmund Ashworth, two brothers from Poynton, Cheshire, who purchased a salmon fishery in Galway. They secured the services of a well-known skilled manipulator, Robert Ramsbottom, a fishing tackle maker from Clitheroe. The Ashworths' apparent success reached the notice of the salmon fishing proprietors on the Tay, who in 1853 decided to set up their own salmon hatching ponds at Stormontfield. Robert Ramsbottom himself came to demonstrate the technique of stripping the ripe fish of eggs and milt. A series of interesting experiments was carried out at Stormontfield during the following years.[94] These received full attention in the columns of *The Field*, as did the development of the establishment at Huningue and the Ashworths' Galway fishery.

The limitations of the artificial rearing of fish are nowadays much more clearly seen than they were at that time, although even then a few doubters queried the value of the technique. Dr J. E. Gray in 1864 said: 'Again, the notion of fishing the breeding-fish out of a river, collecting their eggs and artificially impregnating them, seems to me to be an unnatural mode of proceeding, and such as is not practised in the cultivation of any other animal. I cannot see any practical advantage that can possibly be derived from it.'[83]

To most people however, artificial rearing seemed to be the obvious way of restocking Britain's freshwater fisheries, too often suffering from the effects of pollution by sewage and chemical wastes from gas-works and factories. Many fine salmon rivers were also being ruined by mill dams which thwarted the attempts of the ripe salmon to reach the head-waters of the rivers to spawn. Effective improvement of declining fisheries can be brought about only by removing the causes of the decline, in these instances pollution and physical barriers. Artificial rearing can be used to stock waters with species not found there before, or to restock waters in which numbers have fallen very low but only after removing the cause. It is impossible to make an assessment of the value of any fish hatching operation without some measure of the survival rate to maturity of the young fish released from the hatcheries; few figures were available in the 1860s on which an assessment could be made, and those that were, from Stormontfield, were unduly optimistic. Indeed, the Canadian Government even in this century has supported salmon hatcheries which unsuccessfully attempted to maintain the stocks of salmon in the face of excessive fishing for the canneries.

Nobody was more concerned in fish culture and its potential value than Francis Francis who became one of its most vigorous advocates. Frank Buckland also began to be interested in the subject, and in May, 1861, collected perch spawn at Surley Hall, Eton, and succeeded in hatching out some fish which he demonstrated at a meeting of the Thames Angling Preservation Society, a Society founded in 1838 by a few enthusiasts to protect from poaching the waters in the neighbourhood of Twickenham. According to Bompas, Buckland was '. . . immediately elected upon the committee . . .' of the Society, although this fact may be less significant than it appears, since any member could offer himself for election after subscribing a minimum sum of twenty-one shillings.[95]

A sub-committee consisting of Stephen Ponder, Chairman of the Society, Buckland, Francis Francis and two others was elected to consider the possibilities of setting up a hatchery for the Society. A small hatching apparatus was built in a meadow at Hampton but soon afterwards, at Francis's suggestion, more satisfactory apparatus was fitted into Mr Ponder's own greenhouse at Elm Grove, Hampton. Both Francis and Buckland devoted much attention to Ponder's equipment, and thousands of young trout, salmon and other fish fry were released into the Thames. When Monsieur J. Coumes, Chief Engineer of the French establishment at Huningue, visited England in 1862, Buckland took him to Hampton to see the establishment there.[96]

In January, 1863, Buckland was entrusted with the setting-up of fish hatching apparatus in the windows of *The Field* offices, at that time in the Strand. They attracted a great deal of attention, and he reported fully to his readers on the development of the young fish. He employed as an assistant in this work his friend the old viper-catcher, Thomas White, 'viper catcher twenty years or more, man and boy'. A printed sheet of verse entitled *Our Corner of the Strand* no doubt was run off on *The Field* presses:

But one morning all the Cockneys were taken by surprise,
To see a lot of salmon being hatched before their eyes.
So you soon will all agree that there's not in all the land
Such a place for real sensation as our Corner of the Strand.[23]

Buckland continued to be in great demand as a lecturer on natural history subjects. After a lecture in Oxford the Mayor, Mr C. J. Sadler, wrote to thank him for his '. . . kind, amusing, and instructive lecture which afforded high gratification to a numerous and respectable audience'.[23] Wherever Buckland went, he could now be assured of a large, attentive and fashionable gathering. He spoke at a number of meetings of the Zoological Society of London on the subject of fish hatching, and clearly was beginning to be regarded as an authority on the subject.

He was invited to lecture on Fish Culture at the Royal Institution in Albemarle Street, on April 17, 1863. It was an impressive occasion. The Duke of Northumberland was in the Chair and the audience included Sir Roderick Murchison, Sir Edwin Landseer, Professor Faraday, Professor Daubeny, Professor Tyndall, Professor Frankland '. . . besides a large audience of ladies and gentlemen of position and influence in the social and scientific world'. The lecture was very successful; perhaps Buckland for once was on his mettle to instruct rather than to please. The report of the lecture in *The Field* said that it was '. . . so happily and agreeably rendered that we hardly ever remember to have seen the usually somewhat unimpressionable audience of the Royal Institution so thoroughly thawed into genial good humour and satisfaction, both with themselves and their lecturer. Indeed we heard one or two remark that they had enjoyed it greatly, for "it was very different from the usual sort of lecture they got there".'[97]

These lectures were published in June, 1863, as a book, *Fish Hatching*,[98] of which the *Literary Times* said, 'The mere general reader will find it instructive and suggestive. To the practical pisciculturist, its information and guidance are invaluable.' The *London Review* remarked, 'With respect to fish hatching and acclimatization Mr Buckland has been *par excellence* the most indefatigable of those other indefatigable Englishmen who have associated their names with the promotion and investigation of those subjects', whilst the *Court Journal* described him as '. . . this excellent patron of all culinarians'.[99]

The Field gave a favourable review of *Fish Hatching*. In the previous January it had also reviewed favourably a book on the same subject by Francis Francis. This was *Fish Culture: A Practical Guide to the Modern System of Breeding and Rearing Fish.* One can but wonder whether Francis felt aggrieved at Buckland's apparent poaching on his waters. Francis had, after all, been appointed by Walsh as his Commissioner to report on the state of the fisheries, and his book described in some detail observations made in Mr Ponder's hatchery.

The fish hatching demonstration given in *The Field* window proved so successful that it was decided to show it at the Islington Dog Show:

> *And the next thing that we heard, among the Islington fogs,*
> *Mr Buckland and his salmon had gone straitway to the Dogs,*

wrote the anonymous author of *Our Corner of the Strand.*[23]

Buckland was in charge of the apparatus which was shown at the Dog Show in the Agricultural Hall at Islington in July, 1863, and he described the occasion in *The Field*, which inserted an engraving to illustrate the scene (Plate IX). On the left of the picture is John Crockford, with his back to the lady,

PLATE IX

The Islington Dog Show. July, 1863. On the left of the picture is John Crockford, business manager of *The Field* and founder of Crockford's Clerical Directory, with his back to the lady. He is talking to Capt. Edward Walter (later Sir Edward Walter) who in 1859 had founded the Corps of Commissionaires. On the extreme right is Mr Stephen Ponder and immediately in front of him is Buckland himself.

From *The Field*, July 4, 1863.

PLATE X

No. 37 Albany Street, London. After Mrs Buckland sold the house about 1890, it was used as a lodging house. It may have been at this time that the area railings were altered. From a photograph taken by the late L. R. Brightwell.

talking to Capt. Edward Walter (later Sir Edward Walter) who in 1859 had founded the Corps of Commissionaires. On the extreme right is Mr Stephen Ponder and immediately in front of him is Buckland himself who, '. . . true to his profession, has placed a young salmon in a physic bottle, and is endeavouring to explain *its* beauty to the greater beauty who favours him with her attention'.

The Show attracted many people. Buckland wrote: '. . . it is a great pleasure to think our pains were appreciated, honoured as they were by the careful inspection of the Prince and Princess of Wales, by many persons of influence in the land, by the public in general, and by the poor man with his family on the last day of the show.'[88]

He must have felt that he was beginning to chisel a foothold for himself in the slippery heights of fame. Undoubtedly, he had felt in the past that his efforts were inadequately rewarded for he had confided as much to his friend E. M. Adams, Secretary of the Cremorne Gardens, but he was now greatly in demand as a writer and lecturer, and was beginning to be acknowledged as an expert on fish hatching. He had at last arrived.

CHAPTER NINE

Troubled Waters

WORK FOR THE Acclimatization Society, experiments in fish hatching, writing and lecturing must have made it increasingly difficult for Buckland to carry out his regimental duties. On April 20, 1863, he resigned his Commission as Assistant Surgeon. Bompas[13] suggests that it was not only pressure of work that made him resign. On the death in 1860 of Thomas Tardrew, Surgeon to the 2nd Life Guards, Buckland had hoped to be promoted in his place. Unfortunately for him, the regulations had been altered not long before, so that promotion now went by seniority in the Brigade. In spite of representations from General Lord Seaton, Colonel of the 2nd Life Guards and veteran of the Peninsular War, supported by Sir Roderick Murchison and Sir Benjamin Brodie, it was decided at the Horse Guards that there was no special reason for waiving the rule, and Frederick George Kerin of the Royal Horse Guards was appointed Surgeon-Major in Tardrew's place. There was no ill-feeling between Buckland and Kerin, who was a '. . . kind hearted and popular man in his regiment . . .',[100] but Buckland was clearly disappointed and resigned when he saw that promotion was not going to be rapid.

Shortly after his resignation he moved into the house No. 156, Albany Street (renumbered No. 37 the following year), which was to be his home for the rest of his life. It was conveniently placed on the west side of the street, not far from the junction with what are now the Euston and Marylebone Roads, but was then the New Road; the Zoological Gardens were only ten minutes' walk away, and the Portland Road Station (now Great Portland Street Station) of the Metropolitan Railway was only just across the Marylebone Road. Albany Street was the boundary between, to the east, the working-class area of Cumberland Market, originally intended to replace the Haymarket, Clarence Gardens and Munster Square, and, to the west, the houses of the well-to-do, facing Regent's Park. When the line between Baker Street and Portland Road was under construction, such was the resistance offered by the influential inhabitants of the area, that the railway company had to introduce descending and ascending gradients in the line to avoid a subterranean thoroughfare between the gardens in Park Square and Park Crescent used mainly by nursery-maids and children. This line, the first of the Underground railway system, was opened in January, 1863.[50]

The house itself, which stood in a terrace on a site now occupied by part of the Royal College of Physicians' building, was a pleasing example of late Regency building with a fanlight over the door and a cast-iron balcony to the first floor windows (Plate x). There were four stories in all, in addition to the basement. It had formerly been the home of George Hogarth, Dickens's father-in-law, and to it Buckland now brought Hannah Papps.

They were married by licence on August 11, 1863, at the Church of St Mary Magdalene, Munster Square, where Buckland became a regular and devout worshipper. One of his old college friends officiated, John Edmond Coulson, Vicar of Long Preston, Yorkshire;[24] two of his friends were witnesses. These were Thomas Coulson Carpendale and John Crockford. Carpendale was an artist who '. . . from his long residence in New York, has come to be considered an American, and bears the reputation of being the Trans-atlantic Landseer';[101] he had been chosen by the explorer Paul Du Chaillu, who in 1861 discovered the gorilla, to make the first drawings of that animal.

In consequence of his resignation from the Life Guards, Buckland's income dropped by about £150 a year. On his marriage, he ceased to be a Student of Christ Church, and the last payment to him from this source was for the quarter ending October, 1863.[32] Perhaps he felt that it was time that he began to settle down, and that he was now able to earn a sufficient income from writing and lecturing.

All was not well, however, with his plans for fish hatching.

At the monthly meeting of the Acclimatization Society in July 1863, a letter from Francis Francis was read in which it was pointed out that pisciculture could be made very profitable to the Society. The report in *The Field* said that Francis '. . . was ready to erect an apparatus for the Society upon the most economical and efficient principles, and would carry on the operations under the direction of the Council.' Francis also offered to forgo any profit for himself in the first year of the operation. Buckland, to whom the proposal probably came as a surprise, protested most vigorously against this plan, strongly urging instead the claims of Mr Stephen Ponder, but it was objected that not only was Mr Ponder already committed to the Thames Angling Preservation Society, but he was not even a member of the Acclimatization Society.[86]

The most that Buckland could do was to get the meeting adjourned for a week, so that he could draw up alternative proposals, but Francis's offer was then accepted. 'Without the slightest disparagement to either Mr Buckland or Mr Ponder (both of whom have laboured well and earnestly, each in his own way, and according to his lights),' wrote Walsh, 'it is most clear that a totally independent arrangement will be best.'[101] The decision to set up a hatchery on Francis's land at Twickenham was a serious blow to Buckland's own great hopes for the future of Mr Ponder's establishment; it was very clear that the Thames Angling Preservation Society had not sufficient money to support such a project for long without some financial help, and they might even decide to discontinue hatching on their own account if Francis's hatchery appeared successful. Well might Buckland write to *The Field* to deny the report that he had '. . . highly approved of the proposition before the meeting'.[102] He also mentioned something of his irritation in a private letter to Berkeley.

Berkeley had been fighting a losing battle of his own with Walsh. In 1862 Berkeley had been involved in a lengthy and complicated correspondence in *The Field*, mainly with a Colonel Whyte, on the general subject of Salmon and Civilization. Eventually, Walsh had refused to publish Berkeley's letter, saying, 'As it does not contain any new argument, or any fresh statement of facts, we omit it – cordially approving, as we do, Col Whyte's suggestion that the controversy ought to end now. Argument, logic, fact, and common sense are all on the side of the Colonel.'[103] There the matter rested for a time, although no doubt Berkeley smarted under the rebuke, but a similar situation arose the following year and Walsh again acted with firmness. Berkeley thereupon withdrew his services not only from *The Field*, because it had ceased '. . . to afford fair play to all parties', but he also resigned from the Acclimatization Society.

Berkeley, on receipt of Buckland's letter, wrote to the editor of the *Dorset County Chronicle*. He announced his withdrawal as Vice-President of the Acclimatization Society because '. . . it has fallen into the hands of a clique of men always in town, and who, by the monthly meetings, can control its finances and guide its now misconducted interests.' He added: 'It has become evident to me by the late substitution of the *sub-editor of the Field*, a Mr Francis Francis, to the paid position of manager of the fish-culture to the Society, instead of that really clever gentleman Mr F. Buckland, that a clique having a majority in and around *The Field* office has a great deal too much to do with the Society ever to let its interests stand on their own merits.'

Perhaps a seed was sown in Buckland's mind by Berkeley's further comment: 'We are now without a *leading journal* exclusively devoted to sport and agriculture, for the egregious absurdities that have been published in *The Field*, and its growing scurrility, have deprived its columns of all authority, and rendered it offensive and ridiculous. . . . I cannot help thinking but that the sportsmen of England are numerous enough to start a well-conditioned sporting paper, with a gentleman at its head, and that the defalcation of *The Field* gives an opening to any established journal in which to take up the interests that are now so miserably neglected.'[104]

Buckland was placed in a most embarrassing position. He did not like Francis; he referred to him in 1866 as '. . . my greatest enemy . . .' and added, 'Heaven knows he has done mischief enough to me this last five years but I forgive all'.[23] Nevertheless, it did no good to make his feelings of grievance known and at the November meeting of the Acclimatization Society he did the only thing possible, by making a handsome public apology to the Council of the Society and to Francis for what Berkeley had said, and added that henceforth he hoped they would all work together unanimously for the good of the Society.[105]

As one of the secretaries of the Acclimatization Society, Buckland no doubt felt that it was still his duty to continue to take an active interest in fish hatching. Francis certainly thought that his ideas were being stolen by a relative newcomer to the subject. Buckland made arrangements during 1863 to demonstrate salmon hatching in the buildings of the Science and Art Department at the South Kensington Museum; he also appears to have arranged to set up hatching apparatus in the Crystal Palace and at the Zoological Gardens. In consequence, when he wrote to *The Times* early in 1864 he could announce not only the establishment by the Acclimatization Society of a large hatching apparatus on the premises of Francis Francis at Twickenham, but could also offer his gratuitous services to all those who cared to call at Mr Ponder's hatchery, the Zoological Gardens, the South Kensington Museum, the Crystal Palace or *The Field* office.[106]

It was perhaps Buckland's willingness to throw himself wholeheartedly into any scheme which appeared to be ultimately for the public good, and which involved what he called 'practical natural history', that made him so much in demand. There is no doubt also that his infectious enthusiasm and gentlemanly good humour made him an entertaining and stimulating companion. His interest in fish hatching made it almost inevitable that eventually he would become involved in the attempts being made, mostly under the superintendence of J. A. Youl, to introduce salmonids to the Antipodes. The idea of acclimatizing salmon in Australia and New Zealand waters was put forward by some colonists at a relatively early period and attempts were actually made to carry ova and fry from Britain in 1848, and possibly even before that date. The first successful attempt, however, is associated with the name of James Arndell Youl (1811–1904).[107]

Youl, born in Australia, was sent to England where he was educated privately, and then returned to Tasmania where he spent most of the first forty-three years of his life, becoming a successful agriculturalist and leading member of the community. He returned to England in 1854 and became an active member of a body of colonists known as the Australian Association. From 1860 until about 1890 he was concerned in every attempt, with one exception, to carry salmon and trout to Australia and New Zealand. His interest in the rearing of fish is said to have been awakened by the work of Gottlieb Boccius, whose name has been mentioned earlier. Youl is widely credited with having perfected the '. . . method of packing the ova for transmission on a long sea voyage, by placing them on charcoal and living moss with the roots attached, in perforated wood boxes under blocks of ice, thus preserving the ova in a state of healthy vitality for more than 100 days'.[7] As shown by John Shaw, and many others previously, ova at a lower temperature take longer to develop than those at a higher temperature; ice at that period provided the most convenient, indeed almost the only, method of achieving a constant low temperature.

Buckland assisted Youl in 1863 in some of his experiments on the use of ice and which were described in *The Field*. Boxes of ova were packed in the stores of the Wenham Lake Ice Company in the Strand, and were examined at intervals. Much of the ice used in Britain at that time was imported from the American continent or Norway, where it was cut from the lakes in winter. Buckland's contribution to the discovery, if discovery it was, was mainly as recorder of the results and he himself never appears to have claimed to have done more, although by others he has been credited with a much more positive contribution. Even Youl's part in the experiments was later challenged by others, including E. H. Moscrop, the proprietor at that time of the Wenham Lake Ice Company, who claimed to have suggested to Youl in 1862 the method which was subsequently adopted.[108]

The first two shipments of ova with which Youl was concerned, those in the *Sarah Curling* in 1860 and the *Beautiful Star* in 1862, were failures, and the first shipment which achieved at least partial success was that stowed in the clipper *Norfolk*. She sailed from London on January 21, 1864, carrying about 18,000 salmon ova and 2,700 brown trout ova (*Salmo trutta*). Some 1,200 of the trout ova were collected by Buckland from a pair of trout caught in the River Itchen near Winchester. The remainder of the trout ova were collected by

Francis Francis. The salmon ova were collected by Robert Ramsbottom and others. The ova were packed in boxes as already described, and taken to the vessel: 'All the boxes were placed in the ice-house: the remaining space was filled with blocks of Wenham Lake ice, and the house securely closed.' The *Norfolk* arrived at Melbourne on April 19. Some of the ova, including all the trout ova, were transferred to the sloop *Victoria* which sailed for Tasmania, arriving at Hobart on April 20. Both salmon and trout ova hatched, but the salmon did not become established in Australia or Tasmania as a result of this shipment. The trout, however, thrived in Tasmania and formed the stock from which Tasmania, New Zealand and Australia were subsequently supplied.[107] Buckland was proud of the part he had played in this operation and wrote later: 'Common trout are now plentiful in Australia and New Zealand, and I believe I may fairly say that these colonies owe the existence and almost abundance of trout at the antipodes to myself.' He then described how he caught the fish and how, when he took the ova to the docks, Youl was '. . . nearly pitching them overboard into the dirty water of the docks'. He added: 'It is but fair to say that Mr Francis Francis at the same time sent Youl some eggs, but these were, I believe, those of the *Bouge* or sea-trout, not of the common trout. . . .'[109] Buckland subsequently withdrew this statement; in fact the sea-trout is nowadays regarded merely as one form of the common or brown trout, *Salmo trutta.*

Frank Buckland looked forward to the excursions he made all over the country in search of spawning salmon and trout. 'I candidly confess I amazingly enjoy a day's trout egg collecting; it is a job that just suits me', he said, 'for it requires what I like, very hard work, and there are plenty of new facts happening every minute from which some further knowledge may be derived; then again it is cold work, and I am as fond of cold as a Polar bear.'[109] The conditions under which he worked were sometimes scarcely bearable even for him; 'I spent yesterday in the River Wye freezing', he once wrote to his sister 'Mit', 'nets like wire. Caught 39 salmon monsters. Very cold and slippery.'[110] He always oiled himself all over with hair oil when engaged in collecting ova, and continually rubbed oil on his arms and hands. 'The oil acts as a varnish to the skin', he wrote. The ova were given away to friends and enquirers, or were used for demonstrations at the Zoological Gardens, South Kensington, or in the basement at Albany Street, where he had set up a small hatchery. He jested about this hatchery in his lectures: 'He said he had himself hatched 30,000 salmon in his own kitchen, and as natural history books told them that salmon always returned to the places where they were hatched, they would see that he had a very cheering prospect before him.'[111] He often repeated this joke.

His house became well known for its peculiar visitors and the curious assortment of animals that roamed through the rooms, and sometimes escaped, no doubt to the alarm of some of the neighbours. Here were invited giants, dwarfs, and rat catchers, as well as the leaders of London's intellectual and social life. 'A fish salesman would receive equal courtesy with a Royal duke from the unconventional naturalist in *deshabille* and as he talked with the visitor his hands would be employed in the dissection of some interesting "specimen" ', recalled one writer years later.[112] Buckland often wrote about some of his strange friends and acquaintances whose behaviour occasionally caused even him surprise.

He once invited to lunch six Maori warrior chiefs who were giving a public performance at the Alhambra, Leicester Square, in 1864. Although conversation was limited, for only one of the chieftains could speak English, and Buckland's English guests could speak no Maori, the New Zealanders appear to have enjoyed their lunch and between them consumed fourteen pounds of beef. As a token of gratitude, one of them offered to tattoo Buckland's face, an offer he refused although tempted to have his arm tattooed '. . . just for the fun of the thing'. He wondered whether his guests would be interested in slow worms, and opened up the box for them to see. The effect was dramatic. With one accord the terrified natives were galvanized into activity and leapt downstairs with yells of fear and anger. They reached the garden and leaped the fences like deer, to the extreme consternation of a charming old lady who dwelt near by. She was sitting in the window and looked up in horror to see the enormous natives, one of whom was 6 feet 2 inches tall, bearing down upon her at top speed. Fortunately, the chiefs were pacified when told by their interpreter that the slow worms were not 'Ngarara', the incarnation of the deity, powerful for evil.[48]

A frequent visitor also was Joseph Brice, the French giant, who made a living by exhibiting himself. Buckland had first met Brice in May, 1862, and had done him a considerable service in advising him to find another manager, and subsequently in assisting him to do so. The giant was about 7 feet 6 inches tall and aged 22. He could span eight feet when he streched his arms sideways, and the tallest Life Guardsmen could easily walk beneath them. Buckland had taken him to meet his brother officers at Regent's Park Barracks. When he took Brice round the stables, the troop horses all shied at the sight of the enormous man.[48] One Sunday whilst on church parade, all the men burst out laughing, to the scandal of the colonel, adjutant and sergeant-major, who turned to see Buckland, who was off duty, coming out of his quarters attended by Brice and a dwarf then exhibiting in London.[13]

Brice was a good-natured giant although, to judge by one of his letters that has survived, not particularly literate.[3] During a visit to Ireland, Brice fell in love and married a normal size '. . . very agreeable, good-looking, chatty girl . . .' and on their return to London, Buckland gave a party for them at his house in Albany Street. A cab was sent for on their departure. 'It was very amusing to see the cabman's face of semi-horror and astonishment when his fare came out into the street in the dim gaslight; he seemed half inclined to jump on his box and bolt away as fast as his horse could go. The giant, however, put his elbow on the top of the cab, and told the man where to go. This pacified him a little; for the poor fellow, I believe, fancied we were playing some trick upon him.'[48] Mrs Buckland's great-neice has told the author that her mother remembered, as a little girl, sitting on the giant's knee and also recalled watching him light his cigar at the gas lamp outside the house! It was a black day for Buckland when he returned home to find that the giant's signature had been washed off the ceiling during a bout of cleaning at home.[113]

In 1864 Buckland began to take an active interest in the culture of oysters. Oysters generally occur in shallow water. The young are released as larvae in enormous numbers and after a brief free existence, settle as spat, or baby metamorphosed oysters, on any suitable surface. The success or failure of the spat fall each year depends upon numerous factors, of which water temperature and turbulence are two of the most important, and whilst there is little that man can do to control these factors, he can ensure that suitable surfaces are provided on which the baby oysters can settle. Furthermore, it is found that good spat falls occur more frequently in some areas, where conditions are favourable, than in others. Conditions in other places, however, may be particularly suitable for the rapid fattening of oysters. Oyster culture, which was largely developed by Professor P. Coste in France during the last century, mostly consists in producing 'seed' oysters in those areas where spat falls are generally good, and in transplanting them to other areas where growth is rapid.

Buckland, in company with Thomas Ashworth of the Galway fishery, in August, 1864, visited the Ile de Ré, near La Rochelle, where Professor Coste and others were carrying out experiments.[83] He wrote to Professor Phillips, just before he left: 'I have made up my mind to go to France at once to enquire into [the] oyster question. Shall take your advice and read a paper on "The natural history and cultivation of oysters" at British Association so please put me down *at once* for it in case anybody else turns up.'[72] He read a paper at the meeting in Bath in September; in this he discussed the results of investigations not only in France, but also in many parts of the United Kingdom. It was perhaps during his visit to the Ile de Ré that he obtained one of the tiles laid on the oyster beds for the spat to settle on. It was given him by the '. . . justly celebrated M. Hyacinth Boeuf, the mason who first discovered the art of breeding oysters by artificial means, and which I picked out of his oyster beds with my own hands. . . .'[114]

Buckland was also one of the directors of The Herne Bay, Hampton and Reculver Oyster Fishery Company, set up under the Herne Bay Fishery Act, 1864. The Chairman of the company was Vice Admiral Sir Henry J. Leeke, K.C.B., M.P., and the Deputy Chairman, H. Cholmondeley-Pennell, editor of the *Fisherman's Magazine* and a cousin of Mrs Frank Buckland's brother-in-law. Buckland appears to have been one of the main driving forces behind the company, from which, however, he ultimately withdrew.[23]

It was scarcely surprising, perhaps, in view of his great interest in all matters connected with fish and fishing, that he should have given evidence to the Sea Fisheries Commission set up in 1863, and on which T. H. Huxley served as one of the Commissioners. Buckland's evidence was confined to matters concerning the oyster fisheries.[115]

In July, 1864, the Royal Society for the Prevention of Cruelty to Animals arranged an exhibition of vermin traps on the site now occupied by the Science Museum, but at that time leased to the Royal Horticultural Society. A number of public-spirited people, perturbed at the cruelty involved in the steel traps then in use, had contributed to a prize fund from which awards were to be made to the inventor of a trap which would '. . . serve the purpose of game preservers without inflicting torture'. Frank Buckland was invited to act as one of the judges, an invitation he readily accepted. He was a humane person who never willingly gave pain to animals; he objected, for example, to the wholesale slaughter of sea birds for 'sport' which was all too common in his day, and he started a campaign to reduce the cruelty of the northern seal fishery. He once wrote: 'Many gentlemen, I would venture to remark, start on their travels armed with rod or gun, for the sole purpose of killing or destroying, whether by land or water; to these I would say, do not care so much for the actual killing the animal or fish, as for the investigation of its habits and the conditions of its existence.'[48] Nevertheless, he was a realist. His was not the sentimental approach of some animal lovers of the present day. He appreciated that animals must sometimes be killed, but he did not want it done without good reason and, where possible, he wanted it done rapidly and painlessly.

Buckland had been invited to visit the Galway fishery by Thomas Ashworth and he went, in company with his wife, in the summer of 1864. He gave the inaugural lecture of the Young Man's Mutual Improvement Society in Galway at the end of July, when Ashworth took the chair. The audience included H. Cholmondeley-Pennell and Mrs Buckland.[23] Buckland also studied one of the Irish oyster beds, the Red Bank

Burrin Bed, and later wrote a series of articles on Irish oysters.

He spent much time investigating the Galway fishery and advised Ashworth that his baby salmon were being eaten by the carnivorous water beetle, *Dytiscus*. He awoke early on his first morning in Galway, to find the day was warm and bright. He arose and walked up to the salmon ladder that had been erected to enable the ripe fish to reach Lough Corrib to spawn. It was typical of Buckland that he should wonder what it felt like to be a salmon, making its way up the cataract of the salmon ladder. It was perhaps even more typical of him that he should immediately undress in order to find out. He lowered himself into the rushing stream.

> But all I could think or do, I could not advance one single inch up the ladder against the stream. If I moved, in an instant, the water knocked me about against the stops like a wood-chip in a street gutter after a thunderstorm. So I chose a corner of the ladder where the water boiled and bubbled round, and sat there, wishing and trusting that some salmon would take it into its head to ascend while I was in the ladder. We should hob-nob very well together, thought I, and we would smoke the pipe of peace together. Presently I heard a voice behind me–
>
> 'Bedad! yer honner, you're the finest fish I ever see in the ladder this long time; and, by the powers, if I had got a gaff in my hand I'd just strike it into your scales and see how you would like it!'
>
> I looked up, and there was one of the water-bailiffs, who, watching me from afar off, could not imagine what huge sea monster had got into the ladder and was floundering about in it.

Buckland, on his return, discussed the Galway Fishery in *The Field* in a series of articles which he completed at the end of 1864. He was annoyed by a letter signed 'Your commissioner in Ireland' which attacked him and his findings and which appeared in *The Field* on December 31, 1864. He wrote to the editor on January 7, 1865, expressing his '. . . pain and grief . . .' at what was evidently directed at him; 'For my own part I care not, nor do I heed any observations from the pen of a gentleman who, experience has taught me, is so antagonistic to my best endeavours to promote information on matters relating to fisheries or the cultivation of fish . . .'

'Your Commissioner in Ireland' was, of course, Francis Francis who replied with a savage attack upon Buckland. He said that Buckland claimed success when often there was only failure. Francis quoted Buckland's attempt to produce hybrids between salmon and trout. '. . . I myself was much interested in the experiment, and should have liked a definite account of it, as a guide in future attempts. What became of the hybrids?' He listed a number of similar instances and accused Buckland of misleading the public. He then turned to what was undoubtedly a very considerable source of annoyance.

> What experience has Mr Buckland to offer that will bear comparison with mine? With that vague capriciousness with which he hops from subject to subject – often doing more harm than good, and spoiling it for those who would carry it to a good end – about three years ago he suddenly pounced upon a subject, without any previous knowledge or study of it, which I had for years been striving to bring about, and had at last succeeded in bringing to an issue. I allude to the Thames fish-breeding etc. Now, Sir, there is among literary men a professional etiquette and tacit but understood law, which Mr Buckland has no sort of notion of, and certainly no respect for. It is that when a fellow labourer is known to be engaged upon a subject, and to have been collecting material with respect to it, one ought not to make a descent upon it and take it out of his hands. But Mr Buckland's mode of procedure in *The Field* has been to spread himself over every department, wandering hither and thither like a bee from flower to flower, or a Bedouin of the desert from richly-laden caravan to caravan. The moment a subject has been worked up by another person into notice, down pounces Mr Buckland, and like a blowfly, lays his eggs on the subject, and forthwith pervades it, often to the exclusion of the original proprietor.

There was much more that Francis Francis said; he had clearly been nursing a sense of grievance for a long time and he intended once and for all to make his views known.

Francis Francis may have had another reason for his annoyance: the Acclimatization Society had just decided to suspend the fish hatching operations under his control at Twickenham. Perhaps he believed Buckland to be responsible. An irate life member of the Society complained that he could obtain no reply to his letters from the secretaries and that the operations had been suspended without notice. Francis Francis wrote to *The Field* to say that his position was a most embarrassing one, while James Lowe, Buckland's fellow Secretary, announced that he had been indisposed, and was surprised to learn of the decision to suspend operations.

Meanwhile, Buckland, in answer to Francis's letter, said that as a gentleman he could not reply to a letter couched in such terms, to which Francis retorted that Buckland could not in any event refute the charges. Walsh now stepped in to say, 'This correspondence between two valued contributors is now closed by mutual consent. Of course we cannot attribute to them any disposition to renew it, but we may say that, on our part, we will take care to prevent the occurrence in our columns of anything that might have a tendency to reopen the dispute on this or any similar subject.'

Frank Buckland contributed no more, and the naturalist columns for a time apparently became the responsibility of W. B. Tegetmeier. It may have been that Walsh insisted upon Tegetmeier acting rather as censor of what was contributed by Buckland, who wrote to Owen, 'You will understand from the enclosed my dear Professor how it happened that your humble servant could write no more for *The Field*. The Nat. His. Editor is a vain wretch who does nothing himself but delights in dissecting the writings of all working men and in looking in other people's eyes for "motes" (whatever they may be) and of which he has a fine collection. The "Beam" in his own is ample to supply wood for the park railings of the Richmond Royal Property.'[61] It will be recalled that Owen lived in a grace and favour residence in Richmond Park.

It is probable that the situation would never have reached such a pitch had Buckland's friend and ally John Crockford remained alive, but unfortunately he died on January 21, 1865, at the early age of 41. At the Annual General Meeting of the Acclimatization Society in May, 1865, Buckland was made Naturalist Manager while B. Waterhouse Hawkins, the designer of the statues of prehistoric animals in the grounds of the Crystal Palace at Sydenham, was made Secretary. James Lowe resigned, probably through ill health, for he died shortly afterwards.

Buckland referred to his disagreement with *The Field* at a meeting of the Thames Angling Preservation Society, also held in May. He accused *The Field* of burking, of refusing to publish his articles. Walsh replied, 'We do not bargain to insert every article which every contributor may send us, nor even to insert them intact; and we think that this rule – which is a manifest necessity in the constitution of a paper like *The Field* – is one which Mr Buckland's reputation as a writer has very much more to thank than to blame us for. We can but part with him – however he may part with us – with the best wishes for his success wherever he goes.'[116]

There is no question but that Buckland felt aggrieved and that his pride was hurt by this affair. Even more, no doubt, his pocket was affected. The early months of 1865 cannot have been pleasant for him and the future did not appear very promising, but he had a ready pen and abundant energy and he did not remain idle.

PLATE XI

Buckland's Fish Museum.

(*a*) Before it became established in its 'final' position in the South Kensington Museum in 1872, Buckland's Museum was moved two or three times. This photograph was probably taken in 1871 after narwhal tusks were deposited by Mr Wareham, '. . . the well-known curiosity dealer, of St Martin's Court, Leicester Square'. Note the uncoloured casts.

(*b*) Probably one of the photographs mentioned in *Land and Water*, July 18, 1874, as being taken by Mr Samuel Walker, Photographer.

From photographs in the Library of the Royal College of Surgeons of England.

PLATE XII

Land and Water

(*a*) The illustrated heading was changed after eleven numbers, and

(*b*) remained unaltered until 1869 when the size of the paper was enlarged.

(*c*) This design remained as the heading of the paper until after Buckland's death.

They are good examples of Victorian typographical design.

CHAPTER TEN

The Museum of Economic Fish Culture

BUCKLAND, whose life hitherto had been energetic, now entered a period of feverish activity which continued until shortly before his death in 1880. By 1867 he was engaged in three quite distinct occupations; these were, the superintendence of his Museum of Economic Fish Culture at South Kensington, the editing of the Fishery and Natural History columns of a new weekly journal, *Land and Water*, established in 1866 in opposition to *The Field*, and the carrying out of his duties as Inspector of Salmon Fisheries, a post to which he was appointed in February, 1867. Whilst it is necessary to consider these activities separately, it should be stressed that they were all carried on at the same time by one man. So far as Buckland was concerned, these activities were not distinct, and he often worked at his Museum on matters related to a Salmon Inspection, or dictated letters at the Salmon Fisheries Office in reply to correspondents writing to him in *Land and Water*.

Although his main occupation, writing for *The Field*, had been abruptly taken from him early in 1865, he still had much to occupy his time. It has been already mentioned that in 1863 he had been permitted to set up a small fish hatching apparatus at South Kensington. He now began to develop there a museum largely devoted to the fisheries.

The South Kensington Museum arose directly from the Great Exhibition of 1851 and the site was purchased with some of the profits made in that enormously successful undertaking. The science and art collections were originally housed together in corrugated iron buildings of '. . . a plain and economical character', first opened to the public in 1857. Later, the science collections were exhibited in various buildings on the western side of Exhibition Road, the grounds being leased to the Royal

Horticultural Society for laying out ornamental gardens. The Society also had its own buildings and conservatory on the site.[117]

The original function of the South Kensington Museum was conceived to be that of a teaching institution for artisans and their instructors. The scientific collections were not therefore intended to be comprehensive. Even so, however, they seem to have suffered to some extent from that uncritical approach, and from the tendency to accumulate the jetsam of imperial adventurers, which is so characteristic of Victorian museums generally. Various lecture courses were delivered under the auspices of the Museum, which deserves high praise for its pioneering endeavours to develop the teaching of science in Britain from about 1860 onwards.

In 1864 Buckland's hatching apparatus was displayed in a corner of the Entrance Hall of the Royal Horticultural Society's building, the Society apparently having agreed to contribute towards the running costs. The equipment almost certainly consisted of a series of six long, narrow, slate troughs partly filled with gravel. Water, piped to one end of the first trough, flowed continuously over the gravel, on which fertilized fish eggs, generally of salmon or trout, were thinly spread, and overflowed through a pipe at the other end of the first trough into the top end of the next one, arranged at a slightly lower level. In this way one water supply was made to serve a number of hatching troughs.*

Under these conditions, young fish can be seen developing within the egg, and eventually they hatch as larvae with the yolk sac still attached. This is slowly absorbed during the ensuing few weeks, after which the larvae of many species of fish will feed voraciously on a variety of flesh foods. At a later period, Buckland always endeavoured to have on display in his Museum fish of two or three years of age, in addition to developing eggs or larvae

In January, 1865, Buckland wrote to the Director of the Museum, Henry Cole, C.B., saying that the cultivation of the fisheries of the United Kingdom was now exciting considerable public attention although no public instruction '. . . has

* This equipment was used by A. C. Gardiner and F. T. K. Pentelow for hatching trout eggs at Alresford, Hants, in 1925–7.

ever yet been available for those interested in the supply of food for the people'. He added, '. . . I would now venture to propose to the Lord President, Vice President and members of the Committee of Council on Education that a course of lectures should be given under their authority during the coming summer on "The Cultivation of the Fisheries of Great Britain as providing food for the people". . . . Having studied the subject at great labour and expense I would venture to propose that the commission to deliver the course should be entrusted to myself.' After briefly outlining the subject matter to be covered in each lecture, he went on to say that, if he gave the lectures, he would leave it to the Council to decide '... what would be a fair remuneration for the information and experience therein made for the first time available to the public.'[118]

In another letter to Cole, written the same day, Buckland referred to discussions they had already had about the hatching equipment and proposed to the Museum authorities that they should contribute to the cost of a '. . . larger and more commodious apparatus' and should pay him for '. . . the constant supervision, attendance, and responsibility, for the whole thing. . . . ' He suggested a total fee of £105, which was '. . . the same as that granted by the authorities of the Royal Horticultural Gardens last year', and for this sum he agreed to purchase the apparatus and to provide the fish eggs.

His suggestion does not appear to have met the approval of the Museum authorities who instead appointed him temporarily 'Scientific Referee for Fish Culture', with a personal fee of fifty guineas a year; 'When the attendances exceed fifty during the year, they will be paid for according to arrangement up to a maximum not exceeding two guineas each.' This appointment was continued until Buckland's death. In May and June he gave a course of three lectures on Fish Culture, on the '. . . usual terms of ten guineas a lecture'.[118]

Buckland's responsibilities as Naturalist Manager of the Acclimatization Society were no less than they had been as Secretary. Indeed, the duties were probably more demanding for *The Field*, after the death of John Crockford and the row with Francis Francis, withdrew all support for the Society, and even began to make caustic remarks about its erstwhile child. The *Evening Star* commented in August, 1865: 'In looking over the report for the past year we perceive that the work is done by half a dozen men – notably by Mr Frank Buckland, whose ardour in the cause of pisciculture bespeaks not only the enthusiast, but the practical man of science.' The article added that the piscicultural experiments at Twickenham, which it will be recalled had been under the control of Francis Francis, had not been successful and the Committee were negotiating with the Royal Horticultural Society for the erection of their equipment in the gardens at South Kensington. Meanwhile Buckland had hatched out upwards of 30,000 salmon and trout ova in his kitchen in Albany Street, and had distributed them to members.[119]

He was not satisfied, however, merely to set up a hatchery at South Kensington, which might perhaps have been used to supply the members of the Acclimatization Society, but began to build up a series of displays relating to the fisheries. These included plaster casts of fish. He apparently first saw plaster casts of fish in the Museum of the Royal Society of Dublin, perhaps when he visited Ireland in 1864, and was immediately struck by the effectiveness of this method of showing what the living animal looks like.[60] The corpses of birds and mammals in the hands of a skilled taxidermist can be made to look extremely life-like, but fishes are much more difficult, partly because scales are so readily lost from the skin of many fish, and partly because the natural colours are permanently destroyed by the methods of preservation usually employed. A plaster cast, on the other hand, if well made and artistically coloured, can look very effective. Buckland began to experiment with the plaster casting of animals, and examples of his work which have survived show him eventually to have become a highly skilled operator, perhaps even justifying his boast, made in 1870, that casting was '. . . an art in which I flatter myself no person can now excel me'.[118]

The precise terms of his appointment do not appear to have been defined. His display formed part of the Animal Products and Food Collections under the Keeper of this Division, W. Matchwick. These Collections are singled out for mention in the official history of the Science Museum, which says that they '. . . contained such things as specimens of wool and leather, and examples of things considered to be good to eat. An early Museum Guide gives little technical information but draws attention to the "culinary curiosities from China and Siam", which included birds' nests, sharks' fins, sea-slugs and other delicacies.'[117]

Matchwick's report for the year 1865 describes in detail the purpose of the fish collection. He mentions the intention to obtain '. . . a series of the common varieties of fish brought to the English market for consumption, both marine and those inhabiting fresh waters . . .' the Food Collection being '. . . very obviously deficient in illustrations of the kind'. The fish hatching and rearing apparatus was to display the techniques employed and had proved to be '. . . a very attractive feature to the general body of visitors'. In addition, Buckland had started a separate collection to illustrate more fully '. . . the economy of fish culture and preservation. It consists of hatching and rearing apparatus on a considerable scale, models of breeding ponds, weirs, fish ladders, apparatus for the transport of fertile fish ova to distant countries (Australia, for example); diagrams and models of nets and apparatus used in the illegal destruction of salmon, illustrations of the natural enemies of salmon and trout, a series showing the growth of the salmon from the egg to the full-grown fish; a series of whitebait at various stages of growth, and of fish sold and eaten as whitebait, and an extensive series illustrating the growth and artificial cultivation of oysters from various parts of Europe and other countries; all of which is the private property of Mr Buckland.'[120]

The situation revealed in the last statement soon led to disagreement. An internal minute from a senior member of the Museum staff, Richard A. Thompson, to the Director, dated January 26, 1856, begins: 'The results of the arrangement with Mr Buckland for the past year are not very satisfactory.' It goes on: 'I think it inadvisable that an officer of the Department should be allowed to form and exhibit as his own property such a collection of objects as it is his duty to advise and assist the Department in collecting for itself, the prestige of the Department being used in procuring examples for what is in reality a private collection.' The minute recommends that Buckland be told that he should attend the Museum at stated hours, that all specimens presented to the Collection were the property of the Department, and that his duties included attention to the Animal Products and Food Collections and were not confined to the fish hatching equipment.

In the meantime, however, Buckland himself had written to Cole, pointing out that 'The Museum is entirely my own, and it has cost me much time and trouble.' He observed that bottles, and alcohol for preserving specimens, were expensive, and 'I now tell you fairly that these expenses fall heavily (to say nothing of cab hire to bring them from my house to the Museum) upon my private purse'. He then added: 'My specimens have generally cost me much time and labour to procure and are generally more valuable than the bottles. I am therefore unwilling to enter into the bargain that if the Department find bottles etc., they shall consider the contents of the bottles their own property.'[118]

Nowadays, the argument put forward by Thompson, that the specimens should belong to the Department, appears to be a reasonable one; the great collections in the national museums could never have been built up had every employee regarded the new acquisitions passing through his hands as his own personal property. In the 1860s, however, the national art collections were relatively unimportant, compared with what was in private hands. The scientific collections were only just beginning. Perhaps this is the reason why Cole did not feel compelled to accept Thompson's argument. Perhaps, also, he was apprehensive of the powerful support Buckland might be able to muster. At all events, the Buckland Fish Museum remained, at least in name, as part of the Animal Products and Food Collection, although in reality it was an autonomous unit, presided over by Buckland, whose collection in effect was hired by the authorities.

Buckland spent a good deal of his own money on the Museum. A list of 'Approximate expenses incurred in forming the Museum' includes the following items:

	£
Cast of whale	14
Salmon painted to life	5
Bottles and spirits	20
Buying fish parcels, etc	15
Assistant in casting fish (12 months)	25
Cabs and carts	16

The assistant may have been the Curator, Nevile, who was replaced in 1872 by Richard Edon, a bird and fish stuffer.

The casts of the larger fish were an enormous labour. When possible, Buckland preferred to make them in the basement of his house, where he used the small front kitchen as a work room. He was once sent a sun-fish which had been caught off Folkestone. He wrote that, although it was so large, '. . . being soft I was enabled to tumble it down the stairs into the casting room easy enough, and we could bend it to get it round the corner. The mould, however, with the fins extended, is so long, so heavy, and, of course, perfectly inelastic, that I really do not know how to get the cast or mould out of the kitchen. The total measurements of the fish are, from tip of fin on the back, to tip of fin on belly four feet eight. From nose to stern, three feet five and a half, four feet two in circumference.'[121] He cut up the corpse and gave the pieces to the pigs of a friend '. . . as my little garden is quite full of the graves of stinking fish, and there is no more room for burials'.[109]

A fine sturgeon, nine feet in length and weighing nearly two hundredweight, was once loaned to him for the night by a large firm of fishmongers in Bond Street. The specimen was transported to Albany Street, and was just being lowered gently down the area steps when it broke away, charged the kitchen door head first like a battering ram, and shot into the kitchen and under the table with the velocity of an express train, to the consternation and terror of the cook, housemaid, and domestic pets.[122]

When specimens were too large to cast in his basement, Buckland would sometimes borrow the yard of Grimble and Co.'s distillery, a few yards away in Albany Street, for his operations. Sometimes, also, he would cast exceptionally large fish or marine mammals in the Horticultural Gardens although this could provide unexpected difficulties, as is shown by an account, to be found in the official records at South Kensington, of the casting of a large sturgeon. '1873. June 7. On Thursday this week I inspected a splendid Sturgeon. . . . Mr Dennis of the firm of Groves & Co., Bond Street Fishmongers, kindly sent me a telegram to say they had they believed the largest ever seen in the London Market. I accordingly went to them to their shop and found it was a monster, it measured ten feet seven inches in length and was considered to weigh between five and six hundredweight. I accordingly made arrangements that the fish should be taken to the ground outside my Museum in the evening in Messrs Groves' van and that I would make a mould of the entire fish. I went and ordered four cwt. of plaster to be sent in due time.

'The sturgeon arrived there at about six o'clock and I, my Secretary Mr. Searle and the attendant Mr. Edon at once set to work. The first operation was to get him out of the van, this I did by letting him slide down a board by his own weight . . . '

'Unfortunately there was a flower show on in the Horticultural Gardens and the roadway and every available space in the ground was occupied by the great vans of the various nurserymen so that we only just had room to walk at the sides of our infant fish . . . my secretary superintended mixing the plaster and I manipulated the mould of the fish. After a good four hours hard work we got the Sturgeon out of his case but unfortunately not without the mould being broken into several pieces. Then came the difficulty how the fish was to be got into the van again. We succeeded in doing this for we got a bight of rope round his tail and with the assistance of some half dozen volunteers some pulling on the rope others pushing at the huge carcase we at last got him safely into his carriage and he was on his road home again by about ten o'clock. The fish was afterwards sold, I tasted some, it was very good something between veal and fish.'[118]

Some casts Buckland coloured himself, but many were painted by H. L. Rolfe, whom Buckland described as 'The Landseer among Fishes'. The Museum of Economic Fish Culture attracted very many visitors from every layer of the well-stratified society of the period; all were welcomed by Buckland or the Curator. The display, although by modern standards crude and cramped, was undoubtedly educational. Few Londoners had ever had the opportunity of seeing live fish of any kind, and although most of them were accustomed to seeing specimens of marine species on the fishmonger's slab, comparatively few had any idea of how or where they were caught, and they certainly had no knowledge of their natural history.

The Museum was not, however, of great scientific value.

Buckland wrote that it was '. . . intended as an Educational means of informing the public, not only as to the Natural History of Fish, but also as to their commercial uses, and as to the development of the fisheries of this country'.[109] The visitor would have learnt little about systematics or anatomy, two of the important fields of research of the period, and the details of the natural history of fish seem to have been sketchy in some parts and completely deficient in others. The arrangement of specimens seems to have been haphazard and to have followed no particular plan, although it is difficult to be certain of this since no complete catalogue of Buckland's Museum has survived, if it ever existed.

The visitor would nevertheless have been entertained. He could have watched small fish swimming up a model salmon ladder down which water flowed continuously. He could have admired the numerous casts of fish and perhaps, if he was very fortunate, he might have met Buckland himself, who would no doubt have treated him to a racy dissertation on the specimens in his Museum, illustrated with abundant autobiographical detail (Plate XI). The Museum contained some items whose connexion with fish and fishing was tenuous in the extreme; there was, for example, '. . . a very fine specimen of a man-trap . . .' and the tanned skin of a boa-constrictor fifteen feet long. One bizarre exhibit, preserved in spirit, was that of a mouse trapped by an oyster. The mouse, exploring a larder, had apparently put its head between the valves of the oyster, which had begun to gape through lack of water.[122] Another curious object was a stuffed seagull holding in its beak a copy of an Act of Parliament for the preservation of sea birds.[123]

The Museum attracted people of all types, including Queen Victoria herself and other members of the Royal Family. In April, 1868, their Royal Highnesses Prince Arthur and Prince Christian visited it, perhaps to learn something about fish hatching, since Buckland had been giving advice at least since 1865 on the breeding of trout for Windsor Great Park, where 'An exceedingly pretty rustic house . . . ' was erected for the hatching troughs. Prince Christian of Schleswig-Holstein-Sonderburg (1831–1917) married Princess Helena Victoria in 1866. He was Ranger of Windsor Great Park and a personal friend of Buckland, who in 1875 dedicated his *Log book of a Fisherman and Zoologist* to him.[1]

Even Queen Victoria herself in 1875 requested Prince Christian to summon Mr Buckland. 'Dear Mr Buckland,' he wrote, 'There is a plague of frogs at Frogmore and the Queen wishes me to write to you as she is anxious that you should come down tomorrow Friday to ascertain what could be done to get rid of them. It seems that it is something quite extraordinary.'[124] One wonders whether Buckland's advice, to turn out the ducks to eat the frogs, recalled to her mind the celebrated reply attributed to the Iron Duke when she asked him how to deal with the large numbers of sparrows in the Crystal Palace during the Great Exhibition of 1851: 'Sparrow-hawks, Ma'am.'

Many other famous people visited Buckland's Museum, and from the beginning he took pains to impress upon the authorities the importance of his collection. He once reported to the Lords Commissioners, '. . . . I had the pleasure of meeting at the Museum . . . Capt. Rogers the well known inventor of the spring gun for killing man-eating Tigers and other noxious animals of India'. In July, 1867, he wrote to the Lord President, His Grace the Duke of Marlborough, enclosing letters from Roderick Murchison and Richard Owen which praised the value of the Museum of Economic Fish Culture. Their testimonials were not, however, unsolicited. 'My dear Professor,' Buckland had written to Owen shortly before, 'Would you be so *very kind* as to send me a line approving of my *Museum* of *Economic Fish Culture* at the Horticultural . . . I have spent a considerable sum out of my own pocket for my Museum and I want *your* valuable approval to show the Duke of Marlborough. . . . Please send me your approval of my Museum it may be the nucleus of a fine thing.'[61]

Buckland clearly believed his Museum to be of very great importance. Once, when writing about John Hunter, he said: 'How I should like to show the great physiologist over my Museum of Economic Fish Culture at South Kensington.' How pleased he would be with my hatching-troughs, my yearling salmon, and my four-year-old lake trout; also, I trust, with my "pyloric appendage" theory, and my casts of dissections in plaster-of-paris, especially when painted by my good friend

Rolfe – the dear John was not well up in casting. In my humble way I mean to follow the steps of my great Master, and am trying to make such a Bucklandian fish museum as will be appreciated some of these days. My Father left his museum of Geology to the University of Oxford. It is called the "Bucklandian Museum".'[1] He wrote elsewhere: 'I only trust my museum at South Kensington may one day become the nucleus of such a museum as we have at the College of Surgeons. May the mantle of the great John Hunter descend not only on my humble self but upon all students of St George's Hospital, both past and present.'[125]

Perhaps, also, Buckland attached undue weight in his own mind to the scientific value of casts of fish. Although he was a candidate for Fellowship of the Royal Society on two occasions, 1866–1867 and 1869–1870, he was not successful. His Certificate of Candidature includes the names of Richard Owen, Roderick Murchison, B. C. Brodie and John Phillips.[110] 'Last year', Buckland wrote to Richard Owen in February, 1867, 'I was not successful at the Royal Society but I should much like to try again this year. I should therefore feel *most* obliged to you if you would be kind enough to write a line to Mr White according to the letter enclosed. If you could also be good enough to speak a word for me to any of the Council you know I should feel much obliged.

'I propose to exhibit at the R.S. Soirée Casts of various fish some of them coloured and also *casts* of Crocodile, Water Jack, Puff Adder, Bull Frog etc. These casts will be coloured to nature and I think will meet with your approbation. I want to show the people that I am a *worthy* subject for the F.R.S.'[61]

The undoubted educational value of the fish collection was not, perhaps, sufficiently appreciated by the authorities. The entrance hall of the Royal Horticultural Society's building was not fitted with artificial light, so that the Fish Museum was closed after sunset. It was moved to one of the arcades in the Gardens in 1871 but this was not an ideal situation, and the building was not entirely weatherproof. In November 1870, Buckland applied for an increase in his salary, which had remained at one guinea a week since he joined the staff five years before. 'I have now succeeded with this small allowance', he wrote, 'in making a Museum which, on the testimony of many of my own countrymen, as well as of distinguished foreigners who have visited it and consulted me on fishing matters, is not, of its kind, equalled in any other country. . . . I am very thankful for the opportunity afforded me of educating the people: at the same time I venture to state that in proportion to the increase in my salary as I know I could still further increase my powers of promoting a great national industry which is gradually but quietly claiming its own in the estimation of the public.' His salary was raised to £2 a week the following year.[118]

It is unfortunate that very few specimens from Buckland's Museum survived the hazards of the last War; many suffered damage and deterioration as the result of enemy action. The weekly reports for the half-year ending June, 1873, have, however, been preserved in the official archives, and give some idea of the prodigious labour expended in making casts, painting them, and refurbishing them. In one report Buckland condemns the practice of catching very small haddock, some of which had been sent him by a Grimsby firm. He explained in his report that he had cast a group of these fish for display in his Museum.

Buckland never lost any opportunity of obtaining publicity for his collection. The establishment in 1866 of the new journal *Land and Water* provided him with precisely the platform he required to teach the people, and where he frequently described new additions to his Museum.

CHAPTER ELEVEN

Land and Water

BUCKLAND'S LITERARY OUTPUT during 1865 was comparatively small, although at the end of the year Richard Bentley published two further volumes of *The Curiosities of Natural History*; these are now known as the Third and Fourth Series[60, 48] (see bibliography). Comparison of the four volumes shows the change in the author's style and interests that occurred from 1857, when the First Series was published. The First Series consists of five fairly lengthy essays composed with care and containing many original observations of the behaviour of animals. Its style is in places affected and too consciously 'literary', but in the main it is written in the racy yet naïve manner which is one of Buckland's charms. The Third and Fourth Series are written with a freer and less careful hand; the raciness is there, but there are fewer classical quotations. Also, instead of a few lengthy essays, the reader is presented with a large number of short contributions, some little more than brief notes. The Fourth Series, in particular, is concerned far more with curiosities than natural history, and describes giants, acrobats and wandering mountebanks. In parts it is singularly reminiscent of Henry Mayhew's classic, *London Labour and the London Poor*; it also contains an account of the finding of John Hunter's coffin in the crypt of St Martin-in-the-Fields.

The *Spectator*, in a rather unflattering review of the Third Series, said: '. . . it is difficult, perhaps impossible, to define what is, and what is not, worthy of the attention of any man, but it is also difficult to realize that an individual who has for twenty years devoted his life to training fleas, giving two hours a day to the harnessing of six of them to a tiny chariot, is worthy of the immortality Mr Buckland has striven to secure for him, striven possibly not in vain, for his graphic description of these little creatures . . . will be remembered long after their unfortunate trainer has finished his miserable existence. . . . Perhaps it may yet be our good fortune to find his stature heightens with his heightening aims, and that in the interval which must necessarily elapse before he again challenges criticism he will have found room to grow.' The comment, although perhaps unduly harsh, has some justification, for notwithstanding that the volumes are entertaining, they contain much that is trivial, and the impression remains in the mind of the reader that they were written in a hurry and were inadequately revised.[126]

It is likely that Buckland was in need of money, for he and a few friends were attempting to found a new weekly periodical devoted to sport and natural history and to be called *Land and Water*. Two friends who played a leading part in this venture were William Joshua Ffennell, Inspector of Salmon Fisheries, and Daniel Higford Davall Burr, of Aldermaston Park, near Reading. Buckland had first met Ffennell through their common interest in the artificial propagation of fish; their lives were shortly to become much more closely associated. Higford Burr, as he was generally called, was a former Conservative M.P. for Hereford who may have known the Bucklands at Oxford, for he was a Christ Church man.[127] He was a member of the Council of the Acclimatization Society. Burr's assistance was mainly financial but Ffennell, who was widely known and respected, worked hard to recruit many valuable contributors to the paper and he should bear a measure of the credit for its success.

It is unlikely, however, that *Land and Water* would have ever been born without the help given to it by the famous publishing firm of Chapman and Hall, which seems to have acted as a benevolent godparent in setting the paper on its way in life. Chapman and Hall first achieved prominence in publishing in the 1830s when they commissioned a rising young author to write the adventures of a Nimrod Club; this work, which brought fame and fortune to both author and publisher, was, of course, *The Posthumous Papers of the Pickwick Club* by Charles Dickens. This success was followed by many others, and Chapman and Hall's lists in the following years contained a host of familiar names, including

Thackeray, Carlyle, Trollope, Robert and Elizabeth Barrett Browning, George Meredith, W. H. Ainsworth and Charles Kingsley. By 1865 Chapman and Hall were extremely successful; they had an enviable reputation for honest dealing and treated their authors generously. They turned many away, for they had high standards, and the distinction of appearing in their lists was surely one to be coveted.[128]

The Land and Water Journal Company (Limited) was set up in 1865 at 80 Fleet Street, London. Shareholders included Ffennell and Burr. Frederic Chapman, the principal of Chapman and Hall, held fifteen £50 shares on his own behalf and for his cousin, Edward Chapman, who had recently retired. Buckland received five £50 shares and £250 in cash as his first year's salary, and began energetically to approach his friends and acquaintances for their support. Lord Powerscourt wrote: 'You have done me a good many good turns, and it has struck me lately what an ungrateful beggar I was. Will you accept the enclosed, to stop a gap.' The enclosed was the gift of £100. Lady Chantrey, widow of Buckland's godfather, who was spending the last years of her life in the Star and Garter Hotel in Richmond, Surrey, wrote: 'I never subscribe to anything and therefore must decline subscribing to your newspaper. I wish it success and will put it upon my table with a recommendation. Why not get the *Times* to mention it? You ought not to have left the Horse Guards.'[23]

Towards the end of 1865 rumours of the new magazine began to be heard. 'Mr Frank Buckland is mentioned as the editor of a new magazine to be called *Land and Water*, dealing with the various sports of field and foam', wrote one London newspaper. 'This is to absorb *The Fisherman*, now conducted by Mr Cholmondeley Pennell, and the services of popular writers are said to have been secured.' H. Cholmondeley-Pennell, as already mentioned, was distantly connected with Buckland by marriage and was a co-director of the Herne Bay, Hampton, and Reculver Oyster Fishery Company.[23]

The Prospectus of *Land and Water*, which was issued from Chapman and Hall's office at 193 Piccadilly, promised rich fare. The newspaper was intended to deal with natural history, especially in its practical applications to sport and industry. 'With this in view, it is proposed that *The Land and the Water* shall contain not only all requisite information on the business of the Chase, the Gun and the Rifle, the Net and the Rod, both on the River and the Sea; but that these subjects shall be treated in a style more universally attractive and useful, than has been at present attempted, and in language more intelligible than that which has hitherto found favour in what are ordinarily called "Sporting Circles".' The fisheries were to be given considerable attention as was the science of Acclimatization; the Council of the Acclimatization Society had assured the new journal of its support which, of course, under the circumstances, was hardly surprising. The Prospectus also promised that 'All athletic exercizes which have their strongholds in the Universities and Public Schools, will receive due attention; and Ladies will find in our columns the news of their favourite game, Croquet.'[23]

The first number appeared on Saturday, January 27, 1866, and, like *The Field*, cost 6*d*. Frank Buckland is mentioned in the editorial as the main contributor and manager of the Practical Natural History section, from which it may be inferred that the organization of the paper was similar to that of *The Field*, with each section under the control of its own sub-editor. Support is found for this belief in a brief note in the first number, which states that it was the intention to deal with horticultural matters but that '. . . no trivial or unscientific treatment of these subjects would be worth attempting . . .' and since it had not yet proved possible to come to a satisfactory arrangement with a suitable editor, the indulgence of readers was claimed.

The early issues bear other signs of haste and lack of adequate preparation. The illustrated heading of the newspaper was replaced after eleven numbers by a more ornate design which was in turn replaced in 1869 by an even more ornate design which in its conception and execution could be termed rustic; it is an example of the low level which much periodical typography reached in the second half of Victoria's reign (Plate XII).

Land and Water and *The Field* covered very much the same ground, and eventually, in the 1920s, *The Field* absorbed its rival. The most obvious difference between the two papers was in the great amount of space in *Land and Water*, in the

PLATE XIII

The Bucklands at home (1864). The caption reads: Scene. Enter Frank Buckland with empty Basket in left hand and scalpel and letter in right!

F. B. Did you have a chicken for dinner yesterday when I dined out?

Mrs B. Yes! What about it?

F. B. Well then you have eaten a chicken sent me from *The Field* to dissect and see what it died of!!!

From an original sketch in the Library of the Royal College of Surgeons of England.

I got a cast of this man's hand which I gave to Kinnerton St Museum

NE PLUS ULTRA!

NOW EXHIBITING.

THE

SPANISH GOLIAH

THE CELEBRATED

Senor Joachim Eleizegui,

From the Basque Provinces of Spain.

TWENTY THREE YEARS OF AGE,—STANDS

7 feet 10 inches,

Weighs 450 Pounds,

And whose stature is well-proportioned, having arrived from Paris, will have the honor of appearing at the

COSMORAMA ROOMS

209, REGENT STREET,

In traversing the Continent, Senor Joachim Eleizegui has appeared at various Courts, and been honored with the patronage of

Her Majesty the Queen of Spain,
Her Majesty the Queen of Portugal,
His Majesty Louis Philippe the King of the French.

All of whom have honored him with munificent tokens of approbation. Any attempt to describe this extraordinary Phenomenon would fail to convey to the mind an adequate idea of the immense proportions of

This Modern Giant!!!

Occular demonstration only can verify this assertion. Of all the Accounts that have been recorded in Ancient or Modern European History of persons of large stature, none have equalled him.

Admission,—ONE SHILLING. Children half-price.

The Exhibition to commence at 11 to 5, and 6 to 9. Half-price from 7 to 9.

BIRD, Printer, 67, New Compton Street, Soho.

PLATE XIV

A handbill of Señor Joachim Eleizegui, the Spanish Giant. Buckland has written across the top: 'I got a cast of this man's hand which I gave to Kinnerton St Museum.' The original is in the Devon Record Office and Exeter Diocesan Record Office.

early numbers almost half, devoted to Sea and River Fisheries and Practical Natural History. A more subtle difference is that Buckland's racy style of writing seems to have been adopted by other contributors as well, with the result that *Land and Water* probably made more entertaining reading than *The Field*, although the latter was generally more authoritative. The two papers were clearly competing for the same type of reader, and some friction was inevitable. At the end of 1869 *The Field* unsuccessfully sought in the Court of Chancery to obtain an injunction against their rivals to prevent them publishing a Hunting List, which gave details of the various Hunts in the country. It was admitted by *Land and Water* that their list had been corrected from that published in *The Field*, but presumably the two lists were not identical.[129]

Bompas[13] commented that Buckland's contributions to the paper took the place of the correspondence of other men. Certainly, the work of writing a full length article every week, which in the beginning he seems to have done unaided, and of dealing with the enquiries and comments of readers, was considerable, and cannot have left him much spare time. Some of the letters to the Editor were stimulated by Buckland, who obtained contributions from friends and acquaintances. 'I send you . . . the last number of my new journal *Land and Water*,' he wrote to Professor Phillips in February, 1866. 'I edit the "Practical Natural History and the Fisheries and Archaeology" but the work is simple slavery. Still I must try to get on. . . . Any notes from you would be most acceptable.'[72] There was an accident in January, 1867, when the ice on a pond in Regent's Park gave way and thirty-four people were drowned. Francis Galton, F.R.S., Charles Darwin's cousin and pioneer of the study of heredity, wrote to Buckland complaining of the '. . . blundering efforts and general incapacity of the Humane Society men'.[130] Buckland wrote back at once: 'Many thanks for your kind note which if you will allow me I will print. May I put your name to it? Please scratch Yes or No on an envelope and post it. I want to get up a discussion on the point.'[131]

It is small wonder that even Buckland occasionally felt the strain. 'I felt so unwell that I came down here for a bit of a rest', he wrote to his sister 'Mit' (Mrs Bompas) from Herne

Bay, probably in May, 1866. 'I have been working double tides lately and am now doing the work of two people. I have the paper to look after and also my Museum at South Kensington. In both cases whip and spear and no assistance.'[110] He wrote to Professor Owen in November, 1866: 'Thanks for kind invitation but I always take 3 or 4 hours sleep between churches on Sunday and give my poor head a little rest.'[61] It will be recalled that Buckland worshipped at the church of St Mary Magdalene, Munster Square, where he was married. He was a close friend of the vicar, the Reverend Edward Stuart, M.A., an Eton and Balliol man whose sense of mission led him to sell his estates in order to build and endow this church, which was consecrated in 1852. Mr Stuart, a Puseyite, was a leading spokesman for the Anglo-Catholic movement. The church remains today much as it was in Buckland's time, an example of Gothic Revival architecture.

Buckland himself was deeply religious and some of the passages from his private diary, quoted by Bompas, indicate that he felt God to be very close to him. 'I really cannot help thinking, that the Almighty God has given me great powers, both of thought and of expressing these thoughts. Thanks to Him, but I must cultivate my mind by diligent study, careful reflection in private and intense and quick observation of facts out of doors, combined with quick appreciation of ideas of others. In fact, strive to become a master mind and thus able to influence others of weaker minds, whose shortcomings I must forgive.' On December 16, 1866, the day before his birthday, he wrote: 'The ship is still in good order, ballast not shifted, and the blocks run well; for all this I am most grateful to God, without whose assistance I could do nothing. From Him, of course, all, I know, proceeds; I trust He will continue to pour down His mercies, and I will do my best to fight His cause for Him, and to do my duty to my fellow-creatures.'[13]

In view of his prodigious output, it is scarcely surprising that his contributions to *Land and Water* were uneven. He was, however, never dull, and even when he described the trivial details of his daily life, since he crowded many strange activities into his day, these details were entertaining. They also throw a revealing light on the domestic details of the house in Albany Street. When someone sent him some barnacles from a whale cast up on the shore of Sutherland, Buckland immediately asked for additional and entire specimens, '. . . their being decayed or offensive will not detract from their value to me'. The odour of decay was one to which the neighbourhood was no doubt well accustomed. 'I do not think rats will eat putrid meat;' he wrote in 1866, 'the reason is, that I have lately discovered in my cellar a body of an eagle, which I had entirely forgotten, and which was rather high. I know there are rats in my cellar, because I will not allow them to be killed, as I consider they do me good service in eating the bits which are thrown away in the dust-bin. These rats in my cellar had not touched or gnawed the eagle at all.' As he wrote, 'Dick', one of a long succession of pet rats, was running about the table in front of him. The long-suffering Mrs Buckland and the domestic staff sometimes retaliated, however. Her husband apologized on one occasion for being unable to comment on the corpse of a mature Goldeneye sent to him for examination; 'I regret exceedingly to say that the cook picked and roasted this bird when my back was turned. I have to keep a sharp look-out in my house after specimens kindly sent to me. Directly I am out of the way, if they *look* good to eat, they are cooked; if they stink they are buried. What am I to do?' (Plate XIII).

The columns of *Land and Water* were full of his cheery ramblings; many of them, however, show Buckland as an uncritical, even naïve, person, for all his keen powers of observation. For example, a Mr Wigram asked: 'Is there anything very palatable in duckweed? I noticed to-day three or four pigs, in the marshes near Bromley, that had waded into a cut there up to their necks for the express purpose of eating it, and were doing so with great gusto. It is not an inviting-looking salad.' Buckland's reply was: 'Will any of our correspondents be kind enough to try the experiment, and report the results, of giving duckweed to their pigs? Mr Wigram's observation may possibly lead to the introduction of a new and inexpensive food for pigs.'[132]

On another occasion Buckland wrote: 'Our friend Mr Higford Burr, whose park at Aldermaston, near Reading, is one of the most beautiful bits of spacious woodland and deer frequented scenery near London, now offers asylum to English snakes. This is quite a novel experiment in practical natural history, and we shall be very curious to know what will be the result as affecting the balance of animal life in the park. . . . We trust our correspondents will accede to Mr Burr's request and send him all the live snakes or snakes' eggs they find.' Unfortunately for the modern reader, who no doubt is equally curious to know the effects of this strange experiment, the results were not reported.[133]

Specimens of all kinds were sent to Buckland for comment, and whenever an odd tale was told, he could usually cap it with a better one drawn from his own experience. A capybara was caught, swimming in the sea off Teignmouth, and caused some bewilderment until it was found to belong to the Duke of Somerset. 'Strange things are often found at sea', wrote Buckland, drily. 'Not long ago I received a bottle which had been found floating in the Atlantic. It contained no writing or papers. Simply the two fore feet of an armadillo.' He also engaged in various culinary experiments, the results of which he reported to his readers. He and a friend took some slices of flesh from the head of an old porpoise; they boiled some and fried the rest. Buckland announced that it tasted like '. . . a broiled lamp wick'. On another occasion he was sent some edible snails which he 'fatted on lettuce leaves'. 'The land snails are not quite so good as whelks,' he wrote, 'but perhaps I made a mistake in preparing them; for my cook fled from the kitchen in dismay when told to cook the snails for dinner, and I was obliged to boil them myself.' His offer to send a slice of otter flesh to anyone who wanted to try it does not seem to have been taken up by any reader.

Buckland once remarked that Englishmen always connected the idea of food with their researches into natural history. He told the story of how he bought a tortoise and '. . . on the box-seat of an omnibus showed it to the driver. Jehu turned it about, examined it with great apparent curiosity, and with a sage look said inquiringly, "I wonder how it would eat *biled*!"' Buckland himself was certainly no exception to his own generalization, but there was a good reason for his interest in the edibility of animals. Rising population and the loss of agricultural land to commercial use was, as already pointed out, making it increasingly difficult to supply the working population with home-produced meat. This was probably the reason for attempts to popularize horseflesh as human food.

On February 6, 1868, one hundred and sixty people sat down to a horse-flesh dinner at the Langham Hotel, London. It was no doubt a social success, but it was also a culinary failure. One observer wrote that '. . . the tongue was as nice as an ox; the soup, sausage, and other preparations, in which the real taste of the meat was disguised, were very palatable; but I found the plainly cooked joints, the boiled withers, and roast baron possessed a peculiar flavour and odour which, without my having the slightest prejudice against horse-flesh, rendered it extremely disagreeable to me. . . . I left the table with a strong distaste for it, and . . . from its effect upon myself and a great many others who were present, I am led to the conclusion that it is not good wholesome food.' Buckland, who stolidly ate his way from the soup to the jelly, concurred: 'In my humble opinion . . . hippophagy has not the slightest chance of success in this country.' He mentioned that all the dishes had an unwonted and peculiar taste: 'It reminds one of the peculiar odour which pervades the air in the neighbourhood of a horse that has been hard galloped.' The appearance of one of the horses used for the feast, whose photograph was handed round, seems to have been a final turning point in the argument. Buckland summed up the matter: 'Among the better classes the flesh of the horse will never become popular; for, in the first place, the cooks will not cook it (unless they are placed under martial law); in the second place, the ladies will object to it; and, thirdly, the master of the house will find it vastly inferior to beef and mutton.'[134] Although one or two further attempts were made to interest people in horseflesh, Buckland's assessment proved correct; even when called 'hippocreas' it did not become popular.

Perhaps the last word on the subject came from a correspondent, 'Dab', who suggested that horseflesh should be given to criminals in gaol. 'Now I am certain that many of the criminals now filling our gaols would be industriously at work earning their bread by the sweat of their brow, had they thought or suspected that the allowance of animal food supplied in prison was horseflesh. Be assured these fellows who would garrot you, murder your wives and children or commit the most fearful crimes, would shudder at the thought of dining upon horseflesh. No! they or most of them would die of starvation rather than be reduced to this most dreadful necessity.'[135]

Buckland also gave accounts of his doings during his frequent travels round the country. 'Some little time since, when at Weymouth,' he wrote, 'I espied outside a shop a piece of wood covered with shells. I had not a minute to spare to catch the train, but I still found time to rush into the shop and say "How much?" The price asked seemed to me to be absurdly small, but still I got my piece of wood and shells. On getting into the train I found my new treasure consisted of a broken oar; it is seven feet long, and at one time must have been entirely covered with crows.' The crows referred to are better known as saddle-oysters or silver shells, *Anomia ephippium*.[136]

Not all Buckland's writing was concerned with natural history or the fisheries. He would sometimes discourse upon his youth at Oxford, or would dissect the writings of one of his favourite classical authors from a quite novel and entertaining angle. He sometimes gave medical advice to readers, perhaps in reply to a request for information. For example, 'E.S.', a reader, asked: 'I have heard that snail soup is good for consumption. Can you tell me how to get the snails and how to make the soup?' Buckland replied: 'The great grey and the black slug, I believe, make the best soup. I have a story in my head (but I can't recollect who told me), of a gipsy woman curing a child of a chest complaint with these slugs. She boiled them till a rich firm jelly was obtained, which, when properly served up was not unpalatable. I should be obliged for a dozen or two of these slugs, as I will make a jelly of them and forward it to "E.S." for trial.' Another time he wrote about sleep, and how to procure it. His method was to eat onions, '. . . simple common onions raw, but Spanish onions stewed will do'. His theory was that the essential oil of onions '. . . has I am sure highly soporific powers'.

It would be wrong, however, to give the impression that all Buckland's contributions were of this rather frothy nature. In some ways he was much in advance of his time, especially in his realization of the need for organized fishery research; this aspect of his life will be considered in detail in a later chapter. He was a pioneer in other ways, also. He was a popular educator, and a firm believer in the desirability of teaching natural history to everyone. 'The so-called education of the present day is, in my opinion, too much confined to book learning, and taking for granted the ideas and opinions of others', he wrote. He also said: 'I feel assured that the education of children, both in town and country, might greatly be forwarded if they were taught in the schools what and how to observe. Especially in the country should they be encouraged to make collections of common objects, animal, vegetable, and mineral. They should also be taught to recognize indigenous British birds and beasts, and to send in notes as to what they have observed of their habits. Such studies tend to sharpen the natural faculties, while they humanize the intellect.'[22] He asked his friend from childhood, the Reverend W. Tuckwell, M.A., Headmaster of the College School at Taunton, to write about the teaching of science in his school. It was, after all, something of an innovation in 1868 to make the study of science for two or three hours a week a compulsory part of the curriculum.[137]

Land and Water fairly rapidly became a paper of influence, bringing information before its readers and sometimes, perhaps, tweaking their consciences. Buckland often set an example of humanity to animals or pointed out the cruelty that was so often inherent in their handling. 'The placid beauty and enjoyment of all creation on a fine autumn morning suggests to the British mind the desirability of immediately capturing and slaying something', he wrote in the first number of *Land and Water*. When, in 1880, a correspondent brought to his notice another example of the cruelty of gin traps, he wrote, 'This is . . . a capital case for our friend Mr Colam and the Prevention of Cruelty to Animals Society to enter into a new crusade against those most cruel and barbarous of "fixed engines", toothed spring rabbit and vermin traps.'[138] John Colam was secretary of the Society at this time; he was personally courageous and in 1870 had intervened at a bull fight about to be held under the patronage of the Spanish Consul in the Agricultural Hall, London. He and a number of his inspectors had jumped into the ring and stopped the proceedings. Colam also had much to do with the founding of the N.S.P.C.C. which arose from the work of the R.S.P.C.A.[139] Buckland also preached against the killing of pigs merely by cutting their throats. 'I do not consider the operation at all scientific', he wrote. 'First, the pig has to be hunted and caught; then he is rudely hauled by the hair of his back, which, of course, is more or less sensitive, on to the bench; then the knife is not made to aim at anything in particular, and the result is to be regretted. . . .' He then described an implement shown to him by Colam, and which was similar to a humane killer in principle, but was operated by a mallet.[140] It was more than thirty years after Buckland's death, however, before a suitable humane killer was put on the market and more than seventy years before its use was compulsory for the slaughter of pigs and sheep outside, as well as inside, the slaughterhouse.[139] Buckland had no hesitation, however, in telling Colam that nicking the beaks of swans was greatly to be preferred to the method proposed by the Society, which was to put ivory rings round their necks. A ring with S.P.C.A. on it which was put on the neck of one swan acted like a tourniquet and the bird was found to be starving to death.

Land and Water did not depend entirely upon Buckland for its reputation, even in its early days, and it rapidly acquired an impressive collection of contributors. It soon became the practice to report meetings of the Zoological Society and to announce new arrivals at the Gardens. A. D. Bartlett frequently wrote a brief note on some aspect of the natural history of his charges. The veteran ichthyologist Jonathan Couch (1789–1870), grandfather of Sir Arthur Quiller-Couch, wrote in the early numbers under the pseudonym 'Video', a Latin pun on his initials. The Reverend Francis Orpen Morris (1810–1893), the extreme anti-vivisectionist and naturalist, whose work on British birds and their eggs is still occasionally of value, was a frequent contributor. Francis Day, who, it will be recalled, was trained at St George's with Buckland and had become famous in both medicine and ichthyology, often wrote for the paper and, indeed, twelve years after Couch's death published in *Land and Water* some interesting extracts from Couch's manuscript journals. The full list of occasional contributors would make dull reading indeed, but it included such men as the remarkable Mordecai Cubitt Cooke, who began his working life as an apprentice in the wholesale drapery trade and ended it as an eminent botanist, specially knowledgeable on Cryptogams. Professor W. H. Flower, of the Royal College of Surgeons, and John Gould the ornithologist wrote more than one article, and even Charles Darwin asked for information about the development of horns in the reindeer.

Any discussion of the early history of *Land and Water* must, however, include an account of the extraordinary John Keast Lord (1818–1872), who carried the atmosphere of travel and adventure with him, and breathed into his prose now the exotic scents of the Nile and now the resinous odours of the trapper's log fire. His pen-name, 'The Wanderer', was undoubtedly well chosen. Buckland described his first meeting with Lord in the following words: 'In July, 1863, I attended an entertainment at the Egyptian Hall, entitled "The Canoe, the Rifle, and the Axe". The lecture was full of the highest interest. It was illustrated by well-drawn designs of wild American scenery, and a table by the side was crowded with American trophies. The lecturer was a fine, tall, big-shouldered Englishman, with a great black beard, a handsome, intelligent face, a bold, open, fearless-looking forehead and eyes, that seemed to have concentrated the acuteness and perception of the wild Red Men with the sagacity of a semi-savage fur-trader; while the bright light of education showed that although he wore the dress of a North American trapper, yet he was still a true, noble English gentleman.' Buckland was so impressed with what he heard that he introduced Lord to John Crockford of *The Field*; Lord joined the staff of *Land and Water* when it was established.[141]

Lord's career reads like a novel; he was brought up in Tavistock, Devon, and was apprenticed to a local firm of chemists. He later entered the Royal Veterinary College, London, and returned to set himself up in his profession in Tavistock, '. . . but his convivial tastes led him astray and he suddenly disappeared'. Buckland mentions vaguely that he was shipwrecked off the shore of Anticosta, served for a time on a Greenland whaler and was on an emigrant ship when it was stricken with cholera. Having lived as a trapper in

Minnesota and Hudson Bay for some years, he returned to England. He was appointed to the British Army in the East as a veterinary surgeon and saw service with the Turkish artillery in the Crimea. In 1858 Lord was appointed naturalist to the Commission sent out to map the 49th parallel which was to form the southern boundary of British Columbia. He was in fact to a considerable degree responsible for the success of the Commission through his efficient organization of its transport.

He gathered a valuable collection of the fauna of British Columbia, which he donated to the British Museum. His account of his experiences, *The Naturalist in British Columbia*, still repays reading today. After his return to Britain he was employed by the Viceroy of Egypt and while there made many observations on snakes and snake charmers. His accounts in *Land and Water* of his experiences here show him to have been a brave man, a good naturalist and a kind and considerate companion.

He was a first-rate literary craftsman and it is small wonder that when he died, shortly after he had been appointed manager of the newly opened Brighton Aquarium, his loss was widely felt, nowhere more than on the staff of *Land and Water*.[7, 141]

A rather different type of man was Henry Lee (1826–1888), who also joined the staff of *Land and Water* soon after it began, and took over Lord's job at Brighton. Lee was a clever microscopist and a good experimenter, who wrote well in a slightly forced popular vein. He was, like Lord, a close personal friend of Buckland.[7]

Land and Water was an undoubted success by 1870. It had proved necessary to move to larger premises in September, 1869, when the offices were moved from No. 80 to No. 169 Fleet Street. In May, 1876, a further expansion took place when the offices were transferred to No. 176 Fleet Street. Even today many of the articles and much of the correspondence in the early numbers of the paper are worth reading. Some of the correspondence throws an interesting, and occasionally a macabre, light on the period. During a discussion on how to destroy rats, for example, a contributor using the pseudonym 'Stall fed' wrote: 'One hardly likes to incur the responsibility of placing poison in the hands of any servant or farm-labourer, whose stupidity or carelessness might lead any moment to disastrous results. Foxes would not be safe, for they would run a great risk of being poisoned by eating the dead rats, a diet to which they are rather partial.'[142]

The paper followed with great interest the attempts of Captain Webb to swim the Channel, and indeed assisted that gentleman financially in his attempt. It was also suggested, perhaps by Buckland himself, that Webb should cover himself in porpoise grease, advice which he took. After an abortive attempt by Webb, shortly before he became famous by being the first man to swim the Channel, a J. W. Nicholl-Carne wrote about the impossibility of remaining alive in the water for so long a period; he concluded his letter with an unlikely account of his father, aged 75, swimming for two and a half hours in the Bristol Channel, wearing a tall chimney-pot hat!

This was the period when a train to Brighton and back from London Bridge on a Sunday or Monday cost 3*s*, when coughs, asthma and incipient consumption could be effectually cured by Keating's Cough Lozenges, and when half a dozen bottles of champagne, with three tumblers and an instrument for opening the bottles cost 21*s*. Some unspoiled rural England was still to be found, but it was in full retreat before the massed armies of industry, and perhaps too few people realized how precious was the countryside that remained and how carefully it needed preserving.

CHAPTER TWELVE

H.M. Inspector of Salmon Fisheries

FROM VERY EARLY TIMES Britons have been accustomed to catch fish in their local brooks and ponds. Domesday Book lists numerous inland fisheries, showing the importance of fish in the medieval diet; freshwater fish must have given welcome variety at a time when so many foods were heavily salted or dried. Salmon has always been one of the most highly prized of all species caught in fresh water. The salmon fisheries are mentioned in a clause in Magna Carta, and the first Act of the English Parliament dealing specifically with salmon appears to have been passed in 1285 in the reign of Edward I.[143]

The growth of the sea fisheries during the second half of the nineteenth century and the increasing quantity of fresh sea fish reaching inland markets turned people away from coarse freshwater fish, although in the 1860s many still relished species such as carp, tench and pike and contemporary cookery books are full of ingenious suggestions for masking their muddy flavours. The middle of the nineteenth century also saw the rise throughout England of working men's angling clubs. These were often begun by a few friends, who met together in some local inn to foster good fellowship and the sport of angling, generally for coarse fish. At this time, as the historian of the London Anglers' Association has said, 'The clubs had no ideals, except to take fish; there was no restriction as to size or even season, the waterside was infested with poachers and vagrants, foul language was the order of the day, and general sportsmanship, as we now know it, did not then exist'.[95]

As the demand for coarse fish for food slowly declined, angling increased. The demand for salmon for food, on the other hand, continued to rise, and frequently exceeded the supply; large quantities reached Billingsgate packed in ice and sent by sea from the valuable commercial stake-net fisheries in the Tyne, Tay and Forth estuaries. Significant quantities were also caught with similar 'fixed engines' in the Chester Dee, the Severn and other rivers. Owners of fishing rights farther upstream had a justifiable grievance, for they had formerly been accustomed to catch salmon by net or rod; increased fishing in the estuaries now meant that fewer fish escaped to be caught upstream.

By 1860 there was a strong suspicion amounting to certainty that in many rivers it was not merely a question of who was to catch the fish. The salmon fisheries were in jeopardy, for the total catches from some famous salmon rivers were falling, and in others, such as the Thames, salmon had not been seen for many years. Salmon differ from coarse fish in spawning in fresh water but feeding in the sea. Mature fish enter the rivers and swim upstream to shallow and fast-flowing water and spawn in places where the river bed consists of stones from the size of plums to oranges. Spawning generally takes place in late autumn and winter; the spent and emaciated fish, or kelts, generally die but the few that survive the physiological strain and succeed in reaching the sea rapidly regain condition.

The salmon ova hatch after a period of sixty to 120 days, depending on temperature; the larvae, or alevins, develop into little fish, called parr, with characteristic barred markings. At the end of the first year the parr are three or four inches in length. After a further year or so in the river, during which they grow to a length of about six inches, the parr change shape, lose their barred markings and become more silvery. They migrate in the spring to the sea. These young fish or smolts remain in the sea sometimes for only a year before they return as grilse, but sometimes from two to four years before they return to the rivers of their birth as maiden salmon, when they, like the grilse, spawn for the first time. This account is, of course, a generalized one and may not apply precisely to the fish in certain localities.

It is obvious that unless some control is maintained over the number of salmon captured each year in a particular river, insufficient mature fish will reach the spawning beds, and catches will drop catastrophically after a very few years. As one authority has observed: '. . . each generation of salmon may traverse the whole of the river from somewhere near its source to its mouth twice during its life, and anyone by selfish and greedy action could for immediate gain ruin the fishery not only for himself but for all his neighbours as well'.[143]

Although, however, overfishing might have been the explanation for the decline in catches in some rivers, it was obviously not the reason for the disappearance of salmon in others, such as the Thames. In 1860 a Royal Commission of Inquiry into the Salmon Fisheries of England and Wales was therefore issued '. . . with the view of increasing the supply of a valuable article of food for the public'. The Commissioners were Sir William Jardine, G. K. Rickards and W. J. Ffennell.[144]

The choice of William Joshua Ffennell was a highly suitable one, for few men of the period were so knowledgeable about the management of salmon rivers. He was born of Quaker stock in 1799 at Ballybrado on the River Suir in southern Ireland and seems to have spent his youth largely in hunting, shooting and fishing. He became an expert angler, an authority on the habits of the salmon, and he strove to improve the fisheries of the River Suir. It was largely due to his tact and wisdom that Parliament passed legislation aimed at improving the Irish river fisheries. In 1845 Ffennell was appointed Irish Fishery Inspector, one of his duties being to see that the new law was enforced. As a result of his work a further Act, commonly called Ffennell's Act, was passed in 1848. This gave powers to local boards to administer the law and to raise funds by, for example, the issuing of licences, and so become self-supporting. Ffennell was subsequently made a Commissioner of Irish Fisheries with the responsibility of superintending the work of these local boards. He was an intelligent and kindly man with a reputation for plain speaking and honest dealing.

The Commissioners' Report on the English and Welsh Salmon Fisheries was presented on February 7, 1861. It showed that in some rivers salmon were no longer to be found, in others they were facing extinction, and in yet others numbers were rapidly declining. The Commissioners attributed the decline only in part to excessive netting with fixed nets; they believed part of the trouble was also that poachers took fish on the spawning beds when they were at their most vulnerable or even caught the kelts, which are quite unfit for food.

In many rivers, however, even more potent forces were at work to prevent the salmon finding suitable spawning areas. Industrial plants such as mines, tanneries, chemical factories and gasworks, which had grown up largely after 1815, were pouring toxic liquids into some streams and rivers which in consequence were often incapable of supporting any fish life. Also, ironically, the reforms in public sanitation initiated by Edwin Chadwick in the 1840s had resulted in large volumes of crude sewage polluting some streams, which were in an unmentionable state.

A further problem in many rivers was the presence of dams. The industrial revolution in its early years depended more on water power than on steam, and many rivers were blocked by mill dams, which often formed an insuperable barrier to the salmon migrating up river to spawn. The fish congregated just below the dam and were an easy prey to the poacher, who was often the miller himself. There were seventy-three mill weirs on the Severn alone.[145] Elsewhere, pound locks and weirs, introduced to make rivers more readily navigable and to connect them to the canal systems, also provided an effective barrier to the migrating salmon. Water levels were raised and the currents slowed, so that the fast flowing brooks with gravelly beds, in which the salmon formerly gathered to spawn, were converted to deep sluggish weedy streams in which coarse fish thrived instead.

Parliament had made many attempts in the past to control the river fisheries and the Commissioners commented that as a result of the confused legislation it was now almost impossible to know what was the law, since the river fisheries were affected by at least twenty-six separate statutes, some dating back to the Middle Ages. In some rivers the only way of enforcing the penalty on those who used nets with too small a mesh was in a Court Leet, a mode of procedure long disused.[144]

Parliament accepted the recommendations of the Commissioners, and the Salmon Fisheries Act of 1861 was passed. This Act was designed to replace all previous legislation; certain methods of catching fish were made illegal, an annual close time was enforced during which fishing was not permitted, a weekly close time from noon on Saturdays to 6 a.m. on Mondays was introduced, and it became compulsory to erect fishways or fish passes over dams and weirs. Some attempt was also made to prevent pollution, although in the event the powers provided were found to be quite inadequate. The law was to be enforced by Inspectors of Fisheries who were appointed under the Home Office.

Ffennell was made one of the first Inspectors. His colleague was Frederick Eden. The 1861 Act was found inadequate in certain respects and some amending Acts were later introduced. Perhaps the greatest weakness of the 1861 Act was that it made no real provision for local administration of the law. Justices at Quarter Sessions could appoint conservators or overseers but it was anticipated, mistakenly as it proved, that funds to enable the Boards of Conservators to carry out their duties would be obtained by voluntary contribution. An Act of 1865 defined the fishery districts over which the Boards had jurisdiction and empowered the Boards to raise funds by, for instance, licensing nets and rods and imposing a rate on fisheries. The Inspectors acted mainly as advisers to the local boards and reported annually on the state of the fisheries.[146]

Frederick Eden was ill during 1866 and towards the end of the year decided to resign. Buckland perhaps heard about the impending resignation from an old college friend, George Ward Hunt, or he may have been told by Ffennell, for the two men were both closely involved in *Land and Water*. Hunt was financial secretary to the Treasury and was destined to become for a brief period Chancellor of the Exchequer in Disraeli's first Cabinet, formed in February, 1868. 'Dear Frank', he wrote on October 11, 1866, 'I hear there is just a possibility of a vacancy in the Fishery Inspectorship – I advise you to write a line to Mr Walpole at the Home Office who has the patronage, asking him to consider your claims – I am going to him this morning to urge them but I recommend a formal application.'[23]

Buckland wrote at once to the Right Hon. Spencer Horatio Walpole, who was Home Secretary, and, having obtained from an influential acquaintance, Major General Seymour, a testimonial in support of his application, he wrote again. Meanwhile Hunt had also been working on Buckland's behalf.

PLATE XV

Buckland in working clothes. He preferred to wear only a flannel shirt and trousers in the house and often no shoes or socks. He is holding an oyster breeding tile, perhaps the very tile given him by M. Hyacinth Boeuf, and an oyster shell. Probably about 1875.

From a photograph in the Library of the Royal College of Surgeons of England.

'I have said to Mr Walpole personally and to Lord Bulmore (before you wrote) all I could in favour of you having the Inspectorship of Fisheries. The Board of Trade are concerned with the Oyster Fisheries. I understood when I last enquired that no Inspector would be permanently appointed at present. The Salmon Fisheries is what you should look to.'[23]

Buckland was appointed Inspector in February, 1867. Bompas quotes from the Diary:

> *Wednesday, February* 6.
>
> This day I was appointed Inspector of Fisheries. I had been invited to dine at the Piscatorial Society in St James's Hall, and was sitting on the left hand of the chairman (Mr Sachs), when John brought me in a letter as follows: 'Home Office, February 6, 1867. Sir, – Mr Walpole has desired me to inform you that he has much pleasure in appointing you Inspector of Salmon Fisheries in accordance with your wishes. I am etc, S. Walpole.' – When I read this I felt a most peculiar feeling, not joy, nor grief, but a pleasurable stunning sensation, if there can be such a thing. The first thing I did was to utter a prayer of thanksgiving to Him who really appointed me, and who has thus placed me in a position to look after, and care for, His wonderful works. May He give me strength to do my duty in my new calling! I said not a word to anybody, but in a few minutes I had to make a speech, to propose the health of the prize-givers. I alluded first to the cultivation of the waters, and then to my excellent father's endeavours to do good, saying it was my wish to honour his name, and do my own duty in my generation. I then read out the letter, which was received with great applause. Thus, then, I have gained the object of my life. Surely fortune favours me with great luck; and I am very thankful for it.[13]

It will be noted that the Home Secretary's letter to Buckland was signed by S. Walpole. This was the statesman's elder son who, on his mother's side, was grandson of Spencer Perceval, the Prime Minister who was assassinated in the lobby of the House of Commons in 1812. The young Spencer Walpole had been educated at Eton but owing to lack of adequate funds he had entered the Civil Service instead of going to university and held the post of his father's private secretary.

Buckland by this time was fully conversant with the problems facing the salmon fisheries and he had frequently accompanied Ffennell when the latter was making his inspections. It was as well that he had done so for Ffennell died unexpectedly on March 12, 1867. Spencer Walpole junior before the end of March was appointed by his father in Ffennell's place so that two new and almost completely inexperienced Inspectors were now in office together. Buckland was forty years old whilst his colleague was about twenty-eight. The post of Inspector was apparently worth £700 a year; at least, this was the salary offered to Buckland's successor, Thomas Henry Huxley. Mrs Francis C. Holland, Spencer Walpole's daughter, also mentions her father's salary: 'In 1867 the post of Inspector of Fisheries, one worth, I think, £900 or £1,000 a year, fell vacant. My grand-father, in whose gift it was (as Home Secretary), had conscientious scruples about giving so large a place to his own son, and he therefore cut down the salary to £700 before he offered it to him. Such as it was my father joyfully accepted it. . . .'[147]

Buckland and Walpole were good colleagues. Buckland was a good field naturalist with an intuitive, rather than analytical, approach to problems. His ability to handle figures was atrocious and he generally preferred to ask somebody else to do his arithmetic for him. He once gave the number of eggs in the roe of a specimen of carp as 2,059,759, having obtained this figure by weighing the roe and counting the eggs in a known weight. 'I can guarantee the accuracy of the weighing,' he said, 'and also the calculations, which were made for me by Mr Thomas, a professional accountant.'[22] The final digit in these calculations carried the same importance for him as the first and Walpole remarked, '. . . though he was fond of quoting the figures which his secretary prepared for him in his reports, those who knew him best doubted whether they expressed any clear meaning to him.' Whenever he went on an inspection which was likely to involve him in considerable expenditure, he would arrange his sovereigns in twists of paper, each containing ten coins.[26]

Walpole was a very different man. He had a marvellous head for figures and an incisive mind able to penetrate the legal fog which still drifted over every question concerning the river fisheries. He was not a naturalist, and made no claim to be one, but he was an intelligent man with an engaging manner and perhaps rather more native caution than his colleague. The two men were popular and became widely known as they travelled together or separately through the country, advising, wheedling, coaxing, exhorting and instructing fishery boards, fishermen and riparian owners in all aspects of the management of salmon rivers. Buckland was very amused to find by chance that the two horses harnessed to the carriage belonging to the chairman of one fishery board were named 'Buckland' and 'Walpole'.[148]

The duties of the Inspectors were not always pleasant, for many people from mill owners to fishermen resented Government interference in what they regarded as their rights. Here Buckland's diplomatic and entertaining manner was of considerable value. 'If a close observer were asked to mention the chief quality which Mr Buckland developed as Inspector of Fisheries,' wrote Walpole, 'he would probably reply a capacity for managing men. He had the happiest way of conciliating opposition and of carrying an even hostile audience with him. It frequently occurred that the fishermen, at the many enquiries which his colleague and he held, looked in the first instance with suspicion on the inspectors. They never looked with suspicion on them when they went away. The ice of reserve was thawed by Mr Buckland's genial manner; and the men who, for the first half-hour, shrank from imparting information, in the next three hours vied with one another in contributing it.'[26] Walpole's daughter, however, said of her father, 'I sometimes wonder in how many wayside villages and fishing hamlets may still linger a memory of his genial courteous passing. . . . There was a certain simplicity about him and a ready sympathy, very different from condescension, which was extended to all, both poor and rich, and was so natural to him that he made it seem natural to others.'[147]

The Salmon Fisheries Act of 1873 amended the 1861 and subsequent Acts in certain respects; in particular it gave to the local Boards the right to make their own bye-laws for the better protection and improvement of the rivers under their control. Previously, their powers were limited to the enforcement of regulations laid down at the Home Office, which was a somewhat illogical arrangement since it required that on all rivers the same close times were observed, even though local conditions varied considerably. By the Act of 1873 a new responsibility was added to the Inspectors of advising the Home Secretary on the technical merits of bye-laws proposed by the Boards.

The Inspectors' most important duties throughout, however, were inspections of the rivers of England and Wales, advice to all those who sought it, and the preparation of an Annual Report. The Annual Report was partly a statistical account of the fisheries based on the answers to a series of about twelve questions sent out each autumn to the clerks to the Fishery Boards. The questions covered such points as the prevalence of poaching, numbers of water-bailiffs employed and what steps were taken to prevent pollution and, if so, whether they were successful. The Inspectors in their Annual Reports also drew the attention of Parliament to matters which were apparently of particular importance.

The form which inspections took varied from place to place, and time to time. The Inspectors had to satisfy themselves that salmon could negotiate weirs, and where necessary they assisted in the design of fish passes. Buckland would think nothing of investigating a fish pass from the salmon's point of view, and exceptionally he would wade into the river up to his neck, armed no doubt with the stout bamboo pole he always carried on his inspections (Frontispiece), and would change his clothes on the box of a fly as he was driven away. On other occasions the inspectors would attempt to study the effects of pollutions from factories and mines. Accounts of many inspections are given in the columns of *Land and Water*. An early report of an inspection of the Wear and Tees carried out in July, 1867, says of the two Inspectors: 'They did not go to their business in a kid-glove style, but in a plain, practical, British workmanlike fashion they set about their task, making an impression on the mind of the spectator to the effect that these were indeed the right men in the right place. Not only so, but as becometh cultured gentlemen, the inspectors were exceedingly courteous and affable to every member of the party who essayed a word to them.'[149]

Inevitably, much time was spent in travelling from place to place. 'I send you our annual report just out and hope you will approve', Buckland wrote to Professor Owen on April 22, 1872. 'I was at Lancaster last Wednesday and examined Skerton, Halton and Forge Weirs. The diagonal placed at my suggestion at Skerton is a great success. We have devised passes for Halton and Forge. The Lune fisheries are in a very prosperous state, you will be pleased to hear. I also inspected the Wyre weirs at Garstang, Cleveley, Dolphinholme, Abbeystone Reservoir. Suggested alterations for passes which will make them effective. *No* Salmon in Wyre all sea trout too small for salmon. I wish you would come and see my Fish Museum at South Kensington some afternoon. I shall be away all *this* week inspecting Axe, Exe, Avon, Devon.'[61] Buckland did much of his writing in railway trains, an accomplishment learnt, it is said, from Bishop Samuel Wilberforce. Many of the contributions to *Land and Water* were so written and the manuscript dropped into the nearest letter box at the end of the journey. No doubt he followed the advice he had given to home tourists in 1861 in an article in *The Leisure Hour*. This was, always to be at the station five minutes before the train starts, get into the centre compartment of the centre carriage and 'avoid carriages containing fat men and babies, and get the corner seat'.[150]

Walpole records how Buckland hated boots.

> He lost no opportunity of kicking them off his feet. On one occasion, travelling alone in a railway carriage, he fell asleep with his feet resting on the window-sill. As usual he kicked off his boots and they fell outside the carriage on the line. When he reached his destination the boots could not, of course, be found, and he had to go without them to his hotel. The next morning a platelayer examining the permanent way came upon the boots, and reported to the traffic manager that he had found a pair of gentleman's boots, but that he could not find the gentleman. Someone connected with the railway recollected that Mr Buckland had been seen in the neighbourhood, and, knowing his eccentricities, inferred that the boots must belong to him. They were accordingly sent to the Home Office and were at once claimed.[26]

It is difficult to know what influence the work of the Inspectors had on the condition of the rivers of the country. The Annual Reports, with some exceptions, paint a reasonably optimistic picture of the state of the fisheries, and there seems little doubt that in some rivers the construction of effective fish passes and restriction of the amount of fishing brought about a significant improvement. In others, however, pollution rendered all attempts at improvement useless. Buckland never minced his words when talking about pollution. He regarded '. . . clean and unpolluted water . . . [as] the very foundation of the prosperity of a salmon fishery', and claimed that pollution was the most deadly cause of decline of salmon fisheries. In his first annual report he recommended that a chemist should be given the task of studying how water may be purified.[151] Some manufacturers were prepared to purify toxic waste water before allowing it to flow into river or stream; others were not. One claimed that sulphuric acid, which was released from his works, was a tonic for the fish. 'In England and Wales, as well as in Scotland,' Buckland wrote, 'manufacturers of all kinds of materials, from paper down to stockings, seem to think that rivers are convenient channels kindly given them by nature to carry away at little or no cost the refuse of their works.' He blamed the mine owners even more for they frequently cut off the very sources of the rivers and converted them to poisonous muddy streams. 'The abovementioned individuals and companies for the most part reap no inconsiderable profits from their industrial operations, but while endeavouring to increase their own profits, they treat with indifference the welfare of the public, and an important source of food not only to themselves, but to the public in general.' Buckland claimed industry and the fisheries could exist side by side if the mining interests and manufacturers would make a real effort to purify waste waters.[152] He also pointed out the urgent need for proper treatment of sewage; his description of the state of the rivers near some towns is horrifying. 'Having, as in former years, taken every opportunity of examining the outfalls of sewers into our rivers, I am in a position to warn the authorities who have command of these sewers that the enemy is among them and only awaits time and opportunity to spring from his lair in the form of wide-spread disease.'[153] He performed a very necessary public service in drawing the attention of Parliament and the public to the need for legislation to control pollution.

Although, under the 1861 Act, the penalties for polluting rivers were quite severe, manufacturers broke the law everywhere. There was a saving clause in the 1861 Act which, as Buckland was quick to point out, enabled the offender to escape any penalties if he could prove that he had '. . . used the best practicable Means, within a reasonable cost, to render harmless the liquid or solid Matter so permitted to flow or to be put into Waters. . . .' The Rivers Pollution Commissioners reported, after considering a wide range of types of pollution: 'The remedies for the nuisances which these refuse liquids create have been carefully examined, and after prolonged inquiry and research, we have been able to report that in every case efficient remedies exist, and are available.'[154] In other words, the remedies were there, but the law would not enforce their use.

Buckland acquired a great deal of miscellaneous information about the biology of salmon and trout. He always made a close examination of every fish that came his way, and tried to identify its food from its stomach contents. He demonstrated that the fat round the pyloric caeca, finger-like outgrowths at the base of the stomach, was a food reserve utilized completely during spawning. At the request of the Baden Government, he also gave some attention to various means of marking salmon fry, and commented that the question '. . . has not received the attention it deserved'. He believed that salmon find their way back to the rivers of their birth by their sense of smell, a theory only recently confirmed experimentally in Canada. He also carried on a wide, diffuse and generally uncritical correspondence with people all over the country on the natural history of the salmon. 'Fish will not come up when the water is low', he wrote to one correspondent. 'A salmon is a "Water Fox" and quite as cunning, he knows well enough he will be seen in low water. You never saw a Fox (in his senses) go across an open field when he can go along a hedgerow. For spawning from 44° to 48° is the right temperature. I cannot say *why they rise*. It is generally before a change in the weather. I should be most obliged if you would note down Barometer and Thermometer when they *do* rise and when they do not. We may then get some idea. Depend on it fish and animals have some feelings and susceptibilities which we men have not. Quaere is it Electric or Magnetic probably the latter.'[155]

He was a man of enthusiasms, and often, in a fever of excitement, did or said something not entirely sensible. This tendency was not unnoticed by some of his critics. Every winter from 1864 he collected salmon ova from rivers all over the country. These Mr Stephen Ponder hatched out in his greenhouse and subsequently released as parr into the Thames. When, therefore, news reached Buckland on April 18, 1870, that a salmon had been netted in the lower part of Gravesend Reach, he and Henry Ffennell, W. J. Ffennell's son, immediately went to Gravesend to investigate. The fish was purchased on the spot; '. . . the price I paid for it, as handed over to the fisherman, was two pounds six shillings. I packed up my treasure more carefully and brought it to London. I laid it straight out on a board and surrounded it with sea-weed and then tied newspapers round it. Mr Ffennell . . . and I, carried our treasure, in the dusk of the evening, solemnly along the streets of Gravesend. Our parcel, I must confess, looked amazingly like a child's coffin, with broad shoulders and narrow feet. An old woman, however, came to our rescue. "It's no child them gents is carrying; they don't bury children in sea-weed." '

The two men ceremoniously called into the Athenaeum Club and the salmon was shown to John Gould, the ornithologist. 'The following day I took my fish to Windsor and submitted it to His Royal Highness, Prince Christian, who takes the greatest interest in everything in connection with fish and fish culture. I also exhibited it to a large party of influential gentlemen on board the Steamer of the Thames Conservancy Board, as we had luckily arranged to make an inspection of the Thames weirs on that very day. . . .' Although Buckland reluctantly admitted that this salmon was probably not one of his breeding, he added that his determination to restock the Thames with salmon was now all the greater.[156]

The *Saturday Review* commented:

> Mr Buckland, one of the Inspectors of Salmon Fisheries, realizes the German Doppel-Gänger. He is not one, but two. In his official capacity we have met him this week, and his colleague, Mr S. Walpole, in the grave and ponderous person-

ality of a Blue-book. Here, Mr Buckland, official, does credit to his duties. His Report shows a public servant of great energy throwing much labour, knowledge, and experience into his work, executing it conscientiously, and in difficult and delicate matters exhibiting a patient, tact, and conciliatory temper which might well be imitated in other departments of the Civil Service. . . .

There is also Mr Buckland officious – we use the word according to its etymology – with whom we have also formed acquaintance in the newspapers this week. That is, Mr Buckland persuaded of a mission, Mr Buckland permeated by the sense of a duty (*officium*), Mr Buckland wild, sentimental, sensational, gushing, impetuous, dithyrambic. Nobody could recognize in Mr Buckland pursuing the even tenor of his decorous and useful way in a Blue-book, the Mr Buckland in a fine frenzy writing to the *Times*, or in *Land and Water*, on a 'Salmon caught in the Thames' – rushing down to Gravesend to secure his wonderful prize, bringing the interesting stranger to town in a triumphal procession – turning the smoking-room of the Athenaeum into another Borgo Allegro, to witness this last and most glorious birth of time, 'exhibiting my precious Thames salmon all day at the Horticultural Gardens', then hurrying the noble stranger off to Windsor Castle on a visit to her (the creature was a female) kindred Majesty, and introducing her to 'H.R.H. Prince Christian, much interested in fish culture;' and finally sending a cast of this wonderful wonder of wonders to the Soirée of the Royal Society itself, where we have no doubt Mr Buckland thinks that the plaster of Paris effigy of this memorable brute was a much more important object than the spectroscope or Mr Lockyer's chromosphere of the sun.[157]

Buckland's official position again brought him into contact with James Youl and the attempts to introduce salmon to the Antipodes. It will be recalled that in 1864 Buckland and Francis Francis had both collected trout ova which had been carried in the *Norfolk* to Melbourne and had been successfully hatched in Tasmania. It was from the fish hatched out of these ova that the waters of New Zealand were subsequently stocked with brown trout. In December, 1868, Buckland and Youl were presented with silver claret jugs, together worth about £120, from the Government of New Zealand, as a recognition of the part they had played. Buckland was also made a life member of the Acclimatization Society of Victoria in view of his great services to acclimatization.

Buckland provided 4,000 trout ova for a shipment to Otago in the *Celestial Queen* in January, 1868. This shipment consisted mainly of salmon ova and was organized by Youl. It was a total failure and Youl afterwards wondered whether this was because he had had to reopen the ice-house on the vessel for Buckland, who arrived at the quayside late with the trout ova. At the time Youl felt '. . . that it would have been churlish to refuse my energetic friend room for his Pets, the parents of which he had himself caught and manipulated . . .'[158] Buckland again contributed trout ova to a shipment to Otago in the *Mindora* in 1869. This also was organized by Youl.

When, however, a further shipment to Otago was arranged by Youl in the *Oberon* in January, 1873, Buckland was not invited to assist, and he felt slightly affronted. His help had been requested about the middle of the previous year, and he had obtained official permits from a number of Boards of Conservators; these permits allowed the collection of ova for scientific purposes during the close season.

> The official permits to take Eggs for New Zealand and I must in fairness add for the Thames at the same time remained unused on my table; and I was surprised, as time went on, to find that the assistance of Mr Walpole and myself as H.M. Inspectors of Salmon Fisheries, and of our assistants, as well as the Members of the various Boards of Salmon Conservators, had not been called into requisition.
>
> My surprise was great on hearing that Mr Youl had undertaken the responsible task of collecting the eggs; but of course I took no notice of this; Mr Youl, I learn from a letter in the *Times* had employed skilled Servants to carry out this operation. . . . Of course Mr Walpole and myself and the Members of the Boards of Conservators are all most anxious that the experiment should succeed. Nevertheless, it is a matter for regret to all of us that this great and important undertaking was not allowed to assume the features of an official and international Government transmission of the elements of a vast industry at the Antipodes instead of being entrusted to one individual to whom access to all the above mentioned resources would have been freely open on application which however was never made.

Buckland continued by giving detailed advice on how to look after the ova when they arrived. In the event, however, the shipment was a failure.[159]

It may have been this letter which prompted the Otago Government to commission Buckland and Youl jointly in the shipments of 1875 in the *Timaru*, the *Durham* in 1876 and the *Chimborazo* in 1878. Nicols, in his history of the attempts to acclimatize the salmonidae in the Antipodes is critical of Buckland's part in these shipments, mainly on the grounds that Buckland would not adopt the technique devised by Youl which had previously proved satisfactory, a fact of which there seems no doubt. A few alevins were hatched from the salmon ova carried in some shipments, but although the fry were released into the rivers there was doubt as to whether or not they had returned to the rivers to spawn. Some large salmonids had been caught, but whilst some thought they were salmon others believed they were large trout, which in fact they were.

When Nicols wrote in 1882, however, some of the shipments of salmon ova were believed to have been successful. He commented: 'The whole of the success has been claimed for Mr Buckland repeatedly, and he has not been careful to disavow the honour at all times and in all places. . . .' This criticism, although somewhat uncharitable, was probably not unjust.[159] Nevertheless, it should be recalled that Buckland had been responsible for providing some of the brown trout ova which were carried successfully to Tasmania, as Buckland himself pointed out in 1877. 'I really think we ought to have some official acknowledgement of the fact from the Government authorities, or else in future years it will be forgotten how and who first sent over trout from England.'[160] In June, 1879, a letter was sent from the Chief Secretary's Office in Melbourne setting on record Francis Francis's and Buckland's contribution.

Buckland's energy and enthusiasm in the cause of salmon preservation without any doubt encouraged others to take an interest in the freshwater fisheries. He was Salmon Inspector, and therefore salmon was his prime interest, but he devoted much attention to coarse fish and the more responsible approach of Angling Clubs to their sport, which is very apparent by the time of Buckland's death, was in no small measure due to his influence.

In particular, Buckland played a major part in the preparation of what finally became the Freshwater Fisheries Act of 1878 and which is associated with the name of Mr A. J. Mundella, M.P., one of the members for Nottingham. Indeed, Callcut states, although surely wrongly, that Buckland drafted the Bill.[95] It is more probable that he gave expert advice on its contents, for Mundella himself admitted to complete ignorance of fishery matters. The Act of 1878 extended the law to species other than salmon and empowered the setting up of Boards of Conservators for any rivers containing trout or char. A close season for all freshwater fish was introduced; the period March 15 to June 15 for this close season seems to have been chosen somewhat arbitrarily and partly due to an oversight by Buckland.[95] Buckland very much approved of the provisions of the Act and did much to obtain the support of Angling Clubs for it. He had preached the need for adequate legislation if the freshwater fisheries as a whole were to be improved. The Mundella Act, which was repealed in 1923, was a first attempt to bring about this control; although perhaps not an entirely effective attempt, it was widely welcomed by those interested in angling for coarse fish.

Moreover, Buckland had always stressed the importance of all kinds of coarse fish as food. He wrote to *The Times* newspaper extolling the virtues of eels and pond fish as food '. . . considering the present high price of animal food of all kinds'. His suggestion that pond fish might be fattened by tying on a branch overhanging the water a bunch of rats, a rabbit or two or even a horse's leg so that the gentles would drop into the mouths of the fish waiting below, nowadays sounds unattractive. His reference to stewed eel shops, however, is interesting, sensible and curiously reminiscent of Henry Mayhew, who at one period also lived in Albany Street. 'The poor people of London are very fond of stewed eels. I have been the round of the stewed-eel shops to see for myself. The verdict is that stewed eels are nutritious and capital food. In one shop I counted 32 people, besides myself, eating their quiet pennyworth of stewed eels. I measured (on the quiet) my pennyworth. I had just four inches of eel, each bit about the size of the little finger, plus no end of melted butter and savoury herbs.'[161]

Buckland, Walpole and Archibald Young, the Commissioner of Scottish Salmon Fisheries, were appointed in 1879 to enquire into the causes of a disease which had appeared in salmon in some rivers during the early months of 1878. Affected fish developed greyish-white patches on the skin, particularly on the head and round the fins, and appeared greatly irritated for they dashed about in the river and rubbed themselves against stones. The fish very quickly died, their bodies entirely covered by a paper-like mat of fungus.

The fungus was identified by a number of experts, including Mordecai Cubitt Cooke, as *Saprolegnia ferax*, but the Commissioners admitted their inability to come to any firm conclusions about the causes of the disease.[162] In this they were wiser than Buckland's successor, Professor T. H. Huxley, who carried out some uncritical experiments, in which he attempted to infect the corpses of houseflies by rubbing them on pieces of infected salmon skin, and from his results drew some entirely erroneous conclusions.[163, 164]

The Inspectors had a difficult job and they did it well. They attempted to give advice to the various Boards, although unfortunately, as one chairman of a Board said, everyone through ignorance thought that what was best for himself was best for the river.[165] T. H. Huxley was probably less successful than Buckland because, although he was an eminent biologist, he neither had the approach of the field naturalist to the problem, nor did he obtain the confidence of the local Boards.

Mr J. W. Willis Bund summed the matter up when he wrote in 1885:

> Since Mr Buckland died it seems to be no one's business to collect the various facts relating to Salmon that are reported from time to time. He used to consider no fact to be too small to be noted, and he certainly compiled more information than anyone has done, before or since, as to the habits of fish. . . . Unfortunately his facts are not so useful as they should be, for he noted down everything he was told, whether true or false, and from each of the facts so noted he constructed a theory as to Salmon preservation.[165]

Buckland was a pioneer. It is possible to criticize much that he did and said, but, for all that, to those around him and to those who followed him he set an example of dedicated and selfless service to the public cause.

CHAPTER THIRTEEN

The Sea Fisheries

THE SEA FISHERIES of Britain, especially of England, grew rapidly after 1815 in response to the insatiable demand for cheap food. In no section of the sea fishing industry was this growth more apparent that in trawling, and it is interesting to know why this was so.

Before the development of railways, most fishing communities in Britain were geographically isolated and it was virtually impossible to take fresh fish to the inland consumer except at great cost. In consequence, sea fish were preserved by drying, salting or smoking them and were thus converted to products which, if stored properly, would remain edible for long periods. These traditional products are nowadays generally regarded with disfavour in Britain, where people are no longer accustomed to foods with strong 'cured' flavours, but in former times salt fish and dried fish (stockfish) were essential elements in the national diets.

Not all species of fish will make satisfactory dried, salted or smoked products, and the precise method of manufacture depends upon the species of fish. Dried herring, for example, is unacceptably rancid; if herring is to be preserved in salt, it must be salted in airtight barrels. The preferred species for making dried or dried and salted products are cod and ling, and a few of their near relatives, all of which can be caught on the sea floor. Very many bottom or demersal species, however, cannot be preserved in this way at all. In consequence, highly selective methods of fishing, which catch only those species required for curing, are employed in traditional fisheries.

As methods of transport improved during the nineteenth century, more and more fish was carried 'fresh' from the ports to the growing industrial centres, and it was therefore found possible to sell many species which previously were virtually unused because they could not be cured. Trawling, which is an unselective method of demersal fishing, now began to increase to meet the demand for more fish and more variety. The trawlers caught large quantities of fish in the virgin and largely unexplored North Sea and they landed their catches at any port where they could command a good price. Generally they could undersell their competitors, the established traditional fishermen, and there were inevitable bloody clashes between them.[166]

Successive governments seem to have ignored these developments until about 1860, when charges by traditional fishing interests, that trawling was destroying the sea fisheries, became so vociferous that they had to be investigated. A Royal Commission was set up in 1863 and reported in 1865. It is probably the best known of all the enquiries and commissions that have ever been held into the British fishing industry; its members were James Caird, M.P., G. Shaw Lefevre and Professor Thomas Henry Huxley. Their Report is an invaluable source of information on the state of the sea fisheries at that time. In particular the evidence, which consists of over 50,000 questions and their answers taken from witnesses all round the coasts of the United Kingdom, shows how trawling had developed during the previous fifty years. One witness from Hull, for example, said: '. . . in former years, when we first went out trawling, such fish as haddock and plaice were very little thought of. When I first went out we used to get a quantity of live plaice, and the skipper said, 'Boys, heave them overboard.' I was astonished, but the fact was there was not any market for them. Now, however, everything is sent to market but the very small fish.'[115]

Almost everywhere they went the Commissioners heard of the decline of the traditional fisheries and the increase of trawling. They decided that there was no reason to recommend legislative interference, for the fishing industry appeared to be evolving in response to its changing environment and all the available evidence seemed to point to increased catches. The Commissioners did comment, however, on the lack of precise information about the industry. 'We think it a matter of great importance', they said, 'that fishery statistics should be systematically collected. It is only by such means that the constant recurrence of the panics to which the sea-fishing industry has hitherto been subjected can be prevented, and that any trustworthy conclusions can be arrived at regarding the effect of the modes of fishing which are in use.'[115]

This summary briefly describes the state of the sea fisheries at the time that Buckland was appointed to the Home Office as Inspector of Salmon Fisheries for England and Wales. He had no English counterpart who dealt with the sea fisheries with which, indeed, no official department was greatly concerned; in Scotland, however, the Board of British White Herring Fishery was responsible for the administration not only of the herring fishery but for much else besides including improvement of ports and harbours. The Board of Trade had a general responsibility for ports and harbours of England and Wales and for various details such as the conditions of employment of crews and the enforcement of regulations relating to navigation and other lights on vessels, but fishing vessels tended to be ignored, possibly because there were so many of them, they were so small and each therefore of relatively little value, and many of them regularly landed in one of a number of different ports. Nevertheless, as time went on, it became clear that the sea fisheries, like the river fisheries, presented numerous biological problems which required solution and perhaps legislative action, and since the officials at the Board of Trade included no experts in this field, it was only natural that they should consult their colleagues in the Salmon Fisheries Office.

Although Buckland was never a man to shirk giving an opinion, it was often clear that only an on-the-spot investigation could produce any useful information. It is for this reason, therefore, that Buckland was appointed, either alone or with colleagues, to enquire into various aspects of the sea fisheries. He was in any event interested in marine life and had been collecting marine animals for his museum since it started. His travels as a Commissioner enabled him to extend this interest, to become acquainted with those concerned in the industry at the ports, and to make a contribution to the development of government fishery investigations and policy which has nowadays largely been forgotten.

He was appointed to four Commissions concerned with various aspects of the sea fisheries. These were the Fisheries of Norfolk (1875), Crab and Lobster Fisheries (1877), Herring Fisheries of Scotland (1878) and Sea Fisheries of England and Wales (1879). The first, the enquiry into the state of the sea-coast fisheries of Norfolk, he undertook alone. He held enquiries at various towns on the coast, and also at Norwich, Ludham and Horning Ferry. He learnt that trout were caught in considerable numbers in the sea off Yarmouth and that smelts were taken in some of the Broads. He therefore extended his enquiries to the river fisheries of Norfolk and Suffolk because, he said, 'I considered it essential to discover how far these fish do actually ascend, or might be enabled to ascend, the rivers. . . .' He was encouraged by his friend Dr R. R. B. Norman, a resident of Yarmouth and frequent contributor to *Land and Water*, who often sent specimens to Albany Street. Norman wrote, on behalf of the Yare Angling Association, asking that Buckland should inspect the more important broads and rivers of the county, and including Waveney and Oulton Broad in Suffolk. It was widely felt by gentlemen in the area that the fisheries suffered from excessive netting by a few people. The netted fish were apparently sent to inland towns and sold for 1*s* a stone or used for manure. Buckland investigated the stories that the river fisheries were declining and reported, with evident gusto, that 'one old man, John Green, shoemaker, nearly 90 years old, who gave evidence at Ludham, informed me, "formerly he could go out with his 'pole and tow' (rod and line), and catch a rare mess of good fish in a couple of hours, and now there are hardly any left".' He concluded from this part of the enquiry that '. . . the fresh-water fisheries of Norfolk and Suffolk should be scientifically cultivated. The willingness to take this matter in hand is widely spread amongst all classes of society dwelling in the neighbourhood of the above-named rivers and Broads.' He had probably met many of the influential people in the area already, and during this enquiry he doubtless met many more of them. In his Report he made various recommendations for legislation for the better control of the river fisheries and the Norfolk and Suffolk Fisheries Act of 1877 was largely the result, an Act that Buckland said '. . . has caused the greatest satisfaction, not only to the inhabitants of Norfolk and Suffolk, but also to the angling communities of most of our great manufacturing towns in the London and the Midland districts of England'.[167]

For the Norfolk sea fisheries he recommended various close times and minimum sizes for certain fish and crustacea. Most of these recommendations were embodied in an Act in 1875. The Appendix to his Report contained various miscellaneous pieces of curious information of which the following is an amusing, but not typical, example. After quoting the composition of lobster meat from a treatise on food and dietetics, he goes on to say: 'I am informed by Mr C. C. Fuller, surgeon, 33, Albany Street, Regent's Park, that there is no substance which conveys phosphorus so readily into the human system, and which the system so readily and quickly assimilates, as the flesh of oysters, crabs, and lobsters. For this reason, oysters, crabs, and lobsters should form the diet of those engaged in business or literary pursuits, where much wear and tear of the nerve powers takes place from day to day; care must, of course, be taken that the organs of digestion are not disturbed by too large a quantity of this kind of diet.' It would be difficult to substantiate this theory, and even more difficult to support the 'evidence' adduced by Buckland in 1877 for the presence of phosphorus in lobsters. 'That phosphorus exists in large quantities in lobsters may easily be proved. A Lobster in hot weather, when it ceases to be fresh, assumes a highly phosphorescent appearance when seen in the dark, equal, if not superior to that of a glow-worm or luminous centipede . . . and this phosphorescent appearance is probably caused by the chemical changes in the organic tissues, when life is no longer present to resist the ordained agency of decay and decomposition; in fact, it is slow combustion by combination with oxygen.'[168] The phosphorescence occasionally displayed by stale fish and shell fish is caused by one of a group of luminous micro-organisms; they are quite harmless to man and, of course, their luminous property is quite unconnected with the presence of phosphorus in the tissues.

This Report of 1875 should be looked upon as a first essay, an attempt to bring together from many sources all the relevant information then available. The law affecting the sea fisheries has been changed considerably since Buckland's day, and little would be gained by examining the legislation passed as a result of his advice. The essential point to recognize is that Buckland was attempting to confront legislators with the biological details which must be taken into account in framing laws aimed at conserving the fisheries. His facts were not always correct and he relied too much on hearsay, but he was pioneering in a difficult branch of biology at a time when academic biologists were mainly interested in descriptive morphology and taxonomy. The information he tried to obtain was on the life histories of fish, where and when they spawned, their size ranges and where new fishing grounds could be opened up. Although works of reference were available, such as those by William Yarrell or Jonathan Couch, these either did not give the required information, or they did not cover the precise point which required answering. In any event, it was most unlikely that any legislator would consult such works. It was through the Blue Books, therefore, that Parliament and those responsible for drafting laws began to learn of the importance of the sea fisheries and to hear Buckland's warning voice: 'Vast as are the resources of the sea, yet it is possible that modern appliances and want of scientific cultivation for fishing may draw too much upon the general stock in certain localities.'[167]

Buckland, with his colleague Spencer Walpole, was next commissioned to investigate the crab and lobster fisheries of Scotland, England and Wales. In Scotland, they were joined by Archbibald Young, an advocate who was Commissioner of Scotch Salmon Fisheries. The Irish crab and lobster fisheries were examined at the same time by the Irish Fishery Inspectors. The three Reports, published together in 1877, are filled with material still of interest to the biologist and the historian of the fisheries.[168]

Buckland and Walpole, in commenting on the English and Welsh crab and lobster fisheries, point out the serious lack of adequate background knowledge: 'It would materially have facilitated our labours if we had any reliable data to show at what periods crabs and lobsters cast their shells.' In most areas the story was of increased exploitation; on the Yorkshire coast, for example, 'The railway has created an enormous trade in small crabs which are taken to the great manufacturing towns of Yorkshire, Lancashire, and the midland counties.' The evidence presented to them was conflicting, however, and they concluded that while there had been a marked decrease in the yield of crabs in small fisheries or in confined areas, in large and exposed fisheries there had been no decrease whatsoever. Although for lobsters a minimum size, a close season, and a prohibition on the sale of berried specimens (that is, those carrying eggs) had been suggested to them, they did not see the necessity for any control. There was a large import of Norwegian lobsters and it would therefore be difficult to enforce a minimum size, a close season already existed in effect in many areas because of weather or the existence of other seasonal fisheries, and if the landing of berried lobsters were to be prohibited they believed that the fishermen would merely scrub off the berries (eggs), and so a valuable culinary item would be lost.[168] Such an approach to the problems was a sensible one, for laws which cannot be enforced are worse than useless and, in fisheries as in other forms of human activity, no law should ever be passed unless there is a clear need for it.

It was no doubt Buckland who added to this Report one of those touches of humanity which made him beloved by his friends but which are slightly startling to find in the desiccated contents of a Blue Book.

> The fishermen of Hall Sands keep four or five Newfoundland dogs for the purpose of carrying lines from the shore to the boats in rough weather. The surf is so heavy in certain winds, that the only possible way of landing is for the boat to be drawn through the surf by the friends of the fishermen on the shore, by means of the lines which the dogs take out to them. The fishermen think it a very great hardship that these dogs should be taxed. We promised to draw the attention of Her Majesty's Government to this matter, and we have accordingly noticed it here.[168]

In 1877 Buckland, Walpole and Young were employed as Commissioners to investigate the herring fisheries of Scotland, which were reported to be in an unsatisfactory state. Their Report, presented in 1878, contains much that is new. The increasing size of the herring fishery is noted and no restrictions are advised, except to continue an existing prohibition on the use of movable nets fishing for herring in Scotland on the Sabbath. The Commissioners felt that the heavy penalty attached to breaking the law, forfeiture of the nets which might be worth £200 and so cause ruin of a fisherman, was unduly severe. They also recommended prohibition of beam trawling in certain areas.

Their belief that overfishing for herring was unlikely is worth recording. After giving various calculations of the numbers probably destroyed in other ways, they commented: 'The destructive power of man, therefore, is insignificant when it is compared with the destructive agencies which nature has created; and nothing that man has hitherto done, or which man, so far as we can see, is likely to do, has produced, or will probably produce, any appreciable effect on the number of herrings in the open sea.'[169] This view was repeated shortly afterwards by T. H. Huxley and would probably have been accepted by most marine biologists as a reasonable one until fairly recently; it is only since the last war that man has demonstrated his ability to match the destructive powers of nature by trawling on a massive scale for herring.

In this Report Buckland again attempted to accumulate information which might be useful to the legislator and those in the industry itself. In two appendices he gave 'Notes on the natural history of the herring' and 'The garvie fisheries of Scotland' which contained much original information and observation, quotations from many sources and evidence from witnesses. 'Garvie' is Scottish for a sprat. It is instructive to compare T. H. Huxley's lecture on 'The Herring', given at Norwich in 1881,[170] with Buckland's Notes. Huxley's lecture was witty and erudite, and largely concerned with the anatomy of the herring, whereas Buckland's Notes range from consideration of unfished herring grounds, the method employed for salting and chemical analysis of the fish to spawning grounds, development and the effects of temperature and weather. Buckland attempted too much, perhaps, but he possessed an intuitive sense of the type of information which legislators and the fishing industry itself required for the future efficient development of this natural resource.

Buckland's final commission in connexion with the sea fisheries was that issued in 1878, when he and Walpole were appointed to report on the sea fisheries of England and Wales.

Their Report was published in September, 1879, and resulted from a great many toilsome sittings at towns and villages all round the coast.[171] In an appendix, Buckland gave a brief account of the natural history of the species mentioned in the Report. In another appendix he gave '. . . certain special points connected with the economy of the sea fisheries of England and Wales'. These are comments under eleven separate headings covering, for example, the food of sea-fish, their migrations, their spawning, pollution in estuaries and the effects of trawling on other fish. He stated that the notes were by no means complete and were '. . . offered as mere outlines of investigation, in the hope that the consideration of them may induce gentlemen, fishermen, and others, who have the opportunity of doing so, to continue these observations, and to afford me further details on these important points'.

Buckland and Walpole again drew attention to the absence of reliable statistics of the fisheries and their view is worth quoting at some length:

> During the course of our inquiry we have again and again been struck with the enormous difficulty of obtaining any reliable statistical facts relating to our sea fisheries. . . . The value of the fisheries in this country may be computed in millions; the capital invested in them in millions; the persons dependent on them in hundreds of thousands; and yet there is no really accurate statistical information upon the subject, and there are no means whatever of comparing by figures their yield now with their yield in former years.
>
> Such a state of things seems to us unfortunate. It seems especially deplorable, since it occurs in an age which prides itself on its statistical knowledge, and in which statistics on matters of far less importance than the prosperity of our sea fisheries are diligently collected.

They went on to suggest that the Inspectors of Salmon Fisheries should be made responsible for the collection of the statistics of the sea fisheries and they believed that it would be possible to obtain, within a few years, '. . . a really accurate and comprehensive account of the fisheries of the Kingdom'.

The Report repeats the arguments about the impossibility of overfishing for herring but extends it to cover all species of fish. It is unfortunate that the arguments are put forward in such a pseudo-scientific manner, for some of the premises are highly questionable, yet the prestige of Buckland and Walpole was such that their views were quoted as providing the last word on the subject for the next twenty years, by which time there was no doubt but that they were wrong. One wonders whether Buckland, who by 1879 was a sick man, and whose arithmetic was generally inadequate, understood the full implications of what was being said under his name, for one can be tolerably sure that he himself did not write the passages in question. As early as 1869, he had commented at a British Association meeting that care must be taken to preserve the deep-sea fisheries. The old proverb that there was as good fish in the sea as ever came out of it might have been true twenty years earlier, he had said, but it was no longer true then.

As a result of his work on Royal Commissions, and his appearance before various Parliamentary Committees, he became known to a wide and varied circle of people who sent him specimens of unusual marine organisms not only from all over Britain but from abroad as well. These specimens would often arrive unexpectedly at Albany Street and might remain outside until they announced their own presence. The columns of *Land and Water* were full of descriptions of these trophies. On occasions Mrs Buckland appears to have refused to accommodate excessively odoriferous specimens and to have directed them instead to South Kensington. Buckland once mentioned a specimen, an angler fish, which had been expelled from the house. 'The last I saw of the hamper was that it was standing *outside* the Parcels Delivery Office, not in the shop, and that a dog was sniffing inquiringly through the cracks in the hamper, and there were several blue-bottles flying about over the vicinity.'[172]

His descriptions of fish can scarcely be described as scientific, but they were not, after all, written for scientists and they do hold the interest of the reader. One example from a rich assortment must suffice. A Hull fisherman, Thomas Sparks, in February, 1868, was caught in a gale and blown towards the Norwegian coast. He must have fished there, for he returned to port with some specimens of the curious fish known popularly as Rabbit fish, or King of the Herrings (*Chimaera monstrosa*). A fish salesman obtained them and sent them to Buckland who described them as follows:

> The chimaera can certainly not be classed among the 'Court beauties', but should rather sit for a model to artists who desire to represent nightmares and other demons of darkness. Its general conformation is not unlike that of an elongated carrot with wings.

He went on to describe the external appearance of the animal, whose

> . . . eyes are directed well forward, and, together with the hideous nose, form a figure-head worthy the imagination of the most barbarous Chinaman that ever designed a figure-head for a piratical war junk.

Finally he discussed its habits:

> Mr Couch describes its habits as nocturnal; he is doubtless right, for such a hideous fish can hardly dare to show itself in the day. The other fish who live near his domain have, I trust, strong nerves, for a full-grown chimaera coming round the corner, on a dark night, would be enough to frighten any ordinary fish – such as old Mother Sole, with her dusky dress and demure appearance – into a fit of hysterics.[173]

Before condemning too severely popular writing at this level, it is charitable to remember that the author was writing for an unscientific audience, whose interests were largely centred in the land. He was acting as their guide in a foreign country and he had not time to teach them the language or to point out all the architectural details of each building as they passed it. The most he could do was to try to maintain their interest in all he could show them, and he would often introduce some minor and irrelevant details in what he had to say. It probably entertained his readers to know, for example, that the account they read of a squid found at Herne Bay had been written in the animal's own ink.[174] When this has been said, however, it must be admitted that other authors of the period, notably Philip Henry Gosse, wrote extremely well in a popular vein on marine topics, yet did not find it necessary to sink to the level of triviality which Buckland adopted on numerous occasions.

In 1872 Buckland was invited by the S.P.C.K. to revise one of their books on fishes. He virtually rewrote it and it was published in 1873 under the title of *Familiar History of British Fishes*. The description of each species, which is generally very brief, is illustrated by an engraving and there is much anecdotal material mostly taken from the columns of *Land and Water*. A further edition of this work, completely revised by Buckland as he lay dying, was published posthumously in 1881 under the title *The Natural History of British Fishes*.[175] *The Field*, in a tart review of this second edition, commented that there was no apparent scientific or definite arrangement; it began with Anchovy, Angler and Atherine and passed on in a very irregular alphabetic order, the Bonito and Pelamid appearing between T and W – perhaps an unfair criticism, since the obvious place for these two species is by the side of the Tunny. Unflattering comparisons were made between Buckland's book and the first volume of Francis Day's classic work on the *Fishes of Great Britain and Ireland*, reviewed at the same time. This was unjust, for Day's work was written for specialists and was very much larger. It was also illustrated with numerous full page engravings. No mention was made in the review of the difference in price between the two which, however, must have been considerable.[176]

Nevertheless, *The Natural History of British Fishes* does not show Buckland at his best. As the author of a review in *Nature* commented: '. . . Mr Buckland was nothing if not sketchy and rapid; he would not be tied down to severe statements, but preferred to give an off-hand opinion in a dashing way, no matter that he might find out within a year that what he had advanced was very far wrong. In the present volume, as a glance at the plethoric title-page will show, Mr Buckland attempted too much, with the result that portions of the information conveyed are scrappy, whilst some of it is probably slightly imaginative: books and articles written in railway trains often enough provide hard work for the reader.' The review continues: 'Twenty-five pages of the work are devoted to the salmon (*Salmo salar*), and the essay, confused as it is, is well worthy of perusal, although it contains, as do other portions of the book, a good deal about Mr Buckland, and recapitulates, as usual from *Land and Water*, an account of some of the big fish in "my museum".'[177]

Buckland much enjoyed travelling, particularly in Scotland where he made many friends, and he liked to share his experiences with his readers. He was impressed in Scotland with the desire for education and remarked how, wherever he went, he saw children making their way to and from school. 'Few of the children in the smaller towns and villages wear shoes and stockings. An excellent custom; it saves expense, and makes them healthy.'[178] During his work in 1877 on the Herring Commission, it became necessary to examine the fisheries of Orkney and Shetland and the Admiralty hence provided H.M. gunboat *Jackal* for the Commissioners' use. Buckland described his travels in this vessel, a paddle steamer of 340 tons, built in 1845 and with a complement of sixty officers and men. Archibald Young, his fellow Commissioner, described everything they saw in minute detail, and knew the names of all the landed proprietors and the particulars of every salmon river.

> I cannot pretend to recollect one quarter of what Young told us, but my general impression of these properties is that no one in Scotland has less than £20,000 a year, and that the proper thing to do when a person has made a fortune is to find out a desolate, barren island where Robinson Crusoe himself would be uncomfortable, or a lonely moor where there is nothing but barren rocks and heather, and where, as Col — informed me, the distance from civilization is so great 'that he was obliged to give his chimney-sweep a bed.'

He later commented that he thought he had discovered the reason why people wanted to move to these desolate areas when they had made their fortunes.

> In his original state, man depends for his existence on hunting, and hunts wild beasts and birds, in order to obtain his necessary food and clothes. When he has obtained all the food he can possibly want, and every luxury he can possibly get, then what does he do? Why he immediately goes back to his primitive state, and begins to hunt again. So you see the savage is not instinctively very far removed from the Scotch or English rich proprietors and lessees of grouse-moors and deer-forests.[74]

Buckland watched fishwives arriving in Edinburgh on the train from Newhaven.

> They were all dressed in blue serviceable serge, some were young, some old. They all had their creels or baskets of fish with them. I observed that it required two, and sometimes three railway porters to lift the heavy creels on to the women's backs. . . . The distance these women will walk, and the weight they will carry, is astounding. I was told by an old fish-wife who, living in Dunbar, every morning sets out on a journey of from six to nine miles round the country to sell her fish, that she sometimes carries as much as one hundred-weight on her back. So accustomed is this fine old lady to carry weights on her back, that when having sold her fish, she is returning homewards, she picks up heavy stones from the road-side, and puts them into her creel, finding I suppose that a weighted creel is easier to carry than an empty creel.[179]

Archibald Young and Buckland first became colleagues in 1870 when they were both appointed to inquire into the effect of recent legislation on the salmon fisheries. Young described him as about the most true and genuine man he ever met, without any affectation and always saying what he thought simply and naturally. He was equally at home in the polished society of a luxurious country house or talking to fishermen on the beach. He was at that time in his prime, broad shouldered and powerfully built but somewhat under middle height, with a clever, pleasant face in which the most noticeable features were the large, dark, expressive eyes.[180] Nevertheless, Young does not mention some of Buckland's peculiarities which must occasionally have caused his colleagues both amusement and embarrassment. Buckland once left a parcel of stinking fish, which he had carried about with him and forgotten, neatly wrapped in paper in a fashionable street in Scotland, and stood at the hotel window to watch the face of the first person to examine it. Another time, he spent a Sunday evening preparing herring roe from tapioca pudding and whisky in order to puzzle witnesses at the enquiry the following day.

His luggage usually began to become offensive as enquiries proceeded, for he would fling into his bag specimens of every kind, living, dying and dead. Spencer Walpole also mentions other eccentricities.

> He had almost persuaded himself that inanimate things could be spiteful; and he used to say that he would write a book on their spitefulness. If a railway lamp did not burn properly, he would declare it was sulky, and throw it out of [the] window to see if it could find a better master. He punished his portmanteau on one occasion by knocking it down, and the portmanteau naturally revenged itself by breaking all the bottles of specimens which it contained, and emptying their contents on its master's shirts. To provide himself against possible disasters, he used to carry with him an armoury of implements. On the herring inquiry he went to Scotland with six boxes of cigars, four dozen pencils, five knives, and three thermometers. On his return, three weeks afterwards, he produced one solitary pencil, the remnant of all his property. The knives were lost, the cigars were smoked; one thermometer had lost its temper, and been thrown out of [the] window; another had been drowned in the Pentland Firth, and a third had beaten out its own brains against the bottom of a gun-boat. No human being could have told the fate of the pencils.[26]

His expert opinion was sought by many people, and he was sometimes called as a witness in insurance cases. The most celebrated of these was in December, 1868. The case was a curious one, and was heard before Lord Chief Justice Bovill in the Court of Common Pleas. The plaintiffs had insured their vessel, the *Dreadnought,* with the defendants. The ship had sailed from Colombo in 1864 with a cargo of coffee and when three days out someone had hooked a swordfish which broke the line, but a moment afterwards it leapt out of the water. The following day a leak was reported to the Captain and it was necessary to return to Colombo and thence to Cochin. An almost circular hole about 1″ across was found in the copper sheathing and the planking, but not the lining, and it was suggested that this had been caused by the swordfish. The defendants claimed that the plaintiffs had not shown that the damage was 'caused by contact with some substance other than water'. If the report of the case in *Land and Water* is to be believed, Buckland's evidence caused considerable hilarity in the court.

Professor Owen was also called as a witness. Owen's evidence rather pointed towards the swordfish but he apologised that he could not produce in court specimens from the British Museum to show examples of what a swordfish could do; this being against the Museum regulations. This statement called forth a curt comment from Sir William Bovill that if this was true, the regulations should be changed. Shortly after the case was over, Dr J. E. Gray wrote to *Land and Water* to point out that Owen was wrong, that specimens could be taken from the Museum into Court, and the rules were exactly what Sir William Bovill said they ought to be. This was a stinging rebuke from, nominally at any rate, one of Owen's own staff. Gray added, 'Under all the circumstances I do not believe that a circular hole in a plank about an inch in diameter could have been made by the beak of a swordfish; and it is much more likely to have been the hole made by an auger, which ought to have been filled up with a wooden trenail.'[181]

Buckland's opinion was also sometimes asked about the soundness of particular batches of fish. In 1879 he was called in to examine some of the first commercial consignments of frozen salmon to be imported into Britain. These came from Canada and were brought to Billingsgate. In *Land and Water* it was remarked, '. . . experiments have proved that when properly thawed and cooked they are excellent for the table', although an earlier consignment was condemned.[182] He also carried out experiments into the effectiveness of a new method of preserving fish in fresh condition. In 1875 he was introduced to a Frenchman named Gorges who was reputed to have patented a process for preserving fish in fresh condition by immersing it in a solution prepared from a crystalline powder and a syrupy fluid. Dr Saunders, food analyst for the City of London, had given a certificate to the effect that 'the materials employed in the preparation of the solution are perfectly harmless to human health, and can by no possibility affect the wholesomeness of the fish.' It is most probable that the crystalline powder was boric acid and the syrupy fluid glycerine; boroglyceride, as it was called, was a common preservative for fish in the 1880s. Boric acid is not nowadays a permitted additive to food in Britain. Buckland carried out experiments on this preservative solution in his basement at

Albany Street. He treated a number of different species of sea fish and assembled together a group of his friends who partook of samples and commented on them. From the remarks made by the various members of this taste panel, the results appear to have been very satisfactory, but unfortunately no account is given of the experimental details, not even the length of time for which the samples were kept, and the elementary precaution of keeping at the same time some untreated fish as controls was apparently not taken.[183] Nevertheless, although this report shows Buckland was an inadequate experimentalist, it shows him also as a man with vision, who could see some of the advantages of extending the storage life of fish. Like many others who attempt to introduce to industry what they regard as improvements on existing techniques, Buckland suffered tribulation and disappointment. In spite of its apparent success, the Fish Preserving Fluid was not taken up because '. . . of the opposition of the ice merchants and other difficulties'.[184]

The interest in oysters which Buckland had shown in the early 1860s was continued up to his death, although he resigned his Directorship in the Herne Bay Oyster Company late in 1868 or early in 1869. The precise reasons for his resignation are now obscure, but it was probably due immediately to a disagreement with his co-directors.

He carried on experiments on oysters at his own expense. 'For the last six years Oysters have beaten me', he wrote to Professor Owen on June 28, 1867.

> I am so anxious this should no longer be the case that with 3 friends I have hired an old ditch near Reculvers between Herne Bay and Margate. We have spent £100 upon the experiment which is to give the oysters three requisites:
>
> 1 Plenty of water
> 2 Calm water
> 3 Warm i.e. (about 70) water
>
> The Oysters are now about spawning and in a month's time we shall know if it be a success or not. If so I will let you know and ask you to come down to inspect.
>
> Already I have had one success. We have hatched many *thousand young lobsters* most interesting little things. This

success may be the first thing in a great commercial industry.[61]

Only a week or two before his death he was writing articles for *Land and Water* on the varieties and species of oyster which were of commercial importance, and was asking a correspondent in Scotland for specimens. 'Please do not have the shells washed. Just simply pack them in box with sea weed', he wrote.[155]

His contributions to the development of marine biological science are difficult to assess, for he was a popularizer rather than an innovator, and many of the ideas he put forward had already been expressed by others. His objectives were, however, considerably more utilitarian than those of most of his contemporaries: 'I do not mean to let slip any opportunity of increasing the supply of "Food for the people" ', he wrote to Professor Owen after completing his report on the Norfolk fisheries,[61] and in a number of respects he foreshadowed the attitudes of the twentieth century. This aspect of his life deserves closer attention.

In other respects, however, he was a true child of the first half of the nineteenth century. This is well shown by his determined refusal to accept, or even to understand, Darwin's evolutionary theory and his encyclopaedic interest in the peculiar variations of the human form.

CHAPTER FOURTEEN

Mountebanks, Monsters and Monkeys

BUCKLAND COULD NEVER RESIST a sideshow. A bill-board labelled 'The Talking Fish' or 'The Three-legged Horse' would immediately send him all agog elbowing his way to the front of the crowd, eager to examine the latest wonder the showman had to offer and to cross-question him about it. Since he wrote amusing and interesting accounts of what he saw, promoters of any unusual or important shows often invited him to a special session, because of the publicity his articles provided for them. He became so accustomed to seeing some exhibits on his travels that he was occasionally able to regale his readers with a recent history of some object which had been displayed elsewhere perhaps under a different name.

While Buckland was holding an inquiry in Lowestoft in 1878, for example, he took time off to visit Yarmouth fair, and subsequently described a number of the shows he saw there, including a 'Petrified Mummy'. He wrote: 'This was an old friend that Mr H. Lee and I are continually coming across viz. the "Abogine". The history of the "Abogine" is as follows: He is a dried Australian native, thrown in as a bargain with some shells, spears, etc, in a lot, and bought by a dealer.'

The dealer sold the shells but could not find a buyer for the dried Australian and began to tire of his bargain. At last he called him an 'Abogine' and exchanged him for some monkeys with a penny showman. Buckland added: 'The "Abogine" does not get on; showmen can't make money out of him. . . . "Abogine", of course, means aboriginal native, only the word has got a little twisted.'[185]

Buckland so clearly enjoyed living, in observing his fellow men and learning how they lived. There was nothing he liked better than to talk to the poor showmen who drove a precarious living at fairs or in the streets of the metropolis, and many were those who must have blessed his ready contribution to their catch-pennies. Part of his charm was that nobody was ever too lowly for him to notice, whether they were acrobats, fat women or proprietors of flea circuses.

When Buckland visited Mr Kitchingman, the owner of a flea circus, at home, he reported: 'Mr K. keeps his stock of untrained fleas in a stoppered bottle in flannel wool; cotton wool will not do; he has sometimes two or three hundred fleas on hand, and he very seldom indeed lets one escape.' Shortly afterwards, Mr K. himself wrote to *Land and Water*: 'Will you allow me to add to Mr Buckland's interesting article on my performing fleas that in warm weather I breed fleas from the egg, the larvae feeding on the scurfy excrescence of the human skin. I find these home-bred insects much more tractable. . . .'[186]

In 1877 Buckland reported on the Human Cannon Ball, Zazel. This young lady was shot twice nightly from a cannon, or more correctly a mortar, at the Westminster Aquarium, having first performed a high wire and trapeze act followed by a head-long dive into the safety net below, Zazel achieved considerable fame in Victorian London, and deserved it, for the risks attendant upon becoming a human projectile propelled by gunpowder and guncotton are not small. Buckland always greatly admired examples of human skill, and described many famous acts, such as that of Olmar, who walked upside down above the crowds by placing his feet in rings fixed on the underside of horizontal ladders; of Natator, who carried out numerous remarkable subaqueous feats in a giant fish-tank; and of Blondin, whose daring trapeze and tight-rope act became a legend in his own time.

The sword-swallower Benedetti particularly impressed Buckland. Benedetti began his act by swallowing a single sword, to be followed by seven or eight more, side by side. After withdrawing these and resting briefly, he then attached a bayonet to a musket and swallowed the blade of the bayonet completely, finally gripping its handle between his teeth, bending his body and spinning round so that the musket swung round horizontally. This particular trick was nearly attended by a serious accident shortly after Buckland saw it, for one night the bayonet snapped, leaving over 12 inches of blade in the oesophagus, and it was only Benedetti's great presence of mind in immediately standing on his head that enabled the broken piece to be withdrawn. Benedetti also swallowed such an exceptionally long sword that the point apparently came to rest in the lower abdomen; a number of medical men, including Buckland, were invited by Benedetti to examine him. It was concluded that the point of the sword pushed downwards part of the stomach to a considerable distance.[187]

Every year, if he could manage it, Buckland would go round the exhibitions outside the Cattle Show at Islington, generally in company with A. D. Bartlett or Henry Lee. He particularly liked this show, because it formed a nucleus for very many of the penny and twopenny natural history exhibits of animal and human freaks. Here, side by side, might be seen a sheep with two additional legs growing out of its shoulder and a monstrous pig. The comments of the bystanders added to the fun. 'My eye, Jim,' said one costermonger lad, looking at the pig, 'What prime 'ams he would make. Why, he must be a misery to hisself.'[48] The claims of the showmen were another source of amusement. As Buckland remarked, in characteristic good-humoured manner, 'It is a curious fact (if we believe the showman) that the "crown-ed 'edds of Europe" have nothing else to do but spend their time gazing in admiration at giants, fat women, and at other monstrosities and freaks of nature, living and dead.'

Buckland himself, of course, possessed a remarkable collection of strange objects and it would be of interest to know what became of some of these after his death. There was, for example, the piece of mammoth skin which he inherited from his father. He likewise possessed some hairs from the head of Henry IV which had been obtained by his father, who was present when the King's tomb in Canterbury Cathedral was opened.[188] There were many other items as well, including a fine set of human skulls consisting of Kafir skulls, some skulls dredged from the Thames, two Maori skulls and a Russian skull. The story of this Crimean relic was told by Buckland; the wife of its owner, a sergeant of the Royal Horse Artillery stationed at Aldershot, had complained about this macabre object and her husband had buried it, intending perhaps later to retrieve it. It was, however, unearthed by chance and gave rise to various speculations, one being that it was the remains of a victim of a highwayman, the only difficulty in this theory being that nobody could find the remainder of the corpse![48] Buckland presented his collection of skulls to the Museum of the Royal College of Surgeons shortly before his death. The walls of his house were adorned with heads of curious hybrids and the horns of extinct animals. No doubt it contained other pieces of bric-à-brac, perhaps relics of the pet pony ridden by Buckland and his brother and sister as children. 'People who wish to have relics kept of favourite horses', he wrote, 'should have their ears preserved; they make nice holders for spills; the hoofs also make good inkstands; and the tails mounted on a stick are an excellent thing to kill flies.'[22]

Giants seem to have interested him particularly. Perhaps this was because he himself was rather below average height or maybe it was the memory of John Hunter and the Donegal Giant who had been boiled down in the copper. At all events, Joseph Brice, whose friendship with Buckland has already been mentioned, was only one of many tall men whose bodily dimensions were measured and noted down. Buckland's first personal encounter with a giant appears to have been when he was at St George's Hospital. A celebrated Spanish Basque giant, Señor Joachim Eleizegui, was a frequent visitor to the hospital, where his cousin was a patient. As can be imagined, the giant's sudden appearance, striding down the ward between the beds, caused considerable surprise and consternation amongst the patients.[48] Buckland prepared a cast of the Spaniard's hand and gave it to the Museum in Kinnerton Street which, it will be recalled, was eventually moved into the hospital itself as part of the medical school. It was later an annoyance to him that he had not measured the giant's other dimensions while he had the opportunity. One of the printed bills advertising the Spaniard's exhibition has survived, from which it may be learned that he had appeared at various courts in Europe and had been presented with'. . . munificent tokens of approbation . . .' by the King of the French, and the Queens of Spain and Portugal (Plate XIV). Claims of this type were by no means uncommon at the time, as hinted by Buckland himself, and should perhaps be treated with caution, although some may have been true. Joseph Brice, it was claimed on one of his handbills, was 'Measuring upwards of 8 feet 2 inches, 22 years of age and weighs 30 stone. A golden tribute has recently been presented to him by the Emperor of the French to attest the fact.'[3]

Details of the dimensions of the giants who crossed his path seem to have been collected by Buckland in a fairly systematic manner, although with what end in view does not appear. When Chang, a native of Fychow, exhibited himself in the Egyptian Hall, Piccadilly, London, in 1865, Buckland and a friend went prepared to obtain some idea of the Chinaman's height because, he wrote, 'Giants, I know from experience, are very unwilling to have their proper measurement taken by visitors'.

Before he entered the hall, Buckland ascertained the height to which he could raise his hat above his head, whilst his friend had provided himself with a piece of red tape seven feet in length. As Chang passed through the crowded room, lightly carrying a Chinese dwarf in his arms, Buckland held his hat, as near as he could determine, level with the giant's head; his friend meanwhile held up his tape and stood on a chair. The two men afterwards compared notes and agreed that the giant was '. . . about seven feet three or four inches. . . .' They commented that he looked taller because of the thick Chinese clump shoes which he wore.[48]

The famous Siamese Twins, Chang and Eng Bunker, revisited England in 1869 in an attempt to earn money, for they had lost all their property in the American Civil War. Buckland had heard all about them from his father, and hastened to make their acquaintance. Chang and Eng are probably the best known of all double monsters, the literature is full of references to them and, according to the authors of one standard work on such anomalies, 'The amount of material in the Surgeon-General's library at Washington would surprise an investigator'.[189] They were born of Chinese parents in Maklong, a village about sixty miles from Bangkok, in 1811. A British merchant, Robert Hunter, saw them in 1824 rowing a boat while stripped to the waist and persuaded the parents and King Chowpahyi to allow them to go away to be exhibited. The King was superstitious and could only with difficulty be persuaded to spare their lives. The twins were taken out of the country by an American sea captain, who displayed them in the United States and first brought them to England in 1830. They caused a sensation at the time, and Buckland recalled that in the nursery he used to tie two kittens together and call them Siamese Twins.

Chang and Eng were joined by a cartilaginous band from sternum to sternum. The twins married two English sisters, aged 26 and 28. Chang had ten children and Eng twelve but they were compelled to keep their wives in separate houses, living alternately a week in each. They died in their sixty-third year in 1874. Chang was quite intemperate and suffered a paralytic stroke when returning to America in 1870, but both of them showed severe arterial degeneration when their bodies were examined after their death.[189,190,191]

In order to amuse the twins, Buckland sent the curator of his Museum, Neville, to them with some of the Siamese twin salmon which are not infrequently produced by artificial hatching. 'Although I have elsewhere read articles against the exhibition of the "Siamese Twins", I think our friends ought to go and see them,' he wrote, 'and this, not only because the twins are historical, nay even almost proverbial, characters, but because they are in themselves instances of a most rare and abnormal form of human life which it is very improbable we shall ever see or hear of again in this generation.' Chang and Eng became very attached to Buckland and to Henry Lee. They subsequently carried on a correspondence with Lee after their return to America. A faded sepia photograph of the two men and their wives and some of their children is still to be seen in one of Buckland's scrapbooks.[23,190]

The twins were often entertained at the house in Albany Street, on one occasion in 1869 with Miss Anna H. Swann, the Nova Scotia Giantess, who was 7 feet 5½ inches tall. Anna Swann's parents were both Scottish emigrants to Canada, and although they were of normal size, her mother's family contained some very tall people. Another famous giant whom Buckland knew was Captain Martin van Buren Bates, the Kentucky Giant. He was born in 1845 and enlisted in the Southern army in 1861; he was permitted to do so at the early age of 16 on account of his great size, and at the end of the war was 7 feet 2½ inches tall.[189] He met Anna Swann while they were both crossing the Atlantic to London in 1871. Bates, much to Buckland's disapproval, wore a morning dress which failed to show off his height. Buckland said that he should wear the uniform of an American captain or, failing that, something similar to that worn by the Life Guards, Horse Guards or French Cuirassiers. Captain Bates proposed to Miss Swann and they were married at St Martin-in-the-Fields on June 17, 1871. They made further history, for Mrs Bates was subsequently delivered of a healthy child weighing 23¾ pounds and 30 inches long.[189] The clergyman who officiated at the wedding was himself 6 feet 3 inches tall; the bridesmaids were Christine-Millie, the Two-headed Nightingale.[192]

Christine-Millie were twins joined at the sacra by a cartilaginous and possibly bony union. They were born of Negro slave parents in the United States in 1851 and were exhibited in London with Captain Bates and Anna Swann. Buckland described them as living in perfect concord and able, from long habit, to walk about and even dance without any appearance of effort or constraint. They could dance equally well on two legs or four. They both had pleasant voices, one contralto, the other soprano, and would sing duets together. Christine-Millie did not always agree, however, and when they quarrelled they would knock their heads together. Shortly before the wedding of Captain Bates and Anna Swann, 'H.R.H. the Prince of Wales, accompanied by Prince John of Glucksburg and Mr Paget, and attended by Colonel Keppel, and his Imperial Highness the Grand Duke Wladimir of Russia and suite, attended by Colonel Ellis, paid a visit to the exhibition of the Two-headed Nightingale combination and other natural wonders at Willis's Rooms.' This alone indicates that not all the showmen's claims to royal patronage were false.[191,193]

The house in Albany Street must have been a continuing source of interest and amusement to the neighbourhood where its owner must have been a familiar sight. 'It is his especial delight to entertain celebrities on view in the town', wrote Mrs Priestly, wife of one of the Queen's Physicians, in *The World*. 'This *penchant* makes him the idol of all the children and stray waifs in the neighbourhood, who crowd round the door when a party is expected, or clamber up the railings to get a good view of the giant going in or the dwarf coming away.'[113] His appearance at home may well have shocked the more conventional of his visitors, for he rarely wore a jacket but generally went in a pair of trousers and a flannel shirt. He wore socks and boots only when he had to, and at home apparently merely wore flat slippers on his feet (Plate XV). He was a constant smoker of pipe and cigars, although this habit never spoilt his appetite. His guests must sometimes have found his hospitality slightly unnerving, because of the large assortment of strange animals in the house. Some of these were allowed to roam at large, and frequently they put the house into uproar.

'I have received a new addition to the menagerie in the "Monkeys' Room", as the servants call my studio in Albany-street', he wrote in 1877. 'It is a jackass [an Australian bird]. My jackass is now sitting on the pole I use when out on salmon fishery inspections, and he has just eaten three mice which 'Bilzy', the cat, has been kind enough to kill, when they come out at night to steal the seed from the parrot's cage. . . . The jackass does not bray, but he laughs most heartily. I cannot make him laugh when I like . . . but when he does laugh the ringing sound can be heard all over the house, and the other day much frightened a visitor waiting in the room below.' A few weeks later, he wrote that the jackass was now laughing loudly almost every half-hour, and was being fed on dead mice supplied twice a week by the dustman at a penny a head.[194]

Sometimes animals would escape and create havoc in the house. Buckland once returned home to find his own front door locked against him. The page-boy, John, shouted from inside: 'You can't come in, sir; they are loose!' 'What's they?' Buckland asked. 'I don't know what they are, sir, but they are wild animals of some kind,' John replied. His master managed to sidle round the door to find, in the little ante-hall between the two doors, three badgers. 'Who unpacked them, John?' 'The Missis unpacked them, sir; she couldn't pack them up again, so she's gone to bed.'[195] It was never safe to open any box or parcel delivered at the house. When Buckland was sent by post a dead scorpion in a jeweller's box, it was opened by one of the female members of the household under the mistaken impression that it had been sent from the jeweller's, and the specimen caused some temporary alarm. It might well have been alive.

For a number of years Buckland kept a suricate or meercat as a pet, which was permitted to roam at large through the house. As one died, so it was replaced by another, and all were named 'Jemmy'. The suricate is an African mongoose, fawn-coloured, sharp-nosed and not much bigger than a large rat. In nature it is gregarious and lives in burrows, outside which it is often to be seen squatting on its haunches, ready to disappear in a moment if danger threatens. More than once, Buckland found his boot going round the room, apparently propelled by machinery. This was Jemmy, who, having entered the boot presumably under the mistaken impression that it was a burrow, was endeavouring to excavate it further. Jemmy also would have fights with the monkeys, of which there were generally two or three in cages in the 'Monkeys' Room'.

Mrs Buckland appears to have had a way with animals, and would help to nurse sick specimens back to life and health. A. D. Bartlett would sometimes bring sick animals from the Zoo, and the house in Albany Street was for a period an unofficial sanatorium for small mammals from the Society's Gardens. One of the first specimens of the South African Red River Hog to appear in Europe was so small and delicate when it reached the Zoo that Buckland was given charge of it. It was a scrupulously clean animal, but its boisterous romping created problems as it rapidly grew in size; '. . . he developed a tendency to raid the dinner-table and had a passion for crawling beneath chairs and becoming tightly wedged between their legs. When at a supper-party a solemn D.D. found himself steadily travelling backwards from the table and being carried towards the door, it was decided Dick must go, and more spacious accommodation was therefore found for him at Regent's Park.'[196] Buckland was also sometimes called upon to prescribe for animals in the Gardens themselves. Of all his pets, he seems to have been most attracted by his monkeys, even though they did endless damage and one of them, the 'Old Hag', a Guenon monkey, bit him so badly in the hand that he could not write properly for nine months afterwards.

He was always very upset when his pets died, and he wrote a long article about the 'Old Hag' when she died in 1876:

> For some unknown reason she had taken a most intense dislike to Mrs Bayly, Mrs Buckland's sister: if she only heard her voice she would begin to get in a rage, and more than once she has pulled her dress nearly off her back, and often and often I have seen poor Mrs Bayly caught by the hair by the Hag, and hanging on to the cage like the pictures of Absalom suspended from the tree. The Hag, however, was the greatest possible friend with Mrs Buckland. I don't know who likes the Hag best – the Missis or myself. The Missis used frequently to take her out and nurse her of an evening.[197]

Some of his monkeys habitually drank beer. One of them, when she wanted a drink of beer, would cross her hands in a devotional attitude and look in a supplicating manner first at the glass and then at her master. On Sundays, he gave them a glass of port between them. At least one of his monkeys enjoyed eating cockroaches which apparently swarmed in the kitchen and were caught in traps. Sometimes, however, Buckland would hunt cockroaches himself by shooting at them with a syringe loaded with benzine; 'blackbeetle shooting at night in the kitchen will give as much sport as rabbit-shooting in a warren by day'.

A correspondent writing in the *Sunday Times* in 1937 described her memories of a visit in company with her father to the naturalist at home. The purpose of their call was to deliver a monster salmon from the Tay which Buckland was to cast. Her description must be quoted at length for it conjures up a vivid picture of the atmosphere of the house and its owner.

> We went in a hansom cab, with the packing-case containing the monster fish propped in front of us, and arrived at Albany Street. . . The packing-case was carried down to the basement. We were asked upstairs.
>
> Buckland greeted us. He was coatless and bare-armed. In the middle of a long table was a tray with a dissected animal on it. At the end of the table a large bowl of Irish stew. Buckland was running up and down, now taking a cut at the dissection and now gobbling a spoonful of the stew. 'Have some?' he asked, hospitably waving towards the stew.
>
> On each side of the fireplace was tethered a monkey, their

leashes cleverly arranged so that they could not touch the fire, but could just touch each other's finger-tips, and were not near enough to fight.

Buckland seized a stick and poked behind a bookcase and out rushed a hare – a wild one, said Buckland, but he would soon get it tamed. I mentioned my love for white rats, and he at once produced from somewhere a large white rat and put it on my shoulder. He showed us the original pot of curari poison brought by Bates from the Amazon, put it in my hand, and said I was holding enough to poison half London.

I was sorry when we were told that the casting material was ready, and we left these fascinating surroundings to descend to the basement, where the huge salmon was laid on a special table, with a rim around the edge to prevent the plaster from overflowing and a large bucket of liquid plaster at hand. The fish was duly oiled, and Buckland proceeded to paint on the plaster skilfully. Finally, the whole was covered in thickly. The first part of the job was finished. The plaster was left to harden and we went home.

To me it was a red-letter day which I have never forgotten. I hope there are children to-day who read Buckland.[198]

It seems that Buckland would sometimes help people to find pets. 'If you could call here . . . tomorrow Wednesday between 12 and 1.30 I will try to put you in the way of getting a dog,' he wrote to a Miss Meteyard in 1873, 'and will show you my monkeys and Flying Foxes at the same time.'[155] Buckland at one period had possessed a magnificent Turkish wolfhound named Arslan but had been forced to give it to a friend at Croydon because it killed so many other dogs; apparently he never kept another.

Mention has already been made of Buckland's kindness and generosity. Walpole said: 'Perhaps no man ever lived with a kinder heart. It may be doubted whether he ever willingly said a hard word or did a hard action. . . . He could not resist a cry of distress particularly if it came from a woman. Women, he used to say, are such doe-like, timid things that he could not bear to see them unhappy. One night, walking from his office, he found a poor servant girl crying in the street. She had been turned out of her place that morning as unequal to her duties; she had no money, and no friends nearer than Taunton, where her parents lived. Mr Buckland took her to an eating-house, gave her a dinner, drove her to Paddington, paid for her ticket, and left her in charge of the guard of the train. His nature was so simple and generous that he did not even then seem to realize that he had done an exceptionally kind action.'[26]

Charles Davy, the birdcatcher, whom Buckland had known for many years, became seriously ill in 1879 and finally died of consumption. Buckland gave him much assistance for some time before his death. On yet another occasion, as he was returning home from his office, Buckland encountered a blind man and his dog 'Puss' and wrote an article about them in *Land and Water* and offered to pass on any donations. As a result, over £40 was collected for the blind man.

It is small wonder that Buckland, this unselfconscious and kindly man, should have been so popular, and his harmless eccentricities added to his charm. It was noted at the Annual Dinner of the Piscatorial Society in 1872, when entertainment was provided by professional glee singers, that 'several amateurs also assisted. We particularly noticed . . . Mr Frank Buckland, who introduced an African elephant's tusk and a monster shell, on which, accompanied by Mr Parker, he played some stirring martial music, which seemed to please his hearers amazingly.'[199]

Buckland had numerous friends, and it seems to have been the practice of many of them to write to him on his birthday. E. M. Adams, secretary of the Cremorne Gardens, wrote in 1872, "Some years ago when at Knightsbridge you felt dissatisfied with the return you were receiving for your labour – I remember saying never mind Doctor – The drafts which true genius draws upon posterity although they may not always be honoured at the time they are due are sure to be paid with compound interest eventually. . . . It was only on Sunday night I had a proof of the estimation in which your word is held.

'Two gentlemen were eagerly discussing some subject, the nature of which I had not heard but I was roused by one of them saying "It *must* be so, *Buckland says so*" – This was a clincher – You can fancy how pleased I was. They little thought the authority quoted was my kind, my early friend for whom I wish every earthly blessing.'[23]

Another friend wrote about the same time: 'I earnestly hope you will be spared to enjoy many truly happy returns . . . for your *own* sake and for the good of the general public for I look on *you* as a Public and National benefactor and often hear you spoken of as such – and I trust you will try to prolong your valuable life and when it may please a Great and Just Creator to take it from you that you will bear a great name that may live like your good Father's for many generations to come in the Hearts and memory of a grateful Public.' Even the local Inspector of Police, whose station was not far away from No. 37 on the opposite side of Albany Street, sent to the Inspector of Salmon Fisheries '. . . most sincere congratulations on this anniversary of your Natal day'.[23]

There can be no doubt of Buckland's deep conviction that God was intimately and personally involved in all that he said and did. It was perhaps for this very reason that he found the theory of evolution put forward by Charles Darwin in 1859 so extremely offensive. 'My father was Dean of Westminster. I was brought up in the principles of Church and State; and I will never admit it – I will never admit it', he is reported to have said whenever the subject was raised in discussion.[26] He believed he had evidence that would dispose of Darwinism, but it seems probable that, like Professor Owen, Buckland never fully understood what Darwin was trying to say. Buckland believed in a single act of creation in which everything was made perfect from the beginning and everything showed, to use the words of the will of the Earl of Bridgewater, 'evidence of the power, wisdom, and goodness of the Creator'. It seemed to him, therefore, that if he could demonstrate that animals were fully adapted to their environment, then Darwinism would be proved wrong and discredited. 'I have now another witness to call in evidence of forethought and design on the part of the Great Creator, who has made the machinery of every animal quite perfect, and admirably adapted to its mode of life,' he wrote, after describing the tunny; 'especially do we find this to be the case in creatures which are destined to exist in the depths of the ocean far out of the ken of mortal sight'.[200] This view was not an unusual one when *The Origin of Species* was first published, but rapidly lost adherents, especially under the devastating vehemence of Huxley, partly because whether or not an organism is 'quite perfect, and admirably adapted to its mode of life' begs the question, and can equally well be claimed to be the result of evolution as it can be of special creation.

Darwin's theory is based on the proposition that natural selection takes place because all organisms tend to multiply themselves yet nevertheless the numbers of any particular species remain roughly constant. Therefore, said Darwin, there is competition between individuals of a species for survival or, in other words, a struggle for existence. Nevertheless, this struggle is not entirely haphazard, because no two individuals of the same species are identical and all exhibit variations. In the struggle for existence which occurs between individuals of a species, those showing advantageous variations will on average tend to survive in preference to those with disadvantageous variations. The tendency therefore will be for advantageous characteristics to be accumulated in the genetic stock, to use a modern expression, and species will remain in a state of balance with their environment. In other words, every animal will appear to be 'quite perfect and admirably adapted to its mode of life.' The crux of the argument is not the result, but how the result is achieved.

Buckland felt that Darwin's theories were a sign of the growth of doubt, infidelity and atheism which '. . . must become bitter weeds in future, of no assistance to science, and sure promoters of a dangerous materialism'.[22] One can understand that a man with his background would find particularly unpalatable the suggestion that man also had evolved, and on more than one occasion he wrote against the idea. These articles are of a trivial nature and none of them discusses the real points of difficulty which some other opponents of the theory were quick to point out. Buckland's view, in fact, was summed up when he said: 'Why not rest satisfied with the origin of our race thus revealed to us by the Great Creator Himself – "So God created man in His own image, and in the image of God created He him"?'

'For centuries past this has been, and for centuries to come it will be, the standpoint of human intellect and faith.'[201]

The history of science is full of similar examples of the conflict between faith and scientific theory. Buckland was reacting in very much the same way as many other people at the time, including so eminent a scientist as Owen; it probably did not please Buckland altogether to find that some of the facts noted by him in *Land and Water* and elsewhere had been quoted by Darwin in *The Descent of Man*. Buckland saw in acceptance of the theory, or even perhaps in a preparedness to consider the merits of the theory, the collapse of everything he believed; his simple faith could not be trifled with and his only course was therefore to reject Darwinism entirely.

CHAPTER FIFTEEN

Exhibitions and Aquaria

THE ROOTS OF THE TRADE EXHIBITION, intended not merely for entertainment but rather for stimulating industrial enterprise, are probably to be sought in the trade shows and bazaars of the eighteenth century; the French Government of the Napoleonic era, for example, made considerable use of public displays of manufacturered goods to publicize and encourage national industries. It is in the Great Exhibition of 1851, however, that this phenomenon is to be seen in its most complete and vivid form. This exhibition, the result of an idea of the Prince Consort, fired the imagination of the people, it gave an opportunity for the nation to look at itself and to take stock of the previous miraculous fifty years of progress, and it provided a fascinating glimpse into other lands to see how their peoples lived, for, unlike previous exhibitions, this one was truly international. In the years that followed, many other international exhibitions, generally in more restricted fields, were held here and abroad. They did much to spread the desire for knowledge and to accelerate the pace of industrial progress.

Early in 1866 the French Government decided to organize an International Fish and Agriculture Exhibition at Arcachon near Bordeaux. Arcachon is a fishing port and the centre of an oyster-rearing area. The Exhibition was to be held in July and the cost of the transport of exhibits was to be paid in whole or in part by the organizers. James Caird, one of the members of the famous Royal Commission of 1863 which enquired into the fish industry, was asked by the British Government to act as official representative. Buckland in April wrote to Caird: 'I wish you would kindly make our paper the *Medium* of what you want *done* about Arcachon – we have a *very large* Fishery Connection. So please let me know and I will put your letter in a conspicuous place and anything for the Exhibition I will take charge of it if you have no room.'[155] Meanwhile, the Boulogne Piscicultural Society, not to be outdone, resolved to hold their own international fishery exhibition in September, 1866.

Buckland felt that his countrymen should not be behind the French in holding a fisheries exhibition. 'Though it would seem vainglorious on my part', he wrote to *The Times* on March 14, 1866, 'yet I would suggest that there is a nucleus for an English exhibition of "Fish and Water Products" in the "Museum of Economic Fish Culture" which I have been the means of forming . . . which contains illustrations (as far as I have been able to collect them) of the culture of our rivers with salmon and of our foreshores with oysters.'

He submitted various exhibits, including models of fish ladders and passes, to both shows. At Arcachon he was awarded a silver medal for his contribution to pisciculture; Jonathan Couch, the veteran ichthyologist, at the same time received a gold medal. At Boulogne, Buckland acted as a member of the jury which assessed the exhibits, and was himself given two bronze medals and a silver one.

Although Buckland must frequently have caused his contemporaries annoyance because of his unpredictable behaviour, egotism and seeking after notoriety, yet he had a certain rugged good sense and vision which was lacking in many of his contemporaries who were better scientists. In one respect he was outstanding: this was his realization of the importance of developing popular interest in the problems of the fish industry. In an editorial in *Land and Water* in August, 1866, he said:

> To no country in the world is the development of the Sea and River Fisheries of more importance than Great Britain. Around our coasts, and in the inland waters, thousands of our population are employed in the fisheries. Cod, mackerel, herring, pilchard, salmon, oysters – the richest productions of sea and river, under favourable circumstances, are found in the greatest abundance. Yet we have permitted our shores to be denuded of breeding fish and fry by trawlers working too near inshore at certain seasons, and our rivers to be exhausted for want of rest, or polluted by sewerage and the refuse of our manufactories. The most erroneous

ideas frequently prevail among our fishermen, displaying an amount of ignorance absolutely startling. We have allowed our neighbours to be first in the field to originate International Expositions for the purpose of eliciting popular interest upon the subject. . . . But when we consider the immense amount of ignorance prevailing amongst us on this important subject, and the value of exciting public attention to it, the desirability of an International Fishery Show in England is apparent.[202]

Unfortunately no international exhibition devoted exclusively to the fisheries was arranged in Britain until after Buckland's death, although many were held in Europe. For instance, in 1867 fishery exhibitions were held at The Hague and Amsterdam and in 1868 Buckland was awarded a Diploma of Honour for his contribution to an exhibition at Le Havre.

He had a sense of what the fisheries required for their proper development. When a correspondent to *Land and Water*, signing himself 'Ptarmigan', proposed in 1867 that the Government should take an active part in sponsoring research aquaria and in enabling naturalists to carry out research at sea, Buckland took up the idea at once:

'Ptarmigan' suggests the advisability of establishing under Government supervision aquaria of sufficient magnitude for the accommodation of the larger sea-fishes, in order that properly appointed persons may play the spy upon all their movements, and thus acquire a practical knowledge of their habits, systems, and periods of spawning. We concur *in toto* with this sound and practical advice.[203]

It is a matter of historical interest that the first marine biological station in Europe was founded by Anton Dohrn at Naples only about 1870, and was actually opened in 1873. At a meeting of the British Association in 1873, Dohrn also suggested that the British Association might build either at Plymouth or Torquay an institution similar to that at Naples where admission fees paid by the public to see the aquarium helped to finance the research work and upkeep of the station.[204]

Buckland also, however, supported and extended another suggestion which at the time was probably regarded generally as quite impracticable:

> What objection can be reasonably urged against the employment of revenue cruisers for the accommodation of naturalists appointed by Government, as suggested by 'Ptarmigan', in order that they may make a thoroughly practical examination of the dark and mysterious habits of food fishes. The trawl and tow net, we firmly believe, if judiciously and persistently employed over an extended area of the sea, by men able to identify what the nets drag up and entangle, would do more to bring to light much that is now hidden and unknown than all the evidence ever collected and published by the Sea Fisheries Commission. *It is a Government question*, and not one of private or individual research. We feel confident the time is not far distant when properly-appointed naturalists will be sent by Government to investigate the habits of deep sea fish, and moreover, we predict that aquaria must be established ere long at one or more stations along our coast-line, wherein the larger food-fishes, together with the edible mollusks, may be easily watched from day to day, and their manners and customs investigated.[203]

Although it was more than fifteen years after this was written that the first tentative attempts to carry out biological research were made by Government, there were some private ventures, many very creditable, to combine public instruction and amusement with scientific investigation.* One of the earliest and perhaps best known of these ventures was the Brighton Aquarium. This was designed by the engineer responsible for the construction of Hastings Pier, Edward Birch, who had seen the small aquarium at the Boulogne Fisheries Exhibition of 1866 and had been struck with the possibilities of building a much larger aquarium at one of the English seaside resorts. Brighton was chosen because of its popularity. The construction of the building began in 1869 but for a number of reasons it was not officially opened until August 12, 1872, during the British Association meeting there.[205]

The financial success of aquaria was the result to some extent of the increasing interest in marine life, stimulated by men like Charles Kingsley (1819–1875) and Philip Henry Gosse, F.R.S. (1810–1888). Both wrote books describing how to set up small aquaria, and Gosse for a number of years ran

* The Zoological Society first set up an aquarium in 1853.[56]

courses for those who wished to learn about the mysteries of marine life. During the second half of the Victorian era the improvement in communications and the increasing earnings and savings of all classes made it possible to visit the coasts. 'In remote creeks and fishing hamlets, where families from town came to lodge, children and their parents bathed and dug and searched the tidal treasuries of the rocks; here was at least some mitigation of the divorce of the city-dweller from country life.'[17] When the first childlike curiosity was satisfied, and the tastes of 'trippers' and 'lodgers' turned to more sophisticated pursuits, more than one aquarium, including that at Brighton, fell upon difficult times.

John Keast Lord was appointed the first General Manager and Secretary of the Brighton Aquarium in March, 1872, but died the following December after a long illness. Frank Buckland, Henry Lee and A. D. Bartlett were called in to assist in the running of the Aquarium when Lord was taken ill. One of Buckland's co-directors was his old rival, Francis Francis; it is pleasing to note that they appear to have forgotten their former enmity. Buckland wrote: 'Though this gentleman and myself have had many tiffs together on purely professional matters, still, in all fish matters which indicate progress and developed knowledge, I trust I may be excused for writing we are friends. Time is too short, and there is so much to be done that it's no use driving single harness any more.'[206] After Lord's death, the post of Naturalist Manager was taken by Henry Lee.

The Brighton Aquarium, however, although the first to be begun, was not the first to be opened. There was a highly successful aquarium at the Crystal Palace, opened in February, 1872. The manager, W. A. Lloyd, was a good naturalist who had had great experience in managing aquaria in London, Paris, Hamburg, Breslau, Dresden, Vienna and Moscow. There was also an aquarium at Westminster. The Crystal Palace Aquarium was built by a company with £12,000 capital and was housed in a long arcade-like building 312 feet long, 20 feet high and about 50 feet wide. One side was taken up by tanks, the largest holding 4,000 gallons. Sea water was brought up from Brighton by rail and was held in enormous tanks in the basement, holding 250,000 gallons. The pipes were all of vulcanite, and the engines, boilers and pumps were in duplicate to guard against possible breakdown. Buckland was asked to give an address after Professor Owen had officially opened the Aquarium; he was surprised and not a little annoyed to find that his remarks were totally ignored in the accounts published in *The Times*. He thought this might have been because his observations were not very palatable to the Directors.

It is worth mentioning that Buckland's view, which was not recorded in *The Times*, was that although 'anemones, soldier-crabs, the sensational octopus, barnacles, serpulae, and other non-edible wretches are all very interesting and instructive . . .' it was most desirable to find out something about '. . . the times and manner of the spawning of turbot, soles, plaice, brill, and other commercial sea-fish . . . in order that the legislature may have definite data before them whereon to found laws as to "close times" for sea fish, and the prohibition of in-shore trawling during spring months.' This was only one of a number of occasions when Buckland pointed out the folly of attempting to legislate for fish when their life histories and habits were unknown.[207]

It is tempting to read into Buckland's writings, which are voluminous and diffuse, perhaps more than he himself intended. There is no doubt, however, that he wanted to see aquaria used for research purposes. Although it is nowadays clearly understood that the behaviour of a fish in the highly artificial environment of a tank is not necessarily typical of its behaviour in its natural environment, this fact was not appreciated at that time and, indeed, could only be elucidated by the type of observation that Buckland wished to see carried out. He believed that aquaria could be made more useful by the addition of casts and pictures of fish in the vicinity of the tanks. For more serious students, he also suggested that there should be at the Brighton Aquarium a museum, a reference library of fishery books and microscopic preparations of the minute structures of marine animals. In his desire to see the aquaria, which were being set up in many parts of the country, employed for research, and in his belief that the Government should become involved in fishery research, he was in advance of his time.

'What we want', said an editorial in *Land and Water* in 1870, 'and sooner or later must have, is an inspector of sea fisheries appointed by Government, whose duty it should be to traverse the coast, sail in the trawlers, and inspect the various systems of net and line fishing carried on at the different fishing stations, to take note of the arrival and departure of the migratory species; and to find out, if practicable, by well-conducted experiments, when and where the different kinds of sea fish we consume deposit their spawn. Concerning the sea fisheries at present we are groping our way in the dark, and every step we take is one of doubt and hesitancy, and thus we shall keep stumbling and blundering along until there are no fish left to catch, unless we at once grasp the lamp of science and guided by its light, boldly strive to find out for ourselves, what actually is going on amongst the fish down in daddy Neptune's diggings.'[208] Buckland no doubt inspired this article, but he probably did not write it himself; the bathos of the expression 'daddy Neptune's diggings' suggests that it may have been written by Henry Lee, who once called upon his head the wrath of *Nature* by referring to a new arrival at the Aquarium as 'one of the funniest little "cusses" ever turned out of Nature's workshop, in the shape of a seal. . . .'

The Brighton Aquarium, still the largest building of its kind this side of the Atlantic, was extremely popular, and Buckland seems to have assisted in developing this popularity. He suggested to his friends that they should visit the aquarium. 'I paid my promised visit to the Brighton Aquarium yesterday and was quite delighted with it', wrote E. Stratton F. Berkeley, a former brother officer in the 2nd Life Guards and son of Grantley Berkeley, in 1873. 'I cannot say how much I admire, and approve of, the general design, and way in which it has been carried out. The artistic arrangements of the tanks, etc. are admirable and everything is so neat, clean and well cared for. The appearance and condition of the fish and other tenants of the tanks leave no room for question or doubt as to good management. . . . To my own knowledge many people have run down to Brighton expressly to see the Aquarium, and I hope to do so many another day myself.'[155]

Buckland himself took parties of people round the Aquarium. In 1874 he was asked by the Society of Arts to give two lectures 'On the Structure and Habits of Beasts, Birds, and

Fishes, as showing Beauty and Design'. The lectures appear to have been of a rather diffuse and popular character. Part of the official report of one lecture says: 'Various costly furs, as the silver fox, black fox, and ermine were then shown; and the evening's entertainment was terminated by the exhibition of Mr Saxe's beautiful mechanical piping bullfinch.' At the conclusion of the appointed course, Buckland announced that since he still had a lot to say he would give one more lecture at his Museum and would also conduct a party to the Brighton Aquarium. About 400 people journeyed to Brighton by special train. Tickets were 10*s* 6*d* each and entitled the bearer to first-class travel, admission to the Aquarium and luncheon. The Aquarium was fully equipped to cater for visitors. According to an advertisement of the period it was 'The Largest and most Beautiful Building devoted to Piscatorial Science in the World. Thousands of Fishes and Marine Animals – many of great rarity. The Tanks and Ferneries nightly Illuminated. Promenade Concerts every Saturday at Three o'clock. Band plays thrice daily.' 'For over three decades the Aquarium was not only a popular place of entertainment, and a temple of the Muses,' wrote Brightwell, 'but made very real contributions to marine biology. Despite the counter-attractions of Brill's baths, Ginnett's Circus, the Alhambra, and the growing popularity of the piers, it made a financial success of innumerable stage shows from serious drama to pantomime, and of such Victorian favourites as giants, midgets, Zulu chieftains, and Javanese temple dancers. In more serious vein it offered the greatest singers of the day, with Madame Patti at their head, and an orchestra second to none. Even the catering met with unstinted praise, and what trencher and bottle men they were at that time!'[209] The Aquarium was redesigned in 1927 and remains today a centre of entertainment and instruction for the visitor. Unfortunately all the historical records of the Aquarium were lost in a great storm in 1935.

There were also aquaria in other parts of the country, some of which enjoyed only a brief existence. In January, 1875, for example, a freshwater aquarium was opened by a Mr Charles Partridge in Bishopsgate, opposite the end of Worship Street, London. Buckland gave an address at the opening of the Manchester Aquarium in May, 1874, and at the Southport

Aquarium the following September. The capital involved in building and installing these Aquaria was often very large; the Winter Gardens and Aquarium at Southport cost £90,000. Buckland was also consulted about the possibility of converting plunging baths at Herne Bay to an aquarium. He had become an authority on the subject, and he was a communicating link between these different institutions. He would often ask the manager of an aquarium to attempt to solve some problem in the life history of one or another of the commercial species of fish. He once suggested also that '. . . the attention of future students in the Newcastle College of Physical Science should be directed to the improvement of the fisheries of the northern district'.

Although no major international exhibitions devoted entirely to fisheries were held during Buckland's life, he was closely concerned in the organization of the Fish as Food section of the International Exhibition of 1873. He was also involved in a Piscicultural and Maritime Exhibition held at the Westminster Aquarium in June, 1877. This included 'nets, fishing-tackle, diving apparatus, lifeboats, fog-horns, boats . . .' and it was reported that 'The numerous angling societies and private individuals in London and elsewhere, exhibit a very perfect and valuable collection of British fish as captured by net and rod. . . . Mr Frank Buckland, Inspector of Salmon Fisheries, occupies a large space with his casts and models from his Museum of Economic Fish Culture at South Kensington.'[210] Buckland served on a number of the committees set up to judge the exhibits, which included a fine collection of stuffed Indian fish, recently presented to the Prince of Wales who had just returned from a triumphant tour of India, during which he seems to have given fire engines as presents to some of the native Princes as being one of the few luxuries they were unlikely already to possess!

The Westminster Aquarium was primarily a place of entertainment; Zazel and Benedetti appeared there, for example, and some caged animals were also kept. Buckland once accompanied the Earl of Beaconsfield and a party of ladies to demonstrate the points of Mr Pongo, a live gorilla. 'I have reason to recollect Pongo,' Buckland wrote, 'for one day I was nursing him on my lap, when, all of a sudden, without rhyme or reason, he turned round and made his great canine teeth meet in my left cheek.'

Buckland's contact with many of the influential people in Norfolk and Suffolk, and his desire to see the fishery of the Broads properly controlled, has already been mentioned. He was invited to attend a meeting in August, 1879, at which the possibility of acclimatizing fish in the Broads was discussed; his advice was clearly regarded as of considerable value and he was elected one of the members of the Fish Acclimatization Committee. Although he was present at a meeting of this Committee held in September, illness prevented him from attending a further meeting in the following November, when it was revealed that H.R.H. the Prince of Wales had agreed to become Patron of what was now described as the Norfolk and Suffolk Fish Acclimatization Society. The President of the Society, Mr Edward Birkbeck, M.P., also announced that he had had letters from the German Fishery Association offering assistance and inviting him to visit the International Fishery Exhibition which was to be held in Berlin in April, 1880. This Exhibition was an important one, because it had a considerable influence in this country.

Buckland's advice, and particularly how Britain's co-operation in the Berlin Exhibition was to be obtained, was asked by Herr Georg von Bunsen, son of Baron von Bunsen and an old friend of the Buckland family. Von Bunsen was Vice-President of the Exhibition and of the German Fishery Society. Buckland was not successful in obtaining many exhibits from his countrymen, but he spent much time putting into crates exhibits from his own Museum including casts, maps, diagrams, models of salmon-ladders, tables of statistics and photographs.[211] The fifteen cases were carefully opened at the other end to reveal terrible breakages; Buckland blamed the '. . . rude, uncultivated van men . . .' for the damage. Nevertheless, sufficient remained to make a small display which was little enough compared with the magnificent show of some other countries, notably the United States where the Government had voted £4,000 towards the costs of their national exhibits. Spencer Walpole, who reported on the exhibition, commented: 'The only attempt to give consistency to the collection is due indeed to the private efforts of my colleague

Mr Buckland. Mr Buckland has formed at his own cost a museum of fish culture in London. From the museum he has been able to send many objects of great interest. . . . Mr Buckland's casts of fish are better than those of the Smithsonian Museum.'[212]

There is little doubt that the Berlin Exhibition stimulated the Norfolk and Suffolk Acclimatization Society to attempt to hold a similar function in Norwich; initially their intention was to open a museum but the Secretary of the Society, W. Oldham Chambers, F.R.I.B.A., found that this idea was practically unworkable and suggested an exhibition instead. Much support for the idea was forthcoming from local land-owners, and the Prime Warden and Court of the Worshipful Company of Fishmongers gave a grant of £100 towards it. The Exhibition was held in Norwich in April, 1881. The extent to which Buckland was involved in the later stages of the organization of the Exhibition is not clear, but he was a very sick man by the middle of 1880, and it is improbable that he would have been able to give much assistance from that time until his death at the end of the year. Nevertheless, his energetic championship of the fisheries, his particular concern for the Broads, his attempts to stimulate popular interest in the fisheries, and his earnest desire for a British Fishery Exhibition, were major contributions to the success of the venture, and a gift to posterity which was later to bear rich and unexpected fruit.

Buckland throughout his life was always prepared to try any idea, however far-fetched and impracticable it might seem to other people. Enthusiasm gushed from him like water from a spring; he was not the man to stop working because he was tired or felt that he had done a full day's work. He would never say that a job was not worth the trouble of doing it. He also could throw himself into the schemes and ideas of other people and make them his own, and this is well shown in his adoption of an idea put forward by Mr O. T. Olsen of Grimsby, Lincolnshire.

Olsen suggested in January, 1879, that prizes should be given for the best logs kept by masters of fishing smacks in the North Sea. These logs were designed by Olsen to give details of water temperature, nature of the fishing ground, wind, barometer reading, nature of the fish caught and its quantity.[213] Ole Theodor Olsen was a 'chart maker, compass adjuster, nautical instrument maker, and an authority upon navigation for fishermen'. He was born in Norway in 1839, and went to sea at 14 years of age. He came to Britain in about 1860 and six years later set up in business on his own as a compass adjuster. He published various books for fishermen, including *The Fisherman's Navigator*, *The Piscatorial Atlas* and *The Fisherman's Nautical Almanac*. The Almanac in particular was widely used on the vessels fishing in the North Sea. Olsen died in 1925, but his firm is still in existence although it has no longer any family connexions.[214]

In his many trips to Grimsby Buckland had become acquainted with Olsen, and the two men appear to have thought highly of each other. Olsen's suggestion that prize logs should be kept stemmed from the lack of knowledge of the North Sea and the need to improve fishing charts, which described the nature of the bottom as, for example, 'Fine sand', 'White shells', 'Rubbish' or 'Moor-log from the Texel grounds'. Skippers still found their way about by examining the specimens of sea-floor deposits which stuck to the tallow at the bottom of the sounding lead, by a knowledge of the stars and that sixth sense of direction which all sailors appear to possess. Buckland at once said: 'I think this a most admirable idea on the part of Mr Olsen. The bottom of the sea is in a scientific sense less well known than the deserts of Sahara. . . . We . . . want to know the times and places of the spawning of sea-fish. Where do the soles lay their eggs? When and how does the plaice, turbot, brill, halibut, etc. spawn? Do cod's eggs sink or swim? We know, moreover, as yet, but little of the food of these fishes. We want also samples of the surface-water itself under peculiar conditions; for instance, what is the meaning of that wonderful white appearance of the sea which took place last autumn in nearly all the waters of the northern coast of England? What is the meaning of the occasional red appearance of the sea for many square miles of the ocean surface? Again, how are we to devise a mesh of net that shall let go the small soles and undersized fry of other sea-fish, and keep marketable fish only?'[213] Buckland himself out of his own pocket added to the prizes that Olsen was offering, and persuaded the Fishmongers' Company to bless the enterprise and contribute £25 towards expenses.

The Log Books were called in early in December, 1880. It has unfortunately proved impossible to trace any of them, although some were apparently still in Olsen's possession in this century. *Land and Water* contains some interesting accounts by a skipper, Thomas Salmond, of the catches of the Grimsby smack *Nyanza*, and if these accounts are typical of the logs as a whole, they would be well worth perusing today. As Buckland lay dying, almost his last task was to read and mark these logs. Olsen's idea had taken root, a North Sea Fisheries Prize Committee had been set up and, as usual, the venture had come to depend upon the co-operation and assistance of Buckland, whose early death put an end to the enterprise. The stated aims of the Prize Committee are well worth repeating:

'The study of Deep Sea Fisheries especially the composition of the bed of the Oceans as affecting commercial fish; the capture of trawl and hook fish; the working of fishing nets and gear; a knowledge of the migrations, spawning and food of ground and floating fish; set of tides and temperature of the ocean, as influencing the presence or absence of fish.'

The Government marine laboratories of Britain were, of course, set up to investigate such problems.

As Professor Garstang said in 1930, however,

> . . . the notes that a fisherman can make, and the samples that he can collect, in the course of his regular work, which is exacting enough, can only touch the fringe of all the many matters that affect the life, growth and movements of sea fishes, and Frank Buckland, optimist as he was, must have known that his scheme, however extensively taken up, would never, by itself, have accomplished all that he wanted. The more fully it was carried out, the more difficult it would have been to carry it on. Nevertheless, it is highly probable that in a few years' time, had he lived, there would have been results from this enterprise which would have led to its being placed upon a more solid basis, and the advent of statistical and scientific investigations on fishery problems might accordingly have been hastened.[215]

CHAPTER SIXTEEN

Epilogue

Buckland took little care of his health. He revelled in cold, wet and discomfort. 'I ride generally down to the Fisheries Office on the top of an omnibus. The top of an omnibus is a grand place. One can write notes there. I like to get wet through, and the harder it rains or blows the more I enjoy my ride on the 'bus-top', he wrote in 1877.[216] He had a special rubber diving dress for use when collecting salmon and trout eggs, but netting fish in winter can never be a comfortable task and he was frequently imprudent in exposing himself unnecessarily to frost, snow and rain; and in really cold weather his rubber suit froze on him like armour. He left many descriptions of how he caught and spawned the fish.

> Experience of many years has taught me that if I wished to make a success of egg-collecting I must do it myself. [He wrote in 1872.] On Wednesday morning last, January 17, at sunrise, I anxiously looked out of my bedroom window at the country inn where I was staying. By Jove, what a day! – raining in torrents, the wind coming round the street corners with the rush of a hurricane; the street gutters full, the roads in flood from a stopped-up drain – in fact, everything looking about as miserable and unpromising as possible. . . . At breakfast Mr Bartlett and myself consulted whether we should turn out such a wretched day. 'Turn out?' I said, 'of course we *must* go; but I can tell you we shall have a tremendous day of it'; so away we went to try our luck. We soon came to the water meadows in a sort of country omnibus, which took the water bailiff and ourselves: nets, cans, spawning dishes, a great lot of packages altogether, but all necessary. When we arrived at the appointed place we turned out. The weather, if possible, was getting worse, the river was overbank full and in spate, the 'carriers' in the water meadows

> were overflowing, every inch of ground was saturated, and it was most bitterly cold. 'Never mind,' I said, 'let's go at it'; so in I went with one end of the net; but when the water was nearly up to my arm-pits I must say it was most awfully cold, and I shivered again, even though I had on a wading dress nearly up to my neck . . . I observed there was a water-cress bed, which looked very promising, so I determined to explore it. When I go out on these expeditions I always wear a flannel shirt, the sleeves of which are cut right off, as wet flannel sleeves are a great nuisance, especially when one is catching trout in rat-holes or under mud banks, or among roots of trees, etc. I find I can work better with bare arms, though thorns and briars are decidedly objectionable, and make nasty scratches. I also wear a sealskin cap that I can pull right over my face when I want to push it into the middle of a bush to catch a trout in a hole. If a watercress-bed is to be thoroughly hunted I go on my hands and knees.[217]

Early in 1878, Buckland was involved with James Youl in arranging a shipment of salmon eggs in the S.S. *Chimborazo*. He received the commission late in the season, and exposed himself to appalling weather in a number of rivers in an attempt to collect the ripe fish. Not long afterwards he began to show symptoms of disease. In January, 1879, he assisted in stowing salmon eggs in the ice-house of the S.S. *Durham* and a few days later suffered a severe haemorrhage from the lungs which kept him in bed for ten days and prevented him from returning to work for two months. He had another relapse in April but was well enough to travel later in the year and, for example, conducted an enquiry in Birmingham in June, 1879. Archibald Young, his Scottish colleague, saw him about September and remarked that 'The robust frame had shrunk and the healthy cheek paled. He seemed but the shadow of his former self. Yet his interest in his favourite pursuits was unabated and his mind was as actively vivacious as ever. But sitting in close rooms and examining witnesses during a long day exhausted him, and brought on distressing attacks of asthma, and he was ultimately obliged to give up assisting at the concluding inquiries,'[180] The inquiries referred to were those carried out with Young and Walpole into the fungus disease then attacking salmon in many rivers in England and

Scotland. Buckland did not sit with his colleagues after October, 1879.[162]

The immediate cause of his further relapse, however, was exposure to bad weather whilst engaged on an enquiry in November amongst the fishermen at Cromer. 'Thanks for enquiries,' he wrote in December, 1879, to his friend William (later Sir William) White Cooper, surgeon oculist to the Queen, 'was much better but got caught at Beccles Norfolk Station (when out on a crab and lobster enquiry) in a fearful snow storm and my asthma has come back again which is a great bore. When driving past any time call in and look at John Hunter's Chair made from the bed Professor Owen gave me.'[218]

Professor Owen had given Hunter's four-poster bed to Buckland for his birthday in 1878. Owen had acquired it from his father-in-law, William Clift, who bought it at the sale of Hunter's furniture. After the bed had lain in his house for some months, Buckland suddenly decided to saw it up and make it into a chair. He was unable to complete the job himself and called in a skilled joiner.[219] It is a curious piece of furniture which looks acutely uncomfortable and it must be said that as an historical relic it would have been better to leave it as a bed. It now stands in the Hunterian Museum at the Royal College of Surgeons in London.

Buckland was no longer able to exert himself. In June, 1880, 'dropsy set in' and he underwent an operation, afterwards many times repeated.[13] Perhaps this was to drain fluid from the abdominal cavity. In an attempt to recover something of his old vigour, he went to Margate during July and August, where he stayed at the White Hart Hotel. He was accompanied by his friend Henry Lee. Effort caused him distress, and he mostly rested, but with John, the buttons, to carry the tackle and a friend to help him, he managed to do some fishing at the end of the jetty.

In September, however, a further severe relapse occurred. Although he was now confined to his room, his mental effort appeared rather to be stimulated than otherwise. He dictated the remaining portions of his *Natural History of British Fishes* as he lay racked with pain and gasping for breath.

He had realized for some time that he was dying, and on December 3 signed his will. 'God is so good, so very good to the little fishes,' he is reported to have said, 'I do not believe He would let their inspector suffer shipwreck at last. I am going a long journey where I think I shall see a great many curious animals. This journey I must go alone.'[13] He died at Albany Street, two days after his fifty-fourth birthday, on December 19, 1880. He was buried in Brompton Cemetery on December 24, in the same grave as his little son 'Physie'.

The cause of Buckland's death is not entirely clear. It may have been pulmonary tuberculosis as perhaps implied by Bompas, although from the available evidence this is not very likely. Nevertheless Buckland had seen much of Charles R. Davy, the birdcatcher, who died of phthisis in 1879 and who could have been actively infectious for some years. Buckland also lived in close contact with his monkeys, at least one of which, Little Jack, had a 'tremendous cough' early in 1879.

The death certificate does nothing to solve the mystery, for it states the cause of death as 'Hepatic disease about 2 years. Bronchitis.' He might have suffered from heart disease, giving rise to cardiac asthma and ascites. Recently, Snell has suggested that he was suffering from cor pulmonale with cardiac failure and oedema.[220] The symptoms of disease in January, 1879, and the later accounts of his illness, certainly point to the lungs rather than the liver. Buckland was, of course, a continuous and very heavy smoker of pipe and cigars and it is possible that he developed cancer of the lungs and a secondary growth in the liver, giving rise to pain, signs of hepatic disease and ascites. This would explain the wording of the death certificate, for lung cancer was then a rare disease and not always accurately diagnosed.

Although Buckland was often impetuous and tactless, and therefore caused annoyance, he was without vice and his death caused widespread and genuine sorrow. *Nature*, in an obituary notice, said: 'Although fond of all that pertained to natural science, he was in no sense of the word a profound naturalist; he could seize with alacrity the popular side of a scientific question, but he seldom went deeper. . . . Familiarly known by a large circle of friends as Frank Buckland, he has left them while still in middle life, and it will be long ere they look upon the like of poor Frank again.'[221] *The Times* mentioned Buckland's unremitting labours as a public servant whilst *The Field* gave an unexpectedly kindly note.

> His great merit as a writer was his power of rendering natural history attractive to the multitude; this he did to perfection. . . . Whilst other writers of popular natural history simply compile, Buckland described from his own quaint and singular points of view. His descriptions were therefore vivid, and, if not always consistent, were eminently readable, and doubtless have served their own good turn by attracting many to the study of nature and natural objects.[212]

His successor was Thomas Henry Huxley. Huxley was a year or so older than Buckland, and came from a very different background. He had had a distinguished career, became a Fellow of the Royal Society at 26, and had successfully crossed swords with Owen on more than one occasion. He was also a champion of Darwinism. His knowledge of the sea fisheries and marine biology was wide, from his work on the Sea Fisheries Commission, and also his experience on the cruise of H.M.S. *Rattlesnake* from 1846 to 1850. He was not, however, a practical naturalist, and seems to have preferred the bench to the field. On the whole, Buckland would not have approved of Huxley.

Indeed, Mrs Bompas, Buckland's sister, wrote to her Uncle Samuel in March, 1881:

> He was at work . . . to the very last full of mental energy and vigour as ever, and said he only wished to publish the masses of information he had acquired in his note books to refute the theories of Darwin and Huxley which greatly troubled him, and he would have been troubled indeed to see Huxley put in his place, for he had a horror of his atheistic principles.[41]

Huxley was approached about taking the post soon after Buckland's death. 'If this could be managed,' Huxley wrote to Sir John Donnelly of the Science and Art Department on December 27, 1880, 'I could get great things done in the matter of fish culture and fish diseases at South Kensington, if poor dear X's rattle-trappery could be turned to proper account, without in any way interfering with the work of the School.' He was appointed on January 29, 1881, and found the work congenial. Walpole remained with him during 1881, but was then appointed Governor of the Isle of Man, leaving Huxley as the only Inspector of Salmon Fisheries. Huxley wrote to Walpole in 1883: 'The office would be quite perfect, if they did not want an annual report. I can't go in for a disquisition on river basins after the manner of Buckland, and you have exhausted the other topics. I polished off the Salmon Disease pretty fully last year, so what the deuce am I to write about?'[44] Huxley did not have Buckland's instinctive warmth and geniality and does not appear to have mixed so readily with the members of the Local Boards of Conservators. He also lacked Buckland's impulsive and enthusiastic desire to make science popular and entertaining for the layman, often at the expense of some accuracy. Huxley could, and did, write and lecture well but his popular work was generally at a higher intellectual level than that of Buckland and demanded more effort for understanding.

Buckland bequeathed his Museum of Economic Fish Culture to the nation. He probably intended to do this at least from March, 1872, when he wrote to Mrs Buckland: 'My dear wife, I have this morning dictated the terms of my will to my friend and legal adviser Bennett. I think it right to tell you that I have left you everything – except my museum – all my property in fact – between six and seven thousand pounds altogether.' He also told her that he had so arranged it that if she married again after his death, her future husband would not be able to rob her.[123] The will he signed on December 3, 1880, just before his death, however, not only bequeathed his Museum to the nation '. . . under the name of "Buckland's Fish Museum" . . .' but also provided for £5,000 to be set aside at the death of his wife to endow a trust fund '. . . . . for the foundation of a Professorship of Economic Fish Culture (to be called the Buckland Professorship) . . .' His legal adviser was still William Henry Bennett.[223]

The bequest was formally accepted by the Lord President in July, 1881. Buckland's Museum remained in the immediate care of the Curator, Richard Edon, and although some disquiet was felt by the authorities over the terms of the will, since Bennett, as sole executor and trustee, had complete power over the estate, it was felt that little could be done about it.[118] A Frank Buckland Memorial Fund was opened in 1881 by friends and well-wishers, including the Duke of Beaufort, the Marquis of Conyngham, the Rt Hon. Sir W. Vernon Harcourt, M.P. (Home Secretary), and Professor Owen. H.R.H. Prince Christian agreed to act as President of the Fund. A marble bust of Buckland was executed by J. Warrington Wood and was placed in Buckland's Museum in July, 1882. It had been subscribed to '. . . by a large number of those who appreciated the eminent services of the late Mr Frank Buckland in the interests of British Fisheries'. The remainder of the Fund was employed to purchase an annuity for Mrs Buckland.[224]

Meanwhile, however, the financial affairs of William Henry Bennett were becoming embarrassed; in fact he appears to have absconded with some of the funds. Mrs Buckland was advised by her solicitors to take legal action against him, and half of her estate was eventually recovered. Buckland's Museum itself was also becoming a matter of serious concern to the authorities at South Kensington. Huxley had recommended its acceptance but later altered his view. Perhaps this was partly because the functions of the Science and Art Department were changing, perhaps also because Huxley had originally envisaged a different role for Buckland's Museum. A number of offers were made by outside bodies, notably the National Fish Culture Association whose secretary was W. Oldham Chambers, to take over the contents of the Museum but this was ruled by the Treasury Solicitor to be contrary to the terms of the bequest. The Committee on the Science Collections at South Kensington eventually recommended division of the contents between the Fishery Board for Scotland and the Marine Biological Association, but finding later that nothing had been done they stated in 1898 that '. . . opinion being unanimous, we hope this collection may disappear without delay'.

In their first report they had said: 'No mention of this collection [The Fish Culture Collection] is made in the departmental scheme of classification dated January, 1888; and indeed it seems to bear little relation to the instruction given in the Normal School, to the teaching in science classes connected with the Department, or to the other sections of the Science Museum. Nor is South Kensington a situation naturally adapted for fish-breeding operations. We beg to refer to the weighty opinion of Professor Huxley as to the want of connexion between this collection and its present surroundings, and the small educational or scientific value which it possesses in its present condition.'[118]

An attempt was made to give the Museum back to Mrs Buckland, who might perhaps have been able to sell it to an outside body such as the Fishmongers' Company, but the nation once having accepted a bequest, it apparently has no mechanism for handing it back to the donors again! The collection remained on display at South Kensington into this century but was eventually put into store and, as already stated, little of it now remains. Many of the specimens were of little scientific value and it is difficult to quarrel with the decision to withdraw them from exhibition. Huxley's view of what was educational may not have agreed with that of everyone, but he was undoubtedly right in drawing attention to the lack of connexion of the collection with its surroundings.

Nevertheless, one may regret that something was not done with the collection; attempts were made by the South Kensington Museum authorities to transfer the contents of Buckland's Museum elsewhere, but their efforts were thwarted by the terms of the will. It might perhaps, under other circumstances, have been possible to use some of the exhibits as the nucleus for a National Fisheries Museum. Such a museum would have been very close to what Buckland most desired and might in turn have helped to develop fishery education in this country. There is still no National Museum devoted to the fisheries, and unfortunately little likelihood of one being established.

After Mrs Buckland's death in 1920, at the age of 91, a trust fund was set up, known as the Buckland Foundation. Under this Foundation, a Buckland Professor of Economic Fish Culture is appointed annually to deliver a series of lectures in the United Kingdom or Ireland; the lectures are subsequently published in book form. Buckland clearly understood the term 'Economic Fish Culture' to mean something much wider than fish hatching; he meant the whole science and practice of the fisheries. The topics covered by the lectures since they began indicate that the Trustees have attempted to cover the vast field encompassed by this definition. The first series of lectures was given in 1930 by the late Professor Walter Garstang and they have been continued almost without a break since that time. The lectures provide a valuable opportunity for fishery research workers and others to talk about their work to those engaged in the fish industry and to the general public. They also have another function, which is probably at least of equal importance, and that is of enabling the lecturer himself to see how his work, and the work of others, is related to the industrial scene.

Although, therefore, Buckland's intention of founding a Museum eventually miscarried, the idea of a Professorship of Economic Fish Culture has proved a successful one. Garstang's comment is even more relevant today than it was when he made it in 1930*: 'The advancement of knowledge means, unfortunately, its subdivision into special branches, each of which becomes increasingly technical and intricate. It will be the task of successive Buckland lecturers to act as interpreters – to take up these varied branches one after another, and to show, in plain language, the progress which has been made, and is being made, towards the end he [Buckland] had in view.'[215]

Fate was unkind to the memory of Buckland; had he lived and retained his activity for another year or two, he must surely have received credit for his contribution to the development of the fisheries and fishery research in this country. As it was, his name sank soon after his death into comparative oblivion, and few today know what he did, apart from founding the Buckland Lectures and contributing to a few somewhat obscure Government reports. He deserved better.

His influence on the success of the National Fisheries Exhibition held at Norwich in 1881 has already been discussed in Chapter Fifteen. He had for years talked about the need for such an Exhibition; by the time it was organized and took place, everyone had become so accustomed to the idea, it was so accepted and taken for granted, that nobody thought to acknowledge the contribution of a man who had died four months before the Exhibition opened. Buckland was never-

* Garstang was appointed lecturer for 1929 but first delivered his lectures in February and March, 1930, at Grimsby and Hull respectively.

theless represented there, for a full collection of his casts was lent by the South Kensington Museum.

The Norwich Exhibition led directly to the International Fisheries Exhibition at Edinburgh in 1882, where 'the South Kensington Museum Loan Exhibit, from the collection of the late Mr Frank Buckland, was a centre of constant crowds at the Exhibition.'[225] The Norwich Exhibition had owed a great deal to the influence of Mr Edward Birkbeck, M.P., who had, for example, secured Government recognition of the venture. Mr Birkbeck was again largely responsible for the Great International Fisheries Exhibition held from May to October, 1883, in the grounds immediately behind the Royal Albert Hall in London. This Exhibition was again supported by funds from the State and was a considerable success which greatly stimulated public interest in the fisheries and their problems.

Huxley, when asked by Spencer Walpole what he thought of the Exhibition, replied: 'Well, the chief lesson to be drawn from the exhibition is that London is in want of some open air amusement on summer evenings.'[44] He did not appreciate its enormous educational value, or the great good that was to come of it. The widespread interest aroused in the scientific investigation of the fisheries was very great and resulted in a public meeting at the Royal Society on March 31, 1884. Huxley was asked to take the Chair, and it was there decided to found a marine biological laboratory, the Plymouth Marine Laboratory. Subscriptions were received from many sources; it was due to the liberality of the many donors, including a large number of individual scientists, that the Laboratory was endowed. This, said an American observer in 1910, was '. . . a startling illustration of the limitations of support under which research labors in England, even when explicitly directed to a large extent, as was the Plymouth Station from the beginning, toward investigations of economic significance'.[226]

The author of the Introduction to the Official Catalogue of the 1883 Exhibition mentioned '. . . the endeavours to obtain the establishment of a Government vessel for the instruction and assistance of fishermen, repeatedly made by the late Mr Frank Buckland; to whose memory no monument could be erected either more in accordance with his own desire, or more worthy of the debt of gratitude owed to him by the nation, than such an institution.'[227] It will be recalled that Buckland was in fact more particularly concerned to obtain a Government vessel to carry out research at sea. The Marine Laboratory at Lowestoft began as a daughter station of Plymouth. It is now a Government laboratory under the Ministry of Agriculture, Fisheries and Food. It has a number of research vessels and is, perhaps, the realization of Buckland's dream.

Reference was made in Chapter Thirteen to the insistence of both the 1863 Commissioners, and Walpole and Buckland, on the need for adequate statistics of the industry. It would be natural to assume that the modern system of collection of information about, for example, the quantities and species of fish landed and the areas where they were caught arose from these recommendations. Unfortunately, even here, fate has been unkind to Buckland, and the development of the present-day system of the collection of fishery statistics appears to owe nothing to the recommendations of any of those men who were appointed by Government to make them.

The official account is revealing. 'The Board of Trade began the collection, in a systematic form, of statistics of fish landed on the coasts of England and Wales in 1885. H.R.H. the late Duke of Saxe-Coburg, then Duke of Edinburgh and Admiral-Superintendent of Naval Reserves, collected through the Coastguard some statistics as to the quantity and value of the fish landed, and in 1883 His Royal Highness read a paper on the subject at a conference held in connection with the International Sea-Fisheries Exhibition at South Kensington. Copies of this paper having been sent to the Board of Trade, and the whole question having been duly considered, it was decided to establish a collection of fishery statistics for England and Wales, on the same lines, and generally by the same machinery, as had been recommended by His Royal Highness.'[228] The system adopted was a peculiar one and its details form no part in this narrative; it is enough to say that the method employed before this century in collecting statistics is such as to raise grave doubts as to the reliability of all the figures.*

* Mention has already been made of the Board of British White Herring Fishery. The Board issued statistics relating to the Scottish fisheries from 1809. Only those species earning bounty

In spite, therefore, of Buckland's unremitting efforts for the fish industry and for the development of marine research, there is scarcely one thing that can be ascribed to his efforts. One must ask the question whether his life, which began with so much promise, was frittered away extravagantly and to no good purpose. His interests and energies were so widely diffused that he might have done more by concentrating his energy on a narrower front.

Buckland's charm, however, lies to a considerable degree in the wide scope of his interests. He was not a great scientist, he was not really a scientist at all, but he had the gift of interesting his listeners in what interested him. He was a very acute observer and, above all, he was humane. He wrote simply about animals and his audience read, were enthralled, and assimilated something of his humanity. His life was to him an amusing adventure, shared with thousands of others who were the richer for his writing; they laughed with him, they enjoyed his jokes, they were interested in what interested him. And when he died they lost a friend and a companion and were so much the poorer.

His contribution to the nation, his life's work for the fisheries, cannot be precisely assessed. It was considerable, but Buckland was the ploughman who prepared the soil in which others, like Huxley, sowed and reaped to such good effect. Had he lived a few years more, Buckland might have achieved greater and more lasting fame, but this speculation is fruitless. He was an honest, upright and courageous public servant, and this must be his epitaph.

---

payments were included at first, but as time went on, the statistics were made more complete. It is interesting that the Scottish Board's statistics did not encourage a similar endeavour in England; in fact, two Treasury Commissioners in 1857 recommended that the Scottish statistics be 'made less elaborate'. The Board also initiated some of the earliest marine biological research in this country.[229]

References

1. Buckland, Frank, *Log-book of a Fisherman and Zoologist*. London: Chapman & Hall, 1883 (1st ed. April, 1875).
2. Buckland, William, *Geology and Mineralogy considered with reference to Natural Theology* (Ed. F. Buckland). London: Routledge, 1858.
3. Buckland Papers, Devon Record Office and Exeter Diocesan Record Office (Dep. by the late Prof. M. Gordon).
4. Adamson, J. W., *English Education 1789–1902*. Cambridge: University Press, 1930.
5. Curtis, S. J., *History of Education in Great Britain*. London: U.T.P., 1953, 3rd ed.
6. Wymer, Norman, *Dr Arnold of Rugby*. London: Robert Hale, 1953.
7. Stephen, Leslie (Ed.), *Dictionary of National Biography*. London: Smith, Elder & Co., 1886.
8. Gordon, Mrs. (E. O.), *The Life and Correspondence of William Buckland, D.D., F.R.S.* London: Murray, 1894.
9. Buckland, William, *Reliquiae Diluvianiae*, etc. London: Murray, 1823.
10. Ruskin, John, *Praeterita* (Ed. E. T. Cook & A. Wedderburn). London: George Allen, 1908.
11. *Land and Water*, *21*, January 1, 1876.
12. Buckland, the late Brigadier F. E., Private communication.
13. Bompas, G. C., *Life of Frank Buckland*. London: Smith, Elder & Co., 1885 (9th ed.).
14. Buckland, Frank, *Curiosities of Natural History*. First Series. London: Bentley, 1879 (1st ed. 1857).
15. Buckland, Frank, *Curiosities of Natural History*. Second Series. London: Bentley, 1879 (1st ed. 1860).
16. Woodward, Llewellyn, *The Age of Reform 1815–1870*. Oxford: University Press, 1962.
17. Trevelyan, G. M., *English Social History*. London: Longmans, Green, 1944.
18. Darwin, Charles, *Autobiography* (Ed. Nora Barlow). London: Collins, 1958.
19. Owen, Richard, *The Life of Richard Owen*. London: Murray, 1894.

20. TUCKWELL, W., *Reminiscences of Oxford.* London: Smith, Elder & Co., 1907, 2nd ed.
21. ROSE, R. N., *The Field 1853–1953.* London: Michael Joseph 1953.
22. WHITE, GILBERT, *Natural History of Selborne* (Ed. Frank Buckland). London: Macmillan, 1875.
23. BUCKLAND, FRANK. Papers in Library of Royal College of Surgeons of England (Dep. by the late Prof. M. Gordon).
24. FOSTER, JOSEPH, *Alumni Oxoniensis.* Oxford: Parker, 1888.
25. BUCKLAND, the late C. E. MSS notes in possession of Mrs E. M. Rogers.
26. *Macmillan's Magazine*, 303–309, February, 1881.
27. Revenues and Management of Certain Schools and Colleges. R. Com. [3288] xxi. London: H.M.S.O., 1864.
28. *Temple Bar*, *37*, 175–184, 1873.
29. TUCKWELL, W., *The Ancient Ways – Winchester Fifty Years Ago.* London: Macmillan, 1893.
30. THOMPSON, HENRY L., *Christ Church.* London: Robinson, 1900.
31. MALLET, CHARLES E., *A History of the University of Oxford.* London: Methuen, 1927.
32. Christ Church. College Records. Students' and Chaplains' Accounts, 1861–1864.
33. ASTLEY, JOHN D., *Fifty Years of my Life*, etc. London: Hurst & Blackett, 1894.
34. Christ Church. Collections Record, 1700–1893.
35. HISCOCK, W. G., *A Christ Church Miscellany.* Oxford: U.T.P., 1946.
36. OAKELEY, FREDERICK, in *Reminiscences of Oxford by Oxford Men, 1559–1850* (Ed. L. M. Quiller-Couch). Oxford: Clarendon Press, 1892.
37. BUCKLAND, WILLIAM, Letters to Justus von Liebig in Bayerische Staatisbibliothek, München.
38. PLEDGE, H. T., *Science since 1500.* London: H.M.S.O., 1939.
39. VOLHARD, JAKOB, *Justus von Liebig.* Leipzig: Johann Barth, 1909.
40. HOFMANN, A. W., *The Life-work of Liebig.* London: Macmillan, 1876.
41. Letters in the possession of T. C. Buckland, Esq.
42. WOODHAM-SMITH, CECIL, *Florence Nightingale.* London: Constable, 1950.
43. HOLMES, TIMOTHY, *Sir Benjamin Collins Brodie.* London: T. Fisher Unwin, 1898.
44. HUXLEY, LEONARD, *Life and Letters of Thomas Henry Huxley.* London: Macmillan, 1900.
45. Athenaeum Records. Records of Ballot Sheets.

46. St George's Hospital. The Pupils' Register. Copy in Library of Royal College of Surgeons of England.
47. BLOMFIELD, J., *St George's, 1753–1933*. London: Medici Society for St George's Hospital, 1933.
48. BUCKLAND, FRANK, *Curiosities of Natural History*. Fourth Series. London: Bentley, 1882 (1st ed. 1872).
49. *History, 49*, 299–324, 1964.
50. THORNBURY, WALTER, *Old and New London*. London: Cassell, n.d.
51. GODLEE, R. J., *Lord Lister*. Oxford: Clarendon Press, 1924, 3rd ed.
52. NIGHTINGALE, F. N., *Notes on Hospitals*. London: Longmans, Green, 1863, 3rd ed.
53. *The Times*, June 8, 1866.
54. BUCKLAND, FRANK, in *Fishing Gossip* (ed.) H. Cholmondeley-Pennell. Edinburgh: A. & C. Black, 1866.
55. *Ann. R. Coll. Surg., 10*, 133–139, 1952.
56. CHALMERS MITCHELL, P., *Centenary History of the Zoological Society of London*. London: Zoological Society, 1929.
57. *Leisure Hour, 8*, 54–59, 1859.
58. *Good Words*, 165–169, 1879.
59. *Leisure Hour, 7*, 377–380, 1858.
60. BUCKLAND, FRANK, *Curiosities of Natural History*. Third Series. London: Bentley, 1885 (1st ed. 1865).
61. BUCKLAND, FRANK, Letters to Richard Owen in Library of British Museum (N.H.).
62. Birth Certificate, Francis John Papps. Reg. Dist. St George, Hanover Sq. Registered Oct. 3, 1851, by Hannah Papps.
63. HARVEY, PAUL, *The Oxford Companion to English Literature*. Oxford: Clarendon Press, 1946, 3rd ed.
64. ARTHUR, GEORGE, *The Story of the Household Cavalry*. London: Constable, 1909.
65. *Hansard 3rd Series, ccv*, March 23, 1871. Army Estimates. London: C. Buck, 1871.
66. Household Cavalry Brigade, Gold Stick and Silver Stick Orders. 1854–1874.
67. ANON., *Standing Orders of the Second Regiment of Life Guards*. London: Printed privately, 1856.
68. Death Certificate, Francis John Papps. Reg. Dist. Windsor. Registered February 12, 1856.
69. BUCKLAND, FRANK. Letter in the possession of Dr G. H. O. Burgess.
70. *Literary Gazette*, January 2, 1858.
71. *Leisure Hour, 10*, 55–57, 1861.
72. BUCKLAND, FRANK, Letters to Professor John Phillips. Geological Collections, University Museum, Oxford.
73. *Leisure Hour, 10*, 703–704, 1861.

74. BUCKLAND, FRANK, *Notes and Jottings from Animal Life.* London: Smith, Elder, 1886 (1st ed. 1882).
75. FELLOWS, ALFRED, *The Law of Burial.* London: Hadden, Best, 1952, 2nd ed.
76. *Illustrated London News*, March 1, 1859 (in 23).
77. *Morning Post*, September 21, 1860 (in 23).
78. *The Times*, November 20, 1912.
79. *J. R. Soc. Arts*, *9*, 19–34, 1860.
80. *Edinb. Review*, *61*, 161–188, 1860.
81. *All the Year Round*, *5*, 492–496, 1861.
82. *The Times*, January 21, 1859.
83. *Rep. Br. Ass. Advmt. Sci.* (1864), 1865.
84. 2nd Ann. Rep. Soc. for Acclimatization of Animals, etc. London: The Society's Offices, 1862.
85. 3rd Ann. Rep. Soc. for Acclimatization of Animals, etc. London: The Society's Offices, 1863.
86. *The Field*, July 18, 1863.
87. *The Field*, July 12 and 19, 1862.
88. *The Field*, July 4, 1863.
89. DAY, FRANCIS, *Fish Culture.* London: William Clowes, 1883 [Fish Exhib. Literature].
90. DAVY, HUMPHRY, *Salmonia; or Days of Fly Fishing.* London: Murray, 1851, 4th ed.
91. *Edinb. New Philosoph. J.*, *21*, 99–110, 1836.
Edinb. New Philosoph. J., *24*, 165–176, 1838.
Trans. R. Soc. Edinb., *14*, 547–566, 1840.
Trans. R. Soc. Edinb., *15*, 369–375, 1843.
92. BOCCIUS, GOTTLIEB, *A Treatise on the Management of Fresh-water Fish.* London: van Voorst, 1841.
93. BOCCIUS, GOTTLIEB, *Fish in Rivers and Streams.* London: van Voorst, 1848.
94. BROWN, WILLIAM, *The Natural History of the Salmon.* Glasgow: Thomas Murray, 1862.
95. CALLCUT, W. G., *The History of the London Anglers' Association.* London: W. G. Callcut, 1924.
96. *The Field*, August 23, 1862.
97. *The Field*, April 25, 1863.
98. BUCKLAND, FRANK, *Fish Hatching.* London: Tinsley, 1863.
99. *Literary Times*, June 6, 1863.
London Review, June, 1863.
Court Journal, November 21, 1863 (all in 23).
100. DOLBY, I. E. A. (ed.), *Journal of the Household Brigade for 1876.* London: Pub. for Subscribers only.
101. *John Bull*, November 30, 1861.
102. *The Field*, August 1 and 8, 1863.
103. *The Field*, January 18, 1862.
104. *Dorset County Chronicle*, September 27, 1863.
105. *The Field*, November 14, 1863.

106. *The Times*, January 1, 1864.
107. *Pap. Proc. R. Soc. Tasm. for 1888*, 1–25, 1889.
108. MOSCROP, E. H., *Correspondence relative to the Introduction of Salmon and Trout at the Antipodes.* London: Pub. Privately, 1879.
109. BUCKLAND, FRANK, *Familiar History of British Fishes.* London: S.P.C.K. [1873].
110. BUCKLAND, FRANK, Letters and Records. Royal Society, London.
111. *Bradford Observer*, March 29, 1866 (in 23).
112. *The Globe*, December 20, 1880.
113. *The World*, January 9, 1878.
114. *The Field*, January 28, 1865.
115. *Sea Fisheries of the United Kingdom.* R. Com. [3596 and 3596–I] xvii and xviii. Vols I and II. London: H.M.S.O., 1866.
116. *The Field*, May 27, 1865.
117. ANON, *The Science Museum. The First Hundred Years.* London: H.M.S.O., 1957.
118. Buckland Fish Museum Files. Science Museum, London.
119. *Evening Star*, August 5, 1865 (in 23).
120. *Ann. Rep. Sci. Art Dept. 13 to 18* (1865–1880). London: H.M.S.O., 1866–1881.
121. *Land and Water*, *6*, December 19, 1868.
122. *Land and Water*, *3*, April 27, 1867.
123. *Land and Water*, *8*, October 30, 1869.
124. BUCKLAND, FRANK, Documents in the possession of Miss E. L. Pritchard.
125. *Land and Water*, *16*, October 4, 1873.
126. *The Spectator*, March 3, 1866 (in 23).
127. *The Times*, December 2, 1885.
128. WAUGH, ARTHUR, *A Hundred Years of Publishing.* London: Chapman & Hall, 1930.
129. *Land and Water*, *9*, January 1, 1870.
130. *Land and Water*, *3*, January 26, 1867.
131. BUCKLAND, FRANK, Letters in American Philosophical Society Library, Philadelphia, Pa.
132. *Land and Water*, *2*, October 13, 1866.
133. *Land and Water*, *8*, July 31, 1869.
134. *Land and Water*, *5*, February 22 and 29, 1868.
135. *Land and Water*, *8*, October 30, 1869.
136. *Land and Water*, *7*, April 10, 1869.
137. *Land and Water*, *6*, September 26, 1868.
138. *Land and Water*, *29*, February 21, 1880.
139. MOSS, ARTHUR, W., *Valiant Crusade. The History of the R.S.P.C.A.* London: Cassell, 1961.
140. *Land and Water*, *18*, December 26, 1874.
141. *Land and Water*, *14*, December 14, 1872.

142. *Land and Water*, *1*, March 10, 1866.
143. *Salm. Trout Mag.* No. 142, 517–524, 1954.
144. *Salmon Fisheries, England and Wales.* R. Com. Rep. [2768] xxiii, London: H.M.S.O., 1861.
145. Ashworth, Thomas, *The Salmon Fisheries of England*, 1868. London: Longmans, Green & Co. n.d. ca. 1869.
146. Day, Francis, *British and Irish Salmonidae.* London: Williams & Norgate, 1887.
147. Walpole, Spencer, *Essays Political and Biographical.* London: T. Fisher Unwin, 1908.
148. *Land and Water*, *26*, December 21, 1878.
149. *Land and Water*, *4*, July 27, 1867.
150. *Leisure Hour*, *10*, 357–359, 1861.
151. *Sixth Rep. Insp. Salm. Fish.* [440] London: H.M.S.O., 1867.
152. *Twelfth Rep. Insp. Salm. Fish.* [c 725] London: H.M.S.O., 1873.
153. *Fourteenth Rep. Insp. Salm. Fish.* [c 1254] London: H.M.S.O., 1875.
154. *Pollution of Rivers.* R. Com. 5th Rep. [c 951] xxxiii, London: H.M.S.O., 1874.
155. Buckland, Frank, Letters in the Wellcome Collection, London.
156. *Land and Water*, *9*, April 23, 1870.
157. *Saturday Review*, April 30, 1870.
158. Archives Internal Affairs Department, New Zealand. In and Out Correspondence.
159. Nicols, Arthur, *The Acclimatization of the Salmonidae at the Antipodes.* London: Sampson Low, 1882.
160. *Land and Water*, *23*, March 3, 1877.
161. *The Times*, September 21, 1872.
162. *Salmon Disease.* Inspector's Rep. [c 2660] xiv. London: H.M.S.O., 1880.
163. *Proc. R. Soc.*, *23*, 381–389, 1882.
164. Large, E. C., *The Advance of the Fungi.* London: Jonathan Cape, 1940.
165. Bund, J. W. Willis, *Salmon Problems.* London: Sampson Low, 1885.
166. *Fish Trades Gazette*, March 19, 21–71, 1921.
167. *Fisheries (Norfolk).* Rep. [428] London: H.M.S.O. 1875.
168. *Crab and Lobster Fisheries of England and Wales, Scotland and Ireland* Rep. [c 1695] xxiv. London: H.M.S.O., 1877.
169. *Herring Fisheries of Scotland* Rep. ev. etc. [c 1979] xxi. London: H.M.S.O., 1878.
170. *Norwich Mercury*, April 23, 1881.
171. *Sea Fisheries in England and Wales.* Rep. ev. etc. [c 2449] xvii. London: H.M.S.O., 1878–9.
172. *Land and Water*, *13*, April 27, 1872.
173. *Land and Water*, *5*, July 4, 1868.

174. *Land and Water*, *6*, November 7, 1868.
175. BUCKLAND, FRANK, *The Natural History of British Fishes*. London: S.P.C.K., 1881.
176. *The Field*, February 12, 1881.
177. *Nature, Lond.*, *23*, 576, 1881.
178. *Land and Water*, *9*, June 25, 1870.
179. *Land and Water*, *22*, November 18, 1876.
180. *The Scotsman*, December 23, 1880.
181. *Land and Water*, *6*, December 12 and 19, 1868.
182. *Land and Water*, *28*, November 29, 1879.
183. *Land and Water*, *19*, March 20, 1875.
184. *Land and Water*, *24*, August 18, 1877.
185. *Land and Water*, *25*, May 4, 1878.
186. *Land and Water*, *7*, May 22, 1869.
187. *Land and Water*, *25*, March 23, 1878.
188. *Land and Water*, *3*, July 18 and 25, 1868.
189. GOULD, GEORGE M. & PYLE, WALTER L., *Anomalies and Curiosities of Medicine*. London: Rebman Publishing Co. (Ltd.), 1897.
190. *Land and Water*, *7*, February 20, 1869, and *17*, January 24 and 31, 1874.
191. BLAND-SUTTON, JOHN, *Tumours Innocent and Malignant*. London: Cassell, 1922.
192. *Land and Water*, *12*, July 29, 1871.
193. *Land and Water*, *11*, May 27 and June 10, 1871.
194. *Land and Water 23*, February 24 and March 31, 1877.
195. *Land and Water*, *20*, July 31, 1875.
196. BRIGHTWELL, L. R., *The Zoo Story*. London: Museum Press, 1952.
197. *Land and Water*, *21*, February 19, 1876.
198. *The Sunday Times*, October 3, 1937.
199. *Land and Water*, *13*, February 17, 1872.
200. *Land and Water*, *18*, September 12, 1874.
201. *Land and Water*, *24*, July 28, 1877.
202. *Land and Water*, *2*, August 25, 1866.
203. *Land and Water*, *4*, August 24, 1867.
204. *Rep. Br. Ass. Advmt. Sci.* (1870), 115, 1871.
205. *Land and Water*, *14*, August 17, 1872.
Nature, Lond., *8*, 372, 1873.
206. *Land and Water*, *13*, April 13, 1872.
207. *Land and Water*, *13*, February 10, 1872.
208. *Land and Water*, *9*, January 15, 1870.
209. *Sussex County Magazine*, June, 1952.
210. *Land and Water*, *23*, June, 1877.
211. *Land and Water*, *28*, October 25, 1879.
212. *Twentieth Rep. Insp. Salm. Fish.* [c 2901] London: H.M.S.O., 1881.
213. *Land and Water*, *27*, January 18, 1879.

214. *Grimsby Daily Telegraph*, January 19, 1925.
215. GARSTANG, W., *The Buckland Lectures for 1929*. Aberdeen: Fishing News, 1930.
216. *Land and Water*, *24*, August 18, 1877.
217. *Land and Water*, *13*, January 20, 1872.
218. BUCKLAND, FRANK, Letters in Library of Royal College of Physicians.
219. *Land and Water*, *28*, October 11, 1879.
220. *Proc. R. Soc. Med.*, *60*, 291–298, 1967.
221. *Nature, Lond.*, *23*, *175*, 1881.
222. *The Field*, December 25, 1880.
223. BUCKLAND, FRANK, Will made December 3, 1880.
224. *The Times*, March 29, 1881.
225. HERBERT, DAVID (Ed.), *Fish and Fisheries*. Edinburgh: Blackwood, 1883.
226. KOFOID, CHARLES A., *The Biological Stations of Europe*. U.S. Bureau Education Bull. No. 4. Washington: Govt. Printing Office, 1910.
227. Official Catalogue. International Fisheries Exhibition. London: William Clowes, 1883.
228. *Fishery Statistics:* Inter-Dept. Cttee. Rep. [cd 1063] xv, 1. London: H.M.S.O., 1902.
229. JOHNSTONE, JAMES, *British Fisheries*. London: Williams & Norgate, 1905.

Bibliography

This list does not include references to Buckland's numerous articles in *The Field, Good Words, Leisure Hour, Bentley's Miscellany* and other periodicals, nor does it give his many letters to *The Times* newspaper. His main contributions to *The Field* are to be found in copies for the years 1858 to 1865; articles, letters and replies to correspondents occur in most numbers of *Land and Water* from its inception in 1866 until Buckland's death in December 1880.

Furthermore, various contributions were made by Buckland to volumes of essays by different authors. Some of these have been noted. Details are also given of his official writings as H.M. Inspector of Salmon Fisheries and also as a Commissioner appointed to enquire into certain aspects of the fisheries.

WORKS BY FRANK BUCKLAND

Curiosities of Natural History

These volumes were the most popular of all Buckland's books. They contain essays on a wide variety of topics, and were eventually published as four volumes, known today as Series One to Four. Precise bibliographic references are difficult because the publisher, Richard Bentley, following a practice common in his day did not distinguish between new editions, differing in form or content from previous editions, and mere reprints from the same type. Indeed some of Bentley's 'new editions' may be reissues with only the date changed on the title page. The author has examined many copies of the 'Curiosities', but clearly it would have been impossible to compare them all; the following list may therefore be incomplete in some respects, and some of the earlier editions or reprints may have been overlooked. Bentley perforce brought out individual volumes of the Series at different times but all publishers since have brought them out together.

Richard Bentley editions:

First Series

First Edition	post 8vo *6s* Nov. 1857.
Second Edition	(some corrections) Mar. 1858.
Third Edition	June 1858.
Fourth Edition	Dec. 1858.

Fifth Edition (Notes and Index added) Sept. 1860.
Further editions or reprints:
Dec. 1861; Mar. 1862; June 1863; Dec. 1864; Mar. 1866; June 1868 at 5*s*; Dec. 1870; Dec. 1872; Mar. 1874; Dec. 1876; Dec. 1879 f'cap 8vo at 3*s* 6*d*; June 1883; Mar. 1886; Dec. 1889 at 2*s* 6*d*; June 1893.

Second Series
First Edition post 8vo 6*s* June 1860.
Further editions or reprints:
Dec. 1861; June 1863; Dec. 1865; Mar. 1867; Dec. 1870 at 5*s*; June 1871; Dec. 1872; Dec. 1874; Dec. 1876; Dec. 1879 f'cap 8vo at 3*s* 6*d*; June 1883; June 1886, Dec. 1889 at 2*s* 6*d*; June 1893.

Third Series
First Edition post 8vo 6*s*. Dec. 1865.
Second Edition, revised and with additional notes, published at 5*s*, Dec. 1867. A reprint was published in Dec. 1870, but see under Fourth Series for further editions and reprints.

Fourth Series
The First Edition of the Fourth Series as such was published in 1872 at 3*s* 6*d* at the same time as a revised edition of the Third Series. Much of the material for the Fourth Series was previously incorporated in the Third Series. After 1872 new imprints of the Third and Fourth Series always appeared together:
Dec. 1873; Dec. 1875; Mar. 1878 f'cap 8vo at 3*s* 6*d*; Dec. 1881; Sept. 1885; Sept. 1888 (price reduced in 1889 to 2*s* 6*d*); Sept. 1891.

Editions by other publishers:
Cr 8vo 2*s* 6d each. London: Macmillan, Sept. 1900 (Prize Library. With numerous illustrations).
Cr 8vo 3*s* 6*d* each. London: Methuen, Oct. 1903 (Illustrated by Harry B. Neilson).
Cr 8vo 2*s* 6*d* each. London: Henry Frowde, Oct. 1912 (Hodder & Stoughton) (Herbert Strang's Library).

Buckland's Curiosities of Natural History. A Selection, edited and illustrated by L. R. Brightwell. Cr 8vo 10*s* 6*d* London: Batchworth Press, Aug. 1948.

Fish Hatching post 8vo 5*s* London: Tinsley, 1863.
(An expanded version of a lecture given at the Royal Institution, April 17, 1863.)

Manual of salmon and trout hatching; or an explanation of the fish-hatching apparatus at the Royal Horticultural Gardens, The South Kensington Museum, Zoological Gardens, etc.
12mo 6*d* London: Tinsley, 1864.
(The text begins: 'In the annals of progress there are few steps of greater interest than that of fish hatching.')

Familiar History of British Fishes 8vo 5*s* London: S.P.C.K. [1873].
(In the Preface, Buckland states that '... this little book will be found to be more or less a hand-book to my museum. An engraving of the Museum is given as a Frontispiece. This book was completely rewritten; see *Natural History of British Fishes*, below.)

Log-book of a Fisherman and Zoologist 8vo 12*s* and 5*s* London: Chapman & Hall, April, 1875.
Further editions were published by Chapman & Hall as follows: 1882–1886 at 5*s*; May 1891 at 3*s* 6*d*; Oct. 1896.

In Memoriam. Edward Stuart, M.A., founder and first vicar of the Church of St Mary Magdalene, Munster Square, London. 8vo London: G. J. Palmer, 1877.

The Pollution of Rivers, and its effects upon the fisheries and supply of water to towns and villages. An address, etc. London: C. L. Marsh, 1878.

Natural History of British Fishes cr 8vo 5*s* London: S.P.C.K., 1881.
(This book is a completely rewritten version of the *Familiar History of British Fishes* published in 1873. The Preface was almost the last thing written by Buckland. The neat woodcuts of the earlier version are used again in this work but are very badly printed.)

Notes and Jotting from Animal Life (edited by G. C. Bompas) 8vo 6*s* and 5*s* London: Smith, Elder & Co., 1882.
Further editions were brought out by Smith, Elder & Co. in 1886 and, at 3*s* 6*d*, in 1909.
(Buckland selected and arranged these papers, all of which had previously appeared in *Land and Water*, shortly before his death.)

WORKS TO WHICH BUCKLAND CONTRIBUTED

Buckland, William

Geology and Mineralogy considered with reference to Natural Theology. A new edition, with additions by Professor Owen ... Professor Phillips ... Mr Robert Brown ... and memoir of the author. Edited by Francis T. Buckland. 2 volumes. 8vo 24*s* London: Routledge, 1858.
Fourth Edition. Edited by Francis T. Buckland (and Henry Lee). 2 volumes. 8vo 15*s* London: Bell & Daldy, 1869.

Cholmondeley-Pennell, Harry (ed.)

Fishing Gossip; or stray leaves from the note-books of several anglers. 8vo Edinburgh: Black, 1866.
(Contains 'On the Thames' by Frank Buckland; 'Fish hooks of the earliest date' by Jonathan Couch; 'The Siluris glanis' by Albert Günther; besides essays by Alexander Russell, Thomas Tod Stoddart, Thomas Westwood and others well known to students of angling literature.)

White, Gilbert

The Natural History of Selborne. With notes by Frank Buckland. A Chapter on Antiquities by Lord Selborne and new letters. Illustrated by P. H. Delamotte.
8vo London: Macmillan, 1875. Large paper edition 4to London: Macmillan, 1876. Cheaper edition 8vo London: Macmillan, 1880.
(This was said by *The Field* to have been an undoubted failure, a statement perhaps not supported by the fact that Macmillan brought out a further edition in 1880. Of the total number of 591 pages, White's letters occupy 292 pages, Buckland's notes 147 pages, and Lord Selborne's 112 pages.)

Austen, Nathaniel Laurence

Natural History Papers and Memoir of N. Laurence Austen. Edited by Frank Buckland, etc. 8vo London: Printed for private circulation, 1877.

Birds and Bird-Life. Papers contributed by F. T. Buckland . . . W. C. L. Martin . . . W. Kidd, and other naturalists.
8vo London: Leisure Hour Office [1863].
(The author has not been able to examine copies of the last two publications. Austen died a young man in 1874 as a result of a fall from a horse. He was educated at Cambridge. He was a gifted naturalist and ardent sportsman who chased bears and stalked reindeer in the wildest parts of Norway.)

REPORTS DEALING WITH BUCKLAND'S OFFICIAL DUTIES

Museum of Economic Fish Culture

Reports giving details of the Museum are to be found in the 'Report of the Science and Art Department of the Committee of Council on Education'. London: H.M.S.O. The relevant Reports are the 13th Report for 1865 (1866) to the 28th Report for 1880 (1881) [c 2970].

Salmon Fisheries

'The First Annual Report of the Inspectors of Salmon Fisheries (England and Wales). London: H.M.S.O., 1862, was written by Frederick Eden and William Joshua Ffennell. The first Report to which Buckland contributed was the Sixth Annual Report (for 1866), H.M.S.O., 1867, and the last was the Nineteenth Annual Report (for 1879), H.M.S.O., 1880 [2587].

Commissions and Committees

'Report of the Special Commissioners appointed to enquire into the effect of recent legislation on the salmon fisheries in Scotland. Frank Buckland and Archibald Young. Edinburgh: H.M.S.O., 1871 [c 419].

'Report on the Fisheries of Norfolk, especially crabs, lobsters, herrings and the broads.' Frank Buckland. London: H.M.S.O., 1875 [428].

'Report on the crab and lobster fisheries of England and Wales, Scotland and Ireland.' Frank Buckland and Spencer Walpole (England and Wales), Frank Buckland, Spencer Walpole and Archibald Young (Scotland), J. Aloysius Blake, Joseph Hayes and Thomas F. Brady (Ireland). London: H.M.S.O., 1877 [c 1695].

'Report on the herring fisheries of Scotland.' Frank Buckland, Spencer Walpole and Archibald Young. London: H.M.S.O., 1878 [c 1979].

(Appendices to this Report include 'Notes on the Natural History of the Herring' and 'The Garvie Fisheries of Scotland' (both by Frank Buckland.)

'Report on the Sea Fisheries of England and Wales.' Frank Buckland and Spencer Walpole London: H.M.S.O., 1879 [c 2449].

(This includes appendices by Buckland on commercial species of fish, various aspects of marine ecology, and a table showing the seasons when sea fish are best fit for eating.)

'Report on the disease which has recently prevailed among the salmon in the Tweed, Eden, and other rivers in England and Scotland.' Frank Buckland, Spencer Walpole and Archibald Young. London: H.M.S.O., 1880 [c 2660].

(The appendices include some brief observations on the salmon disease by Mordecai Cooke, Henry Lee, Professor Rolleston, C. L. Jackson [consulting naturalist to the Southport Aquarium]. and Erasmus Wilson.)

'Report as to the use of dynamite for killing fish.' Frank Buckland and Spencer Walpole. London: H.M.S.O., 1877.

'Report on the fisheries of the English Lake District.' Frank Buckland and Spencer Walpole. London: H.M.S.O., 1878.

(Although the columns of *Land and Water* contain references to the sittings of the two Inspectors at various towns to hear evidence in connexion with the matters dealt with in the last two Reports, and although the existence of the Reports seems to be credited by Westwood and Satchell in *Bibliotheca Piscatoria*, the author has been unable to examine copies of either of them.)

Index

INDEX